introduction to wave mechanics

introduction to wave mechanics

Louis Harris

Associate Professor of Physical Chemistry
Massachusetts Institute of Technology

Arthur L. Loeb

Associate Professor of Electrical Engineering
Massachusetts Institute of Technology

McGraw-Hill Book Company, Inc.

New York San Francisco Toronto London

introduction to wave mechanics

Library of Congress Catalog Card Number 62-21571

26810

preface

The purpose of this book is to present within the scope of a one-semester course most of the principles of nonrelativistic wave mechanics, together with examples illustrating the applications of these principles. The origin of the book lies in a set of notes issued by the authors over a period of years with the aim of supplementing existing texts and adapting them for students having a background of about two years of college mathematics and physics, including atomic physics.

The change of the role of wave mechanics in science curricula, and its introduction into engineering curricula, has influenced our presentation of the subject. It is no longer realistic to assume that only those students already having a highly specialized preparation in mathematics and physics will study wave mechanics in a quantitative fashion, while all the others can manage with a qualitative model. Rather we wish to acquaint the student as early as possible with the fundamental principles of wave mechanics and to give him practice in applying these principles. By providing incentive for self-study, we hope to make the student sufficiently versatile in coping with future problems in the ever-increasing field of applications of wave mechanics.

The authors have consistently aimed at a logical sequence of topics and a detailed discussion of each. Mathematical topics beyond partial differentiation, integration, and the most elementary differential equations are presented in detail, and with sufficient generality to allow applications outside the immediate scope of this book. Thus a self-contained volume has evolved, in which the important principles are first illustrated by examples and then again by problems interspersed throughout the text. The emphasis is more on depth in detail than on a broad coverage of topics.

As an introduction to the postulates of wave mechanics such elements of wave theory as expansion in terms of orthogonal functions and the dispersion of wave packets are discussed. The statistical nature of wave mechanics is stressed, and a separate chapter is devoted to the uncertainty principle and operator commutation. The solution of Schroedinger's equation is preceded by various applications of the postulates illustrating how information is extracted from wave functions. Only when the student has had sufficient practice in the use of wave functions is he asked to solve the wave equation. Each analytical solution of Schroedinger's equation is obtained by operator algebra; this method has been found more satisfactory than the polynomial expansion method, because it illustrates quantization more directly, because it gives a more unified approach to the generation of Hermite, Legendre, and Laguerre polynomials, and because it relates the wave mechanical approach to that of matrix mechanics. Moreover, the operator form of these polynomials, as exemplified by Rodrigues's formula for Legendre polynomials, is particularly useful in deriving selection rules. Operator algebra is also used in the discussion of electron spin.

In the chapter on perturbation theory a good deal of the preceding material is applied again. This chapter is based on the foundation laid by the introductory chapter on orthogonal functions, and its application to an anharmonic oscillator further illustrates the usefulness of the operator form of the eigenfunctions of the harmonic oscillator. Finally, this chapter forms the basis for a discussion of direct spin exchange interactions and the helium atom.

The book is concluded by a review of the various interactions that determine the electronic configuration of atoms. An earlier chapter on the resonance of an electron between two identical atoms provides the introductory material for the study of molecular binding.

The authors are aware of many omissions, but in order to restrict the material to a single semester, a choice often had to be made between topics. The decision was always made in favor of wide applicability and of relevance to the remainder of the book. Such topics as the variation method, the continuous spectrum of hydrogen, and the Russell-Saunders and other spin-orbit coupling models regretfully had to be omitted; in each case it was felt that the material in this volume would provide a sufficient basis for continued study. One of the authors has omitted Chaps. 8 and 9 in his class presentation without impairment of the continuity of the material.

It is a pleasure to acknowledge the assistance of our colleagues and students during the development of this text; their names are too numerous to be mentioned separately here. We are particularly grateful to Norman Menyuk, Arthur J. Schneider, and Oscar Grosch for their assistance in the preparation of various drafts of this book. The support of the Westinghouse Educational Foundation and the Westinghouse Research Division is gratefully acknowledged. Special thanks are due Miss Frances M. Doherty and Mrs. Laurence R. Swain, Jr., who typed many drafts of the manuscript.

Louis Harris
Arthur L. Loeb

contents

11

the central field

12

spherical harmonics and selection rules

13

radial dependence of wave functions in a coulomb field

14

the hydrogen molecule-ion

15

separation of variables

16

electron spin and the exclusion principle

17

perturbation theory

18

the helium atom

introduction

chapter

1

1-1 Stationary states. So much of our knowledge of the structure of atoms and molecules is based on the results of spectroscopy that it is worthwhile to recall the development of ideas that have led to our present concepts.

The correlation between spectroscopic term values and the energy levels of the stationary states of atoms was first postulated by Bohr. He proposed that an atom could exist only in certain stationary states, each of which has a definite energy. The discrete radiation emitted by an atomic system was the result of atoms going from an excited stationary state to a less excited stationary state or to the nonexcited state. This last state is usually designated as the normal or the ground state. The frequency of the radiation emitted, as a result of the transition from one stationary state to another, is found from the relation

$$E_2 - E_1 = h\nu \tag{1-1}$$

where E_2 is the energy of the atom in the more excited state, E_1 is the energy in the less excited state, h is Planck's radiation constant, and ν is the frequency of the radiation.

1-2 Excitation potentials. Soon after Bohr's proposal, Franck and Hertz, and others, carried out experiments in which electrons were accelerated through tubes containing elements in their gaseous state. As the accelerating voltage was gradually increased, the electrons passed through the gas without change in energy until a critical accelerating voltage was reached, when the electrons were found to have lost most of their energy. The critical accelerating voltages were found to be different for each gaseous element. Franck and Hertz concluded from their measurements that energy was transferred from the electrons to the atoms in the gas by inelastic collisions and that these atoms in turn lost the energy by radiation. When the region in which the inelastic collisions occurred was exposed to the slit of a spectrograph the spectral line observed had a frequency given by the relation

$$(\Delta V)e = h\nu$$

where e is the charge on the electron and $(\Delta V)e$ corresponds to the loss in energy of the accelerated electron. The spectral line was the result of transitions from a state with energy E_2 to a state with lower energy, E_1. The value of the frequency of the spectral line was in agreement with Eq. (1-1).

As the accelerating voltage was increased, additional inelastic collisions corresponding to greater excitation potentials of an atom were observed and simultaneously new spectral lines of the atomic spectrum appeared, corresponding to excitation of atoms to higher levels. As the accelerating voltage was increased still further, the complete atomic spectrum of the element appeared. These experiments provide an excellent experimental confirmation of Bohr's postulate for the mechanism of the emission of spectral lines.

In practice, much greater accuracy for the energy (term value) differences is obtained from spectroscopic than from electron-impact measurements. The latter type of measurements supplemented the former in determining the difference between the energy of the excited states and that of the ground state.

1-3 Selection rules for transitions. Early empirical spectroscopic studies showed that the apparent complexity of the spectrum of an element could be resolved as follows. For each element a comparatively small set of numerical terms was found to exist, such that the frequency of each spectral line equals the difference between the numerical value of a pair of terms.

Even before Bohr's postulate it was recognized that every spectral term of an atomic system did not combine with every other term to give a spectral line. Bohr correlated this behavior with certain quantized changes of the angular momentum of the atom in the two energy states involved in a transition. This "selection rule" was partially successful in predicting the presence and absence of certain transitions.

The concept of transitions between stationary states to give spectral lines has been found to have general application to nuclear and molecular systems as well as to atomic systems. It is one of the important concepts used in physics today.

---

problem 1-1. As the accelerating voltage of electrons through mercury vapor is gradually increased, one finds excitation potentials at

$$4.69, 4.91, 5.48, 6.73, 7.75, 7.94 \cdots \text{volts}$$

and finally the ionization potential at 10.5 volts. Transitions with radiation emission are observed only from the 4.91, 6.73, and 7.75 excited levels.

(*a*) Calculate the wavelength (angstroms) of the first spectral line to appear as the accelerating potential is gradually increased (from zero).

(*b*) Three strong spectral lines in the visible emission spectrum of mercury are at 4040, 4358, and 5460 A. Demonstrate that these levels have a common upper level, from this information.

---

problem 1-2. When neon gas at a low pressure is exposed to radiation of the following wavelengths:

$\lambda = 745$ A	the 745-A resonance line is reemitted
$\lambda = 627$ A	the 8900-A, 7180-A, and 745-A lines are emitted
$\lambda = 502$ A	photoelectrons of 3.11-volt energy as well as the complete spectrum are observed

Predict the results of the following separate experiments:

(*a*) Irradiation of neon gas with $\lambda = 7180$ A
(*b*) Passage of 15-volt accelerated electrons through neon gas
(*c*) Passage of 19-volt accelerated electrons through neon gas
(*d*) Passage of 22-volt accelerated electrons through neon gas

---

1-4 Bohr theory of the hydrogen atom. Bohr also derived an expression for the energies of the different stationary states of the hydrogen atom, from a consideration of the internal motion of the atom, namely, that of the electron with relation to its proton. He assumed that the electron moved in a circular orbit around the nucleus and that the electric force of attraction between the proton and electron just balanced the centrifugal force of the rotating electron. If Ze represents the charge on the nucleus, e the charge on the electron, r the distance of the electron from the nucleus, m_e the mass of the electron, and v the velocity of the electron

$$\frac{Ze^2}{r^2} = \frac{m_e v^2}{r} \tag{1-2}$$

In the excited states the electron moved around the proton also in distinct circular orbits, but further from the proton. The postulate of discrete energy levels restricted the circles in which the electron might move. Here, Bohr introduced his second postulate which predicted exactly which circles are permitted for the electron motion. The quantization condition is

$$2\pi m_e r v = nh \tag{1-3}$$

where n is a quantum number, which may take on integral values from 1 to ∞, and h is Planck's constant. According to Eq. (1-3), the angular momentum of the system can assume only multiple values of $h/2\pi$.

In terms of the quantum number n, the velocities of the electron and the radii of the orbits for the different stationary states are therefore

$$v = \frac{2\pi Ze^2}{nh} \tag{1-4}$$

$$r = \frac{n^2h^2}{4\pi^2 Ze^2 m_e} \tag{1-5}$$

The total energy E is equal to the sum of the kinetic energy and the potential energy

$$E = \frac{1}{2} m_e v^2 - \frac{Ze^2}{r} \tag{1-6}$$

Substitution of Eq. (1-2) into Eq. (1-6) gives

$$E = -\frac{1}{2}\frac{Ze^2}{r} = -\frac{1}{2} m_e v^2 \tag{1-7}$$

Substitution of Eq. (1-4) into Eq. (1-7) gives

$$E = \frac{-2\pi^2 Z^2 e^4 m_e}{n^2h^2} \tag{1-8}$$

When correction is made for the motion of the proton around the center of mass of the hydrogen atom, the energy for the system becomes

$$E = \frac{-2\pi^2 Z^2 e^4 \mu}{n^2 h^2} \tag{1-9}$$

where μ is the reduced mass of the proton-electron system.

1-5 Sommerfeld's action integral. A more general formulation of the quantum restriction used by Bohr was given by Sommerfeld. He considered a more general type of motion in which each degree of freedom for the system was quantized and the relation between the generalized coordinate q and its associated momentum p was

$$\oint p_i \, dq_i = nh \tag{1-10}$$

The subscript i refers to the particular degree of freedom involved, $\oint$ denotes integration over a complete cycle of motion, and n and h have the same meaning as in Eq. (1-3). When Eq. (1-10) is used to represent the motion of the electron in a circular orbit in the hydrogen atom,

$$\oint p_\phi \, d\phi = \oint (I\omega) \, d\phi = I\omega \oint d\phi = nh$$

$I\omega$ is the angular momentum. I is the moment of inertia, ω is the angular frequency, and ϕ is the angular coordinate. Since the angular momentum is constant here, the $I\omega$ was moved to the front of the integral. Solving for the kinetic energy of the system in terms of the moment of inertia and angular frequency gives

$$\tfrac{1}{2}I\omega^2 = \frac{(I\omega)^2}{2I} = \frac{(nh/2\pi)^2}{2\mu r^2} = \frac{1}{2}\frac{n^2h^2}{4\pi^2\mu r^2} \tag{1-11}$$

When r from Eq. (1-5) is substituted in the denominator of the above equation, one finds that this kinetic energy is equal to $(-E)$ of Eq. (1-9), a result that was just obtained from the Bohr theory, Eq. (1-7).

---

problem 1-3. Using Sommerfeld's action integral, find the allowed energies for a rotor, with constant r, in terms of its moment of inertia.

---

problem 1-4. Using Sommerfeld's action integral, find the allowed energies of a harmonic oscillator in terms of its angular frequency ω.

(The potential energy of the harmonic oscillator in one dimension is $\frac{1}{2}kq^2$, where q is the displacement from equilibrium, $k = \mu\omega^2$, and μ is the reduced mass of the oscillator.)

1-6 Applications of the Bohr theory. When Eq. (1-1) is combined with Eq. (1-9),

$$\nu = Z^2 \left(\frac{2\pi^2 e^4 \mu}{h^3}\right)\left(\frac{1}{n_1^2} - \frac{1}{n_2^2}\right) \tag{1-12}$$

where ν, the frequency of an emitted line, is a function of two quantum numbers, n_2 for the upper state and n_1 for the lower state. Equation (1-12) is in the form in which the experimental results for the different series in the spectrum of atomic hydrogen had been expressed prior to Bohr's theory:

$$\nu = R_A \left(\frac{1}{n_1^2} - \frac{1}{n_2^2}\right) \tag{1-13}$$

The n_1 in Eqs. (1-12) or (1-13) is constant for a spectral series, while n_2 may take on values from $(n_1 + 1)$ to ∞. Thus, for the Balmer series of the hydrogen atom, $n_1 = 2$ and $n_2 = 3, 4, 5, 6 \ldots$. The Rydberg constant, R_A, in the experimental equation, Eq. (1-13), is equal to the expression in the first parentheses in Eq. (1-12), when $Z = 1$, as is the case for the hydrogen atom. Thus Bohr succeeded in expressing the empirical constant R_A in terms of natural constants. Use has been made of this relation to derive the best value of h, by combining the results of Eq. (1-12) with other independent measurements of e and e/m for the electron.

Equation (1-12) can be used to predict the frequencies of the spectral lines in the He^+ and Li^{++} spectra. It was used to predict the frequencies of the spectral lines in the deuterium spectrum before that isotope of hydrogen was found.

---

problem 1-5. The Rydberg constant as evaluated from the Balmer series of the hydrogen atom is 109,677.6 cm^{-1}. For heavy elements, the Rydberg constant approaches the value 109,737.3 cm^{-1}.

Calculate the ratio of the rest mass of the electron to that of the proton, to three significant figures from these data.

The assumption of elliptical as well as circular orbits and the application of the relativity correction for the electron moving in elliptical orbits permitted Sommerfeld to explain the detailed fine structure in the spectrum of atomic hydrogen that is observed with a spectrometer of high resolution. The conditions for quantization of the motion in the elliptical orbits were obtained by use of Eq. (1-10).

1-7 Limitations of the Bohr theory. As successful as Bohr's method for calculating the energy levels of the H atom (and He^+ and Li^{++}) appeared to be, it could not be satisfactorily extended to other atomic systems. Application of the Sommerfeld action integral to calculation of the energy levels of the free rotor and the harmonic oscillator gave expressions in general accord with the results of the spectra of diatomic molecules. Later, more extensive measurements showed that the energy expressions derived in this manner were incorrect. For example, it follows from Probs. 1-3 and 1-4 that the energy levels of the rotor are $E = J^2h^2/8\pi^2I$, where J is the quantum number representing rotational energy; for the oscillator one obtains $E = vh\nu$, where v is the quantum number representing vibrational energy and ν is the vibrational frequency. Both J and v range from zero to infinity and take on successive integer values. The later, more correct measurements are represented by $E = J(J + 1)h^2/8\pi^2I$ and $E = (v + \frac{1}{2})h\nu$, respectively.

Bohr was able to apply the electromagnetic theory of radiation to account for the fact that transitions with emission of radiation did not occur between all the stationary states, and thus he was able to account for the presence of strong lines and the absence of other possible lines. However, his treatment could not account for some weak lines which occurred in the spectra.

The basic difficulties of the Bohr theory of atomic structure are not due to lack of refinements in the original model, but rather to the fact that the description of atomic systems is subject to natural limitations.

1-8 The wave properties of particles. While many investigators were extending Bohr's ideas, other physicists tried to find a different method for treating the mechanics of atomic and molecular motion. In 1924, L. de Broglie suggested that just as it had been useful to endow photons with particle behavior (as had been done for the photoelectric effect), it might be interesting to consider the results of endowing particles with wave properties. Using the modified relativity relations, $E = mc^2$, and the relation $E = h\nu$, he predicted that a group of particles having a linear momentum p could be associated with a wave whose wavelength is

$$\lambda = \frac{h}{p} \tag{1-14}$$

Within three years, experiments involving the collisions of electrons with matter were described; the results of which were easily explained using de Broglie's ideas, and could not be explained otherwise.

When a narrow beam of fast (50,000-volt acceleration) electrons is incident on a thin metal foil, the emerging beam of electrons has an intensity pattern comprising a center image (the trace of the original, unscattered beam), around which are grouped circular zones of different intensity, and of greater intensity than the regions between zones. A photographic plate, used for recording the pattern, shows a series of concentric halos. The spacing of the halos was found to depend on the spacing of the atoms in the foil, the geometry of the apparatus, and the accelerating potential of the incident electrons. The halos were displaced by a strong magnetic field, so that the scattered beam must be composed essentially of electrons and not X rays. The pattern produced can be explained quantitatively if it is assumed that the atoms of the metal foil behave as components of a ruled grating and that the atoms of the foil diffract the electron beam. The value of p in Eq. (1-14) can be calculated from the accelerating voltage; the spacing of the atoms in the foil is known from X-ray studies. Thus with the knowledge of the geometry of the apparatus and the use of the diffraction law, it is possible to calculate the spacing of the halos. The agreement between the observed and calculated spacing is excellent. Such were the results of G. P. Thomson, in England.

---

problem 1-6. (*a*) Derive a relation, for small angles of forward scattering, between the diameter d of a halo formed as a result of electron scattering, from a metal foil with a structure represented by an atomic distance a, when the recording screen is at a distance l from the metal foil, and the accelerating voltage for the incident electrons is V.

(*b*) A metal foil with an atomic spacing of 2.5×10^{-8} cm is studied with electrons accelerated through 60,000 volts, and a recording screen 50 cm beyond the foil.

Calculate the diameter of the innermost halo.

Measurements on the backscattering of much slower electrons by metals were carried out at the same time in the United States by

Davisson and Germer. They used a narrow beam of low-voltage electrons incident normal to the face of a single crystal of nickel cut parallel to its (111) face and observed the angular distribution of the backscattering of the electrons. For electrons originally accelerated through 54 volts, they found a maximum in the scattering at an angle of 50° from the normal.

A quantitative evaluation of the phenomenon, on the basis of the diffraction theory of waves, using the diffraction angle of 50° and the known grating spacing presented by the crystal gives a wavelength, associated with the phenomenon, of 1.65 A. The wavelength associated with a beam of electrons accelerated through 54 volts is 1.67 A, in quite satisfactory agreement with the 1.65 A. Measurements with other metals showed corresponding agreement between the wavelengths calculated by the two methods.

In addition to the diffraction effects of electron beams, diffraction effects have also been demonstrated for beams of helium atoms, hydrogen molecules, and beams of thermal neutrons. This behavior of neutron beams has promoted them to an important tool for locating the relative positions of hydrogen atoms in crystals.

Thus the wave character of particles in motion has a practical as well as a theoretical basis.

1-9 Wave mechanics. Schroedinger and others had meanwhile extended the ideas of de Broglie and had developed a new dynamics for atomic and molecular systems. Atoms and molecular systems are represented by wave functions, just as in macrooscillating systems sound and radiation are represented by wave functions. In the parlance of the newer wave mechanics, the motion of electrons in an atom can be represented by waves, whose wavelengths, velocities, and amplitudes are determined when the wave function of the system is known. The quantized angular momenta and energies of the stationary states that a system may manifest are found from the solutions to the general wave equation, when boundary conditions are imposed.

Although, in many cases, wave mechanics does not predict the parameters of an atomic system to the accuracy suggested by the Bohr theory, it is found that under those circumstances, the accuracy suggested by the Bohr theory is illusory. Consider, for example, Eq. (1-3), where $mrv = h/2\pi$, for $n = 1$. Since $h/2\pi$ is known to better than one part in a thousand, the product on the left-hand side of the equation should be known to this accuracy. As we shall see in later chapters, the uncertainty principle of wave mechanics predicts that the above product may not be known to better than $\sim h/2\pi$. Thus the

Bohr theory assumes an accuracy in the *rv* product very much greater than is possible.

A good introduction to wave mechanics is made by considering some aspects of the theory of waves. Chapter 2 presents a mathematical treatment of those aspects of wave theory that should be helpful for an understanding of wave mechanics.

wave theory

chapter

2

2-1 Introduction. In Chap. 1 the similarity between beams of electrons and beams of electromagnetic radiation was noted, in particular in the diffraction of these beams by periodic structures. For this reason we shall review here certain aspects of wave theory that are relevant to the motion of lightweight particles. We consider first the propagation of monochromatic harmonic waves *in vacuo*, and the superposition of several such monochromatic waves. Next, we shall review the creation of standing waves, and the conditions imposed on their frequencies by the geometry of the vessel containing these waves. Finally, we shall consider the creation of wave packets by the so-called Fourier synthesis of monochromatic harmonic waves, and conversely the analysis of wave packets in terms of component monochromatic waves.

In addition to the propagation of waves *in vacuo*, their propagation in dispersive media will also be considered. Extension to nonhomogeneous media leads to a generalization of Fourier expansion, namely, to the expansion in terms of a complete set of orthogonal functions. Just as the monochromatic harmonic wave functions are characteristic of homogeneous media, each heterogeneous medium has a characteristic set of orthogonal functions associated with it.

2-2 Harmonic waves. The harmonic wave is a simple example of a wave traveling with a constant velocity through any medium, without change in profile. The shape of this profile is described by a wave function; for harmonic waves the general form of the wave function is

$$\Psi = \phi \exp i\left[2\pi\left(\frac{q}{\lambda} - \frac{t}{\tau}\right)\right] \tag{2-1}$$

where ϕ = maximum amplitude
q = coordinate along which the wave is propagated
λ = wavelength
τ = period

The maximum amplitude ϕ is generally complex; it can be written in the form $\phi = |\phi| \exp -i\beta$, in which case Eq. (2-1) becomes

$$\Psi = |\phi| \exp i\left[2\pi\left(\frac{q}{\lambda} - \frac{t}{\tau}\right) - \beta\right] \tag{2-1a}$$

Here $|\phi|$ and β are real, as are q, λ, t, and τ. The quantity β is called the "phase angle." The following parameters are also frequently used to describe the properties of a harmonic wave:

$k \equiv 1/\lambda \equiv$ wave number
$\gamma \equiv 2\pi/\lambda \equiv$ angular wave number
$\nu \equiv 1/\tau \equiv$ frequency
$\omega \equiv 2\pi/\tau \equiv$ angular frequency
v_p = velocity of propagation

Figure 2-1 represents the propagation of a harmonic wave; the real and imaginary parts of the wave function Ψ are plotted against the coordinate q for two values of the time t. The wavelength is the distance between adjacent crests, and the wave number represents the number of wavelengths that fit into a unit of distance. The solid and the dotted curves represent the wave at two moments between which there is a time interval Δt. When this time interval equals the period τ, then the dotted curve just coincides with the solid one; in this case each crest has moved up one wavelength. Therefore the wave covers a distance λ in a time τ; hence it travels with a velocity v_p which equals λ/τ. Since $\lambda = 2\pi/\gamma$, and $1/\tau = \omega/2\pi$, $v_p = \omega/\gamma$; v_p is also known as the phase velocity.

Equation (2-1) can be rewritten in terms of γ and ω:

$$\Psi = \phi \exp i(\gamma q - \omega t) \tag{2-2}$$

Similarly Eq. (2-1*a*) can be transformed into Eq. (2-3):

$$\Psi = |\phi| \exp i(\gamma q - \omega t - \beta) \tag{2-3}$$

2-3 Superposition of waves. Generally, in wave mechanics, the wave function representing a system results from the superposition

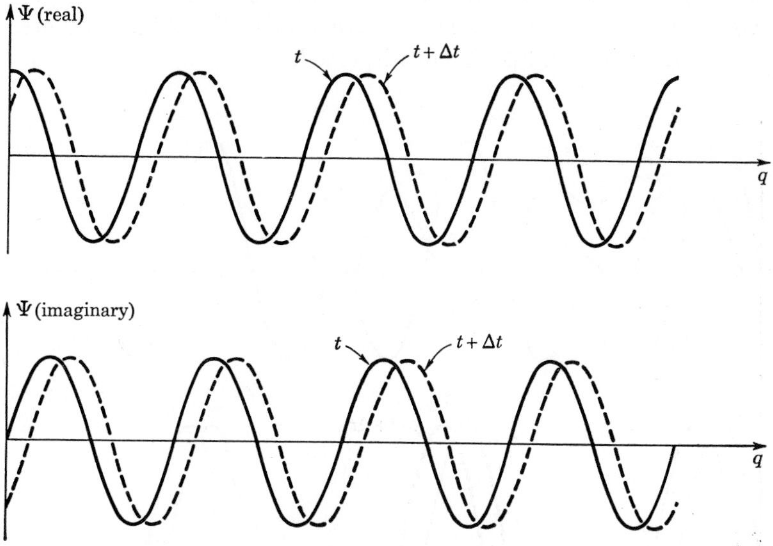

fig. 2-1 propagation of a monochromatic wave

of several other wave functions. A method for superimposing waves was postulated by Young, who showed that when two light waves cross each other, the resultant amplitude at the point of crossing is the sum of the amplitudes of each separate wave at the point of crossing. Young's observation is represented mathematically by Eq. (2-4), which expresses the wave function Ψ as a linear combination of the functions

$$\Psi_1 = \phi_1 \exp i(\gamma_1 q - \omega_1 t) \qquad \text{and} \qquad \Psi_2 = \phi_2 \exp i(\gamma_2 q - \omega_2 t):$$

$$\Psi = \phi_1 \exp i(\gamma_1 q - \omega_1 t) + \phi_2 \exp i(\gamma_2 q - \omega_2 t) \tag{2-4}$$

Equation (2-4) is illustrated in Fig. (2-2); it is observed that the profile of a function such as given by Eq. (2-4) is generally *not preserved* as time progresses.

Observe that in Fig. 2-2*a* the propagation velocities of the two waves represented by Ψ_1 and Ψ_2 differ and that the profile of the resulting wave changes with time. On the other hand each wave in Fig. 2-2*b* has the same propagation velocity; the profile of the resulting wave remains constant. When harmonic waves are superimposed whose wave propagation velocities are the same, even though their wave numbers and angular frequencies differ, then the profile of the wave does not change with time. The superposition of harmonic waves with different propagation velocities results in a wave with changing profile; such a wave is said to be dispersed. The wave shown in Fig. 2-2*a* is dispersed; the one shown in Fig. 2-2*b* is not dispersed.

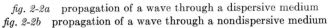

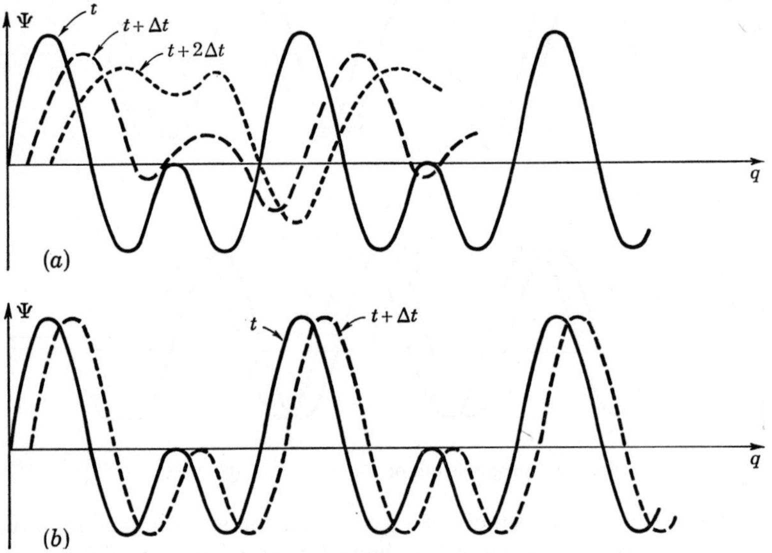

fig. 2-2a propagation of a wave through a dispersive medium
fig. 2-2b propagation of a wave through a nondispersive medium

When a third wave is added to the result of superimposing two waves, the resulting amplitude is the sum of the amplitudes of all three component waves. Equation (2-4) can be generalized to include the superposition of any number of harmonic waves:

$$\Psi = \sum_{n=-\infty}^{\infty} \phi_n \exp i(\gamma_n q - \omega_n t) \tag{2-5}$$

Such a wave is dispersed unless Eq. (2-6) is satisfied:

$$\frac{\omega_1}{\gamma_1} = \frac{\omega_2}{\gamma_2} = \cdots = \frac{\omega_n}{\gamma_n} = v_p \tag{2-6}$$

It should be emphasized that in Eq. (2-5) the quantity γ_n may well be negative; in that case the propagation velocity is negative so that a wave with negative γ_n propagates in the negative q direction. The quantity ω_n may similarly be negative.

---

problem 2-1. Show that a necessary condition for maintaining the same profile of a wave is that the wave function be a linear combination of the wave functions of a number of harmonic waves, all having the same velocity of propagation.

2-4 Real wave functions. While the most general harmonic wave function is complex, as given by Eq. (2-2), two such wave functions can always be superimposed to give a real wave function. Consider Eq. (2-4); if we set $\gamma_1 = -\gamma_2 = \gamma$, and $\omega_1 = -\omega_2 = \omega$,

$$\Psi = \phi_1 \exp i(\gamma q - \omega t) + \phi_2 \exp - i(\gamma q - \omega t)$$

Two cases are of interest:

If $\phi_1 = \phi_2 = \frac{1}{2}\phi$,

$$\Psi = \phi \cos (\gamma q - \omega t)$$

If $\phi_1 = -\phi_2 = -\frac{1}{2}i\phi$,

$$\Psi = \phi \sin (\gamma q - \omega t)$$

In both cases real wave functions are produced as long as ϕ is chosen real. It should be noted that the two component waves constituting these real waves are propagated in the *same* direction with the *same* velocity, for $v_1 = \omega/\gamma$, and $v_2 = (-\omega)/(-\gamma)$.

---

problem 2-2. Below is a list of wave functions. Find the wave functions that result when these are added in pairs. For each superposition give the propagation velocities of the component waves and of the resultant wave.

(*a*) $\cos (\gamma q - \omega t)$
(*b*) $i \sin (\gamma q - \omega t)$
(*c*) $\cos (\gamma q + \omega t)$
(*d*) $i \sin (\gamma q + \omega t)$

2-5 Standing waves. Of special interest in Prob. 2-2 is the addition of the wave functions $\cos(\gamma q - \omega t)$ and $\cos(\gamma q + \omega t)$. The waves described by these two wave functions travel with equal speeds, but in *opposite* directions. The resultant wave has the wave function

$$2 \cos \gamma q \cos \omega t$$

It is a function that has several remarkable properties. In the first place the locations of its nodes are independent of time, for the wave function $2 \cos \gamma q \cos \omega t$ vanishes whenever the function $2 \cos \gamma q$ does, irrespective of t. Furthermore, the profile of the resulting wave only changes its scale as time progresses, but its shape remains geometrically similar at all times, as shown in Fig. 2-3. The wave thus

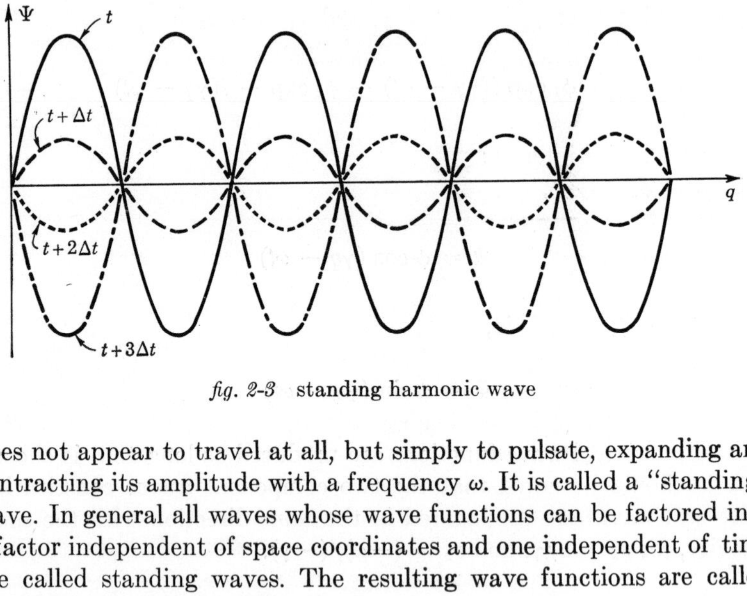

fig. 2-3 standing harmonic wave

does not appear to travel at all, but simply to pulsate, expanding and contracting its amplitude with a frequency ω. It is called a "standing" wave. In general all waves whose wave functions can be factored into a factor independent of space coordinates and one independent of time are called standing waves. The resulting wave functions are called "stationary" wave functions.

---

problem 2-3. (*a*) Prove that the function $\Psi = 2\phi \sin \gamma q \sin \omega t$ represents a standing wave with nodes at $q = n\pi/\gamma$ (where n is an integer), regardless of the value of t.

(*b*) Find the nodes in the wave whose wave function is given by $\Psi = 2\phi \cos \gamma q \cos \omega t$.

---

problem 2-4. Find the wave function representing the wave obtained by the superposition of two waves whose respective wave functions are

$$\Psi_1 = +\phi \sin (\gamma q - \omega t)$$
$$\Psi_2 = -\phi \cos (\gamma q + \omega t)$$

Where, if any, are the nodes in the resulting wave?

---

problem 2-5. What are the propagation velocities of the waves whose wave functions are, respectively,

$$\Psi_1 = \cos (\gamma q - \omega t) \quad \text{and} \quad \Psi_2 = i \sin (\gamma q + \omega t)?$$

Does the addition of these two waves result in a standing wave? Determine which of the waves found in Prob. 2-2 are standing waves.

---

problem 2-6. The waves whose respective wave functions are

$$\Psi_1 = \phi \exp i(\gamma q + \omega t) \quad \text{and} \quad \Psi_2 = \phi \exp i(\gamma q - \omega t)$$

are added.

Is the resultant wave stationary?
Does it have any nodes?
Do its real and imaginary parts have any nodes?
(Assume that ϕ is real.)

2-6 The wave equation and its solutions. All waves, whether pressure waves, electromagnetic waves, or particle waves, have wave functions that satisfy a differential equation of the form of Eq. (2-7).

$$\nabla^2\Psi + g^2(\mathbf{q})\Psi = a\frac{\partial\Psi}{\partial t} + b\frac{\partial^2\Psi}{\partial t^2} \tag{2-7}$$

where ∇^2 is Laplace's operator and $g^2(\mathbf{q})$ is a real function of space coordinates. The function $g^2(\mathbf{q})$ depends on the properties of the medium in which the wave is propagated. In homogeneous media g^2 is independent of $\mathbf{q}$. The coefficients a and b are independent of space and time coordinates. Equation (2-7) is called a wave equation; its solutions depend on the particular form of the function $g^2(\mathbf{q})$. We can find the particular form which the wave equation assumes for harmonic waves by substituting Eq. (2-2) into Eq. (2-7).

$$(g^2 - \gamma^2)\Psi = (-i\omega a - \omega^2 b)\Psi \tag{2-8}$$

Since generally Ψ does not vanish, it can be canceled out of both sides of the equation. Since, furthermore, $\omega = v\gamma$,

$$g^2 = \gamma^2(1 - bv^2) - iv\gamma a \tag{2-9}$$

Accordingly, g^2 is independent of q for harmonic waves.

---

problem 2-7. (*a*) Prove that for harmonic waves

$$a + a^* = +i\gamma v(b - b^*)$$

(*Hint:* Take the complex conjugate of both sides of Eq. (2-9) and remember that g^2 is real.)

(*b*) Prove that if b is real in the harmonic wave equation, a is purely imaginary.

Since Eq. (2-7) is a linear, homogeneous differential equation, any linear combination of several of its solutions is also a solution.

---

problem 2-8. In Eq. (2-7) replace Ψ by $(c\Psi)$. Show that the resulting equation is equivalent to Eq. (2-7) by dividing both sides by c.

---

problem 2-9. State the conditions for which

$$\Psi = \phi_1 \cos(\gamma q - \omega t) \qquad \text{and} \qquad \Psi = \phi_2 \sin(\gamma q - \omega t)$$

are both solutions of Eq. (2-7). Prove that under these conditions, $\Psi = \phi \exp i(\gamma q - \omega t)$ is also a solution, by two methods:

(*a*) Direct substitution

(*b*) Linear combination of two solutions

In general, if $\Psi = \chi_1$ is a solution of Eq. (2-7), then

$$\nabla^2\chi_1 + g^2\chi_1 = a\,\frac{\partial\chi_1}{\partial t} + b\,\frac{\partial^2\chi_1}{\partial t^2} \tag{2-10}$$

and similarly if $\Psi = \chi_2$ is a solution of the same equation, then

$$\nabla^2\chi_2 + g^2\chi_2 = a\,\frac{\partial\chi_2}{\partial t} + b\,\frac{\partial^2\chi_2}{\partial t^2} \tag{2-11}$$

where ∇^2 is the Laplace operator. To prove that a linear combination of χ_1 and χ_2 is also a solution of Eq. (2-7), multiply both sides of Eq. (2-10) by ϕ_1 and both sides of Eq. (2-11) by ϕ_2, where ϕ_1 and ϕ_2 are both independent of space coordinates and of time, and add the two resulting equations together:

$$\nabla^2(\phi_1\chi_1 + \phi_2\chi_2) + g^2(\phi_1\chi_1 + \phi_2\chi_2) = a\,\frac{\partial}{\partial t}\,(\phi_1\chi_1 + \phi_2\chi_2) + b\,\frac{\partial^2}{\partial t^2}\,(\phi_1\chi_1 + \phi_2\chi_2) \tag{2-12}$$

According to Eq. (2-12) then, the function $\phi_1\chi_1 + \phi_2\chi_2$, which is a linear combination of χ_1 and χ_2, is also a solution of Eq. (2-7).

While we have shown that there is an infinite number of solutions to a differential equation such as the wave equation, the number of *linearly independent* solutions of a linear homogeneous differential equation equals the degree of that equation; for partial differential equations this applies to *each* of the *independent* variables. (Solutions are linearly *independent* if no linear combination exists that is identically equal to zero for all values of the independent variables. For instance, $\sin \gamma q$ and $\cos \gamma q$ are linearly independent because the linear combination $(\phi_s \sin \gamma q + \phi_c \cos \gamma q)$ vanishes only if $\phi_s/\phi_c = -\cot \gamma q$; this is generally not true if ϕ_s and ϕ_c are independent of q.)

---

problem 2-10. (*a*) Prove that $\exp i\gamma q$ and $\exp -i\gamma q$ are linearly independent.

(*b*) Determine whether $\exp i\gamma q$ and $\sin \gamma q$ are linearly independent.

(*c*) Prove that the following functions are all linearly independent:

$\exp i(\gamma q - \omega t) \qquad \exp -i(\gamma q - \omega t)$
$\exp i(\gamma q + \omega t) \qquad \exp -i(\gamma q + \omega t)$

(*d*) Write the *most general* solution of the harmonic wave equation.

Since a second-order differential equation has two linearly independent solutions, any other solution can be expressed as a linear combination of these solutions. In Sec. 2-5 we considered a particular combination of harmonic wave functions, namely, the one leading to standing waves. In Sec. 2-7 we shall consider the wave equation peculiar to standing waves.

2-7 The stationary wave equation. In Sec. 2-5 we found that the superposition of two harmonic waves traveling in opposite directions with equal speeds may lead to a standing wave. We then defined a stationary wave function as one that may be written in the form

$$\Psi = \psi T \tag{2-13}$$

where ψ is independent of time and T is independent of coordinates. When Eq. (2-13) is substituted into Eq. (2-7) and both sides of the equation are divided by Ψ,

$$\frac{1}{\psi}\nabla^2\psi + g^2(\mathbf{q}) = \frac{a}{T}\frac{\partial T}{\partial t} + \frac{b}{T}\frac{\partial^2 T}{\partial t^2} \tag{2-14}$$

Since ψ and g^2 are independent of time, the left-hand side of Eq. (2-14) is independent of time. In order for Eq. (2-14) to be valid, its right-hand side must also be independent of time. Since this right-hand side is independent of the space coordinates, the left-hand side must also be independent of coordinates. Consequently *both* sides of Eq. (2-14) must be independent of *both* time and coordinates. In other words, Eq. (2-14) is for standing waves equivalent to Eqs. (2-15) and (2-16):

$$\nabla^2\psi + g^2\psi = -K^2\psi \tag{2-15}$$

$$b\frac{\partial^2 T}{\partial t^2} + a\frac{\partial T}{\partial t} = -K^2 T \tag{2-16}$$

where K is independent of time and of coordinates. Equation (2-15) is called the stationary wave equation; its solution depends on the particular form of $g^2(\mathbf{q})$. Equation (2-16), with constant coefficients, is easily solved. In the particular case of *harmonic* waves, Eqs. (2-2) and (2-13) give

$$\psi = \phi \exp i\gamma q$$
$$T = \exp -i\omega t$$

These are substituted in Eqs. (2-15) and (2-16), with the result that

$$-\gamma^2 + g^2 = -K^2 \tag{2-17}$$
$$-\omega^2 b - ia\omega = -K^2 \tag{2-18}$$

From Eqs. (2-17) and (2-18),

$$\gamma^2 = g^2 + \omega^2 b + ia\omega$$

Therefore, the speed of propagation is

$$v = \frac{\omega}{\gamma} = \pm \frac{\omega}{(g^2 + \omega^2 b + ia\omega)^{1/2}}$$

Here v is a function of ω, so that, in general, waves obtained by the superposition of harmonic waves are dispersed. On the other hand, if $g^2 = 0$ and $a = 0$, then v^2 is independent of ω; in this case the superposition of harmonic waves leads to a wave that is not dispersed. (Electromagnetic waves *in vacuo* obey the special wave equation

$$\nabla^2 \Psi = \frac{1}{v^2}\frac{\partial^2 \Psi}{\partial t^2})$$

Since Eq. (2-15) is homogeneous, linear, and of second order, it has two linearly independent solutions for each value of K^2. Similarly, Eq. (2-16) has two linearly independent solutions for each value of K^2. There are, therefore, generally four linearly independent solutions of the stationary wave equation for each value of K^2. There remains the evaluation of this parameter K. We shall see in the next section that K is determined by the boundary conditions imposed on the wave functions.

---

problem 2-11. Prove that if ψ is a solution of Eq. (2-15) and T is a solution of Eq. (2-16), then $\Psi = \psi T$ is a solution of the wave equation, Eq. (2-7).

---

problem 2-12. Write a general solution of Eq. (2-16) in terms of a, b, and K, and also in terms of γ and ω.

2-8 Boundary conditions and quantization. Since in this chapter we confine our attention to linear motion, the stationary wave equation, Eq. (2-15), becomes here

$$\frac{d^2\psi}{dq^2} + g^2(q)\psi = -K^2\psi \qquad \text{(2-15}a\text{)}$$

In particular, we can substitute Eq. (2-17) for harmonic waves to obtain the stationary harmonic wave equation

$$\frac{d^2\psi}{dq^2} = -\gamma^2\psi \qquad \text{(2-19)}$$

As we know, two linearly independent solutions of Eq. (2-19) are $\exp i\gamma q$ and $\exp -i\gamma q$, so that the most general solution of the stationary harmonic wave equation can be written

$$\psi = \phi_+ \exp i\gamma q + \phi_- \exp -i\gamma q \qquad \text{(2-20)}$$

where ϕ_+ and ϕ_- are independent of q.

Similarly, if χ_+ and χ_- are two linearly independent solutions of the general stationary wave equation, Eq. (2-15), then its general solution is

$$\psi = \phi_+\chi_+ + \phi_-\chi_- \qquad \text{(2-21)}$$

To evaluate ϕ_+ and ϕ_-, two boundary conditions must be given. Let us consider boundary conditions at two values of q, namely, $q = \pm\frac{1}{2}q_0$:

$$\psi(-\tfrac{1}{2}q_0) = A \quad \text{and} \quad \psi(+\tfrac{1}{2}q_0) = B$$

From Eq. (2-21),

$$A = \phi_+\chi_+(-\tfrac{1}{2}q_0) + \phi_-\chi_-(-\tfrac{1}{2}q_0) \qquad \text{(2-22)}$$
$$B = \phi_+\chi_+(+\tfrac{1}{2}q_0) + \phi_-\chi_-(+\tfrac{1}{2}q_0) \qquad \text{(2-23)}$$

In particular, for the harmonic wave equation we obtain, from Eq. (2-20),

$$A = \phi_+ \exp(-\tfrac{1}{2}i\gamma q_0) + \phi_- \exp(+\tfrac{1}{2}i\gamma q_0) \qquad \text{(2-24)}$$
$$B = \phi_+ \exp(+\tfrac{1}{2}i\gamma q_0) + \phi_- \exp(-\tfrac{1}{2}i\gamma q_0) \qquad \text{(2-25)}$$

In both the general and the harmonic case there are two equations, and two unknowns, ϕ_+ and ϕ_-. We shall first discuss the harmonic case, and later generalize to any wave equation.

Equations (2-24) and (2-25) can be solved by determinants as long as A and B do not both vanish:

$$\phi_+ = \frac{A \exp(-\tfrac{1}{2}i\gamma q_0) - B \exp(+\tfrac{1}{2}i\gamma q_0)}{\exp(-i\gamma q_0) - \exp(i\gamma q_0)}$$

and

$$\phi_- = \frac{B \exp(-\tfrac{1}{2}i\gamma q_0) - A \exp(+\tfrac{1}{2}i\gamma q_0)}{\exp(-i\gamma q_0) - \exp(i\gamma q_0)}$$

Substitution of these expressions for ϕ_+ and ϕ_- into Eq. (2-20) gives:

$$\psi = \frac{A \sin \gamma(\tfrac{1}{2}q_0 - q) + B \sin \gamma(\tfrac{1}{2}q_0 + q)}{\sin \gamma q_0} \tag{2-26}$$

---

problem 2-13. Check by direct substitution in Eq. (2-26) whether $\psi(-\tfrac{1}{2}q_0) = A$ and $\psi(+\tfrac{1}{2}q_0) = B$.

This solution fails, however, when A and B both vanish. In that case Eqs. (2-24) and (2-25), and also Eqs. (2-22) and (2-23), form a set of linear, homogeneous algebraic equations. In general such a set of equations has nonvanishing solutions *only* if the determinant of the coefficients vanishes. Thus if A and B vanish, nonvanishing values of ϕ_+ and ϕ_- exist only if the determinant of the coefficients of ϕ_+ and ϕ_- in Eqs. (2-24) and (2-25) vanishes, in other words, if

$$\begin{vmatrix} \exp(-\tfrac{1}{2}i\gamma q_0) & \exp(+\tfrac{1}{2}i\gamma q_0) \\ \exp(+\tfrac{1}{2}i\gamma q_0) & \exp(-\tfrac{1}{2}i\gamma q_0) \end{vmatrix} = 0$$

Hence

$$\sin \gamma q_0 = 0 \tag{2-27}$$

$$\gamma q_0 = n\pi \tag{2-28}$$

where n is an integer that may be negative as well as positive. Equation (2-28) indicates that when a standing wave is required to vanish at two points a distance q_0 apart, its angular wave number is limited to a discrete set of values. If we remember that $\gamma = 2\pi/\lambda$, we see that q_0 equals $n(\tfrac{1}{2}\lambda)$, so that exactly an integral number of half wavelengths fits between the two points where the wave function vanishes, as shown in Fig. 2-4. Since γ is limited to the values $n\pi/q_0$, it follows from Eq. (2-17) that $K^2 = n^2\pi^2/q_0^2 - g^2$. Thus both Eqs. (2-15) and (2-16) can only be solved for discrete sets of values of K^2; the solutions of the harmonic wave equation are therefore limited to a discrete set of functions that vanish at $q = \pm \frac{1}{2}q_0$. We say that the waves are "quantized" by the condition that they vanish at two points.

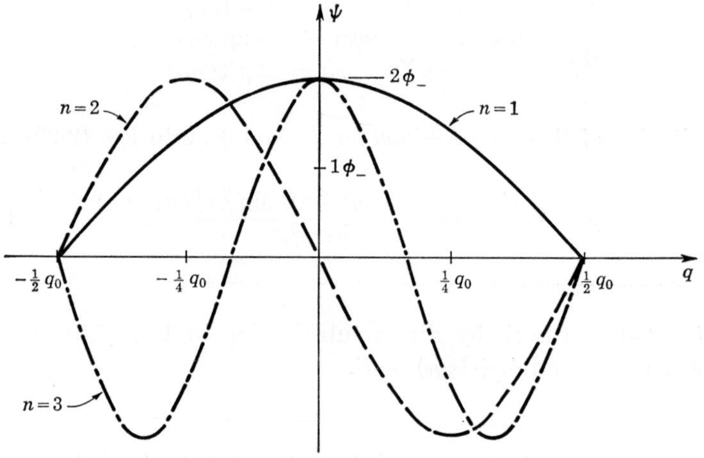

$\psi = \phi_-[(-1)^{n+1}\exp(in\pi q/q_0) + \exp(-in\pi q/q_0)]$

fig. 2-4 quantization of the wave number

When A and B vanish, it follows from Eqs. (2-24) and (2-25) that

$$\phi_+ \exp -\tfrac{1}{2}i\gamma q_0 = -\phi_- \exp +\tfrac{1}{2}i\gamma q_0$$

and

$$\phi_+ = -\phi_- \exp i\gamma q_0 = -\phi_- \exp in\pi = -\phi_-(-1)^n = (-1)^{n+1}\phi_-$$

Therefore

$$\begin{aligned}\psi &= \phi_-[(-1)^{n+1}\exp i\gamma q + \exp -i\gamma q] \\ &= \phi_-\left[(-1)^{n+1}\exp\left(\frac{in\pi q}{q_0}\right) + \exp\left(-\frac{in\pi q}{q_0}\right)\right] \qquad (2\text{-}29)\end{aligned}$$

---

problem 2-14. (*a*) Prove that the wave function given by Eq. (2-29) vanishes at $q = \pm\frac{1}{2}q_0$ for all integer values of n.

(*b*) If ϕ is real, for which values of n is ψ real everywhere, and for which values is it pure imaginary everywhere?

We can extend the same argument as used above to the solutions of the general stationary wave equation. If $A = B = 0$, then Eqs. (2-22) and (2-23) have nonvanishing solutions only if

$$\chi_+(-\tfrac{1}{2}q_0)\chi_-(+\tfrac{1}{2}q_0) = \chi_+(+\tfrac{1}{2}q_0)\chi_-(-\tfrac{1}{2}q_0)$$

In general, this is true only for a discrete set of values of $(-K^2)$. We can denote the general solution of the stationary wave equation vanishing at two points, by ψ_n, and that of the associated time-dependent equation, by T_n; the permitted values of K are designated K_n. Then $\Psi_n = \psi_n T_n$ is a solution of the general wave equation, Eq. (2-7), vanishing at two designated points, for all integer values of n. The most general solution of Eq. (2-7) that vanishes at those two points can then be written

$$\Psi = \sum_{n=-\infty}^{\infty} C_n \psi_n T_n \tag{2-30}$$

where C_n is independent of q and t.

The parameters C_n denote the relative weight given each function Ψ_n, in taking the linear combination. For harmonic waves we can substitute for ψ_n the expression given by Eq. (2-29); the parameters C_n can be combined with ϕ_- by defining $\phi_n \equiv C_n\phi_-$. Then

$$\Psi = \sum_{n=-\infty}^{\infty} \phi_n \left[(-1)^{n+1} \exp\left(\frac{in\pi q}{q_0}\right) + \exp\left(-\frac{in\pi q}{q_0}\right)\right] T_n \tag{2-31}$$

---

problem 2-15. Show by using the expressions

$$\exp \pm \frac{in\pi q}{q_0} = \cos \frac{n\pi q}{q_0} \pm i \sin \frac{n\pi q}{q_0}$$

that Eq. (2-31) is equivalent at any given time to a real Fourier series expansion.

---

problem 2-16. Show that, while $\Psi_n = \psi_n T_n$ is a stationary solution of Eq. (2-7), $\Psi = \sum_n C_n \psi_n T_n$ is generally not a stationary solution of that equation.

2-9 Interpretation of K_n and quantization of frequencies. Equation (2-30) gives an expression for the general solution of the wave equation that vanishes at two points; Eq. (2-31) is an equally general expression for a *harmonic* wave with nodes at $q = \pm\frac{1}{2}q_0$. In both of these expressions T_n represents a solution of Eq. (2-16) for allowed values of K. Since Eq. (2-16) is of second order, it has two linearly independent solutions for each value of K. Since, furthermore, Eq. (2-16) is independent of $g^2(\mathbf{q})$, T_n always has the form that we already know for harmonic waves:

$$T_n = \exp -i\omega_n t \tag{2-32}$$

where according to Eq. (2-18),

$$-\omega_n^2 b - ia\omega_n = -K_n^2 \tag{2-33}$$

In the case of vibrating strings or air columns encountered in many musical instruments, both the function $g^2(\mathbf{q})$ and the coefficient a vanish, while b is finite. For these cases Eq. (2-33) becomes

$$K_n^2 = \omega_n^2 b$$

while Eq. (2-17) becomes

$$K_n^2 = \gamma_n^2$$

so that

$$\omega_n^2 = \frac{\gamma_n^2}{b}$$

When Eq. (2-28) is substituted for γ_n,

$$\omega_n^2 = \frac{(n\pi)^2}{bq_0^2}$$

Therefore, for vibrating strings or air columns the allowed frequencies are integral multiples of a fundamental frequency, $\pi/b^{1/2}q_0$. Generally, a and g^2 do not vanish, so that the relationships between the various allowed frequencies are not so simple; bells, for instance, have frequencies that are not so simply related.

In wave mechanics, we usually deal with vanishing b, but finite g^2 and a. In Prob. 2-7 it was shown that, in this case, a must be purely imaginary. Therefore, in wave mechanics, Eq. (2-33) becomes

$$K_n^2 = ia\omega_n$$

where K_n^2 is real.

Furthermore, when b vanishes, Eq. (2-16) is of first order, so that, in wave mechanics, it has only one linearly independent solution. The allowed values of ω_n depend on the quantization of K_n, in other words on boundary constraints.

Because of the importance in later chapters of the wave equation with vanishing b, we summarize below the various wave equations and their solutions, substituting for K_n^2 the expression $ia\omega_n$,

$$\nabla^2\Psi + g^2(\mathbf{q})\Psi = a\frac{\partial\Psi}{\partial t} \qquad \text{[from Eq. (2-7)]} \qquad (2\text{-}34)$$

$$\Psi = \sum_n C_n\psi_n T_n \qquad (2\text{-}30)$$

$$\frac{d^2\psi_n}{dq^2} + g^2(q)\psi_n = -ia\omega_n\psi_n \qquad \text{[from Eq. (2-15)]} \qquad (2\text{-}35)$$

$$T_n = \exp -i\omega_n t \qquad (2\text{-}32)$$

Thus Ψ is known everywhere, and at all times, when ψ_n, ω_n, and C_n are known. In some cases ψ_n and ω_n can be found by solving Eq. (2-35) analytically; in general, however, the determination of ψ_n and ω_n involve fairly elaborate approximation techniques. Both the analytical solutions and some approximation methods will be discussed in later chapters. The constants C_n in Eq. (2-30) can be determined when an initial condition is given. We shall first discuss the method of finding the set C_n for the example of harmonic waves, and then extend this method to the general wave equation.

---

problem 2-17. Find the most general expression for the solution of the harmonic wave equation that satisfies the condition $\partial\Psi/\partial q = 0$ when $q = \pm\frac{1}{2}q_0$.

2-10 Harmonic analysis. In Sec. 2-8 it was pointed out that any linear combination of stationary solutions of a wave equation, while not itself stationary, is also a solution of that wave equation. Thus since the wave functions $\Psi_n = \exp i(n\pi q/q_0 - \omega_n t)$ are solutions of the harmonic wave equation, their linear combination

$$\Psi = \sum_{n=-\infty}^{\infty} \phi_n \exp i\left(\frac{n\pi q}{q_0} - \omega_n t\right) \qquad (2\text{-}36)$$

is also a solution of that same equation.

We shall now show that, if the function Ψ is known at a particular time, say $t = 0$, then it is possible to find the function Ψ at any other time. For this purpose the procedure called "harmonic analysis" is applied. This procedure consists of finding the coefficients ϕ_n in Eq. (2-36) in terms of the known function $\Psi(q,0)$. When these coefficients are then substituted in Eq. (2-36), a general expression is obtained for $\Psi(q,t)$.

In this section we do not limit ourselves to functions vanishing at

$$q = \pm \tfrac{1}{2} q_0$$

as was done in Sec. 2-8. At $t = 0$ the wave function is

$$\Psi(q,0) = \sum_{n=-\infty}^{\infty} \phi_n \exp i \frac{n\pi q}{q_0} \tag{2-36a}$$

Multiply both sides of Eq. (2-36a) by the function $\exp(-im\pi q/q_0)$, where m is an integer, and integrate both sides of the resulting equation over the interval $-q_0 < q < +q_0$. (The reason for choosing this particular interval will be given in Sec. 2-11; see also Prob. 2-18.) Then

$$\int_{-q_0}^{+q_0} \exp\left(-i\frac{m\pi q}{q_0}\right) \Psi(q,0)\, dq = \sum_{n=-\infty}^{\infty} \phi_n \int_{-q_0}^{+q_0} \exp\left[i\frac{(n-m)\pi q}{q_0}\right] dq \tag{2-37}$$

The integral on the right-hand side of the last equation is evaluated for two separate cases:

1. $n \neq m$:

$$\int_{-q_0}^{+q_0} \exp\left[i\frac{(n-m)\pi q}{q_0}\right] dq = \frac{-iq_0}{(n-m)\pi} \{\exp[i(n-m)\pi] - \exp[-i(n-m)\pi]\} = 0$$

2. $n = m$:

$$\int_{-q_0}^{+q_0} \exp\left[i\frac{(n-m)\pi q}{q_0}\right] dq = \int_{-q_0}^{+q_0} dq = 2q_0$$

Therefore, in the summation on the right-hand side of Eq. (2-37) all terms vanish except the one having $n = m$, so that

$$\phi_m = \frac{1}{2q_0} \int_{-q_0}^{+q_0} \exp\left(-i\frac{m\pi q}{q_0}\right) \Psi(q,0)\, dq$$

and because the subscript m could represent any one of the integers n,

$$\phi_n = \frac{1}{2q_0} \int_{-q_0}^{+q_0} \exp\left(-i\frac{n\pi q}{q_0}\right) \Psi(q,0)\, dq \tag{2-38}$$

Since $\Psi(q,t) = \sum_n \phi_n \exp i(n\pi q/q_0 - \omega_n t)$, Eq. (2-38) leads to the following relation between the wave function at any time $\Psi(q,t)$ and the wave function at a given time $\Psi(q,0)$:

$$\Psi(q,t) = \frac{1}{2q_0} \sum_n \left[\int_{-q_0}^{+q_0} \exp\left(-i\frac{n\pi q}{q_0}\right) \Psi(q,0)\, dq\right] \exp i\left(\frac{n\pi q}{q_0} - \omega_n t\right) \tag{2-39}$$

As an example, consider a uniform string that is clamped between points at $q = \pm\frac{1}{2}q_0$ and plucked and released at time $t = 0$ at a position halfway between these points. At time $t = 0$ the wave function describing the profile of this string is

$$\Psi(q,0) = \Psi(0,0)\left(1 - \frac{2|q|}{q_0}\right)$$

where $\Psi(0,0)$ represents the displacement of the string when and where it is plucked. When this expression is substituted into Eq. (2-38), a general expression for ϕ_n is found, excluding for the time being ϕ_0,

$$\begin{aligned}\phi_n &= \frac{1}{2q_0} \int_{-q_0}^{+q_0} \exp\left(-i\frac{n\pi q}{q_0}\right) \Psi(0,0)\left(1 - \frac{2|q|}{q_0}\right) dq \\ &= \frac{\Psi(0,0)}{2q_0} \int_{-q_0}^{+q_0} \exp\left(-i\frac{n\pi q}{q_0}\right)\left(1 - \frac{2|q|}{q_0}\right) dq\end{aligned}$$

The second factor in the integrand is even, while for the first factor the real part is even, the imaginary part odd.† Consequently, the

† Even and odd functions are defined as follows:

$f(x)$ is even if $f(-x) = f(x)$ $\qquad$ $f(x)$ is odd if $f(-x) = -f(x)$

The product of an odd by an even function gives an odd function. Integration of an odd function over an interval that is bisected by the origin results in zero.

imaginary part of the integral vanishes. Integration by parts gives

$$\phi_n = \frac{\Psi(0,0)}{q_0}\,\mathrm{Re}\left[\left(1-\frac{2q}{q_0}\right)\left(\frac{iq_0}{n\pi}\exp -i\frac{n\pi q}{q_0}\right)\Big|_0^{q_0} + \frac{2i}{n\pi}\int_0^{q_0}\exp\left(-i\frac{n\pi q}{q_0}\right)dq\right]$$

$$= \frac{2\Psi(0,0)}{(n\pi)^2}\left[(-1)^{n+1}+1\right]$$

Thus

$$\begin{aligned}\phi_1 &= +\frac{4}{\pi^2}\Psi(0,0) = \phi_{-1}\\ \phi_2 &= 0 = \phi_{-2}\\ \phi_3 &= \frac{4}{9\pi^2}\Psi(0,0) = \phi_{-3}\\ \phi_4 &= 0 = \phi_{-4}\end{aligned}$$

A separate case is ϕ_0:

$$\phi_0 = \frac{\Psi(0,0)}{q_0}\int_0^{q_0}\left(1-\frac{2q}{q_0}\right)dq = \frac{\Psi(0,0)}{q_0}(q_0-q_0) = 0$$

Thus

$$\begin{aligned}\Psi(q,t) &= \Psi(0,0)\left\{\frac{4}{\pi^2}\left(\exp\frac{i\pi q}{q_0}+\exp\frac{-i\pi q}{q_0}\right)\exp -i\omega t\right.\\ &\qquad \left. +\frac{4}{9\pi^2}\left(\exp\frac{3i\pi q}{q_0}+\exp\frac{-3i\pi q}{q_0}\right)\exp -i\omega_3 t+\cdots\right\}\\ &= \Psi(0,0)\left[\frac{8}{\pi^2}\cos\frac{\pi q}{q_0}\exp(-i\omega_1 t)+\frac{8}{9\pi^2}\cos\frac{3\pi q}{q_0}\exp(-i\omega_3 t)+\cdots\right]\end{aligned}$$

This last result agrees with that obtained by conventional Fourier expansion; it is observed that the vibration of the string plucked at the center contains only odd harmonics. Figure 2-5 shows the amplitudes, ϕ_n, of the various admixed harmonics as a function of the wave number of that harmonic. The wave number is given by the relation $\gamma_n = n\pi/q_0$.

2-11 Orthogonal functions. In the harmonic analysis discussed in Sec. 2-10, use was made of the fact that

$$\int_{-q_0}^{+q_0}\exp\frac{-im\pi q}{q_0}\exp\frac{in\pi q}{q_0}\,dq = 0 \qquad \text{when } m \neq n$$

This behavior is a special case of the general phenomenon of orthogonality. Two functions $v(q)$ and $w(q)$ are said to be orthogonal over the interval $q_1 < q < q_2$ if

$$\int_{q_1}^{q_2} v^*(q)w(q)\,dq = 0 \qquad (2\text{-}40)$$

where v^* is the complex conjugate of v.

---

problem 2-18. Show that the functions $\exp im\pi q/q_0$ and $\exp in\pi q/q_0$ with $m \neq n$, are orthogonal over the interval $-q_0 < q < +q_0$, and the interval $0 < q < 2q_0$, but not over the intervals $-\frac{1}{2}q_0 < q < \frac{1}{2}q_0$ and $0 < q < q_0$.

---

problem 2-19. (*a*) Find the smallest interval over which $\sin(\pi q/q_0)$ and $\cos(\pi q/q_0)$ are orthogonal.

(*b*) Are $\sin(\pi q/q_0)$ and $\sin(2\pi q/q_0)$ orthogonal?

(*c*) Are $\sin(\pi q/q_0)$ and $\exp(i\pi q/q_0)$ orthogonal?

We noted in Sec. 2-10 that if *all* stationary wave functions are known, then a general solution can be expressed as a linear combination

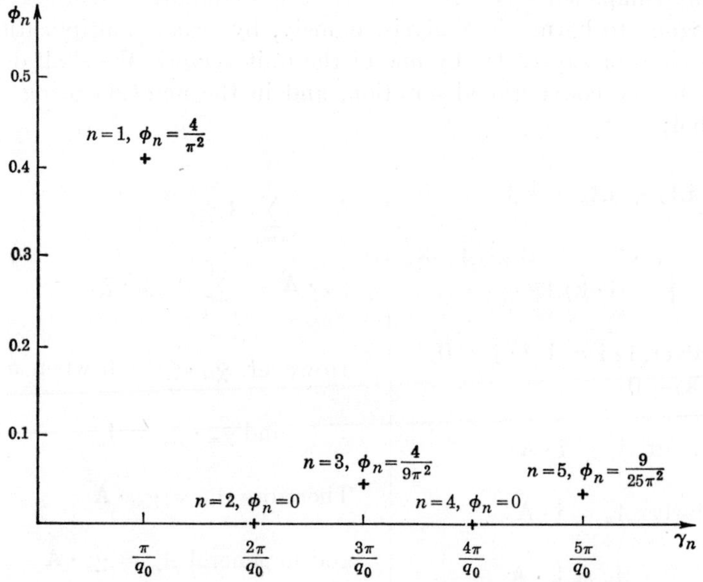

fig. 2-5 amplitudes vs. quantized wave number for a plucked string

of *all* these. Thus the stationary functions are a frame of reference with respect to which the solution is expressed. The coefficient of each stationary function is a measure of how much each function contributes to the desired solution. There is a close analogy between the expansion in terms of orthogonal functions and the expansion of three-dimensional vectors in terms of orthogonal unit vectors:

$$\mathbf{A} = \hat{\mathbf{i}}A_x + \hat{\mathbf{j}}A_y + \hat{\mathbf{k}}A_z$$

which can be rewritten
$$\mathbf{A} = \sum_{n=1}^{3} A_n \hat{\mathfrak{x}}_n \qquad (2\text{-}41)$$

where
$$A_1 = A_x \qquad \hat{\mathfrak{x}}_1 = \hat{\mathbf{i}}$$
$$A_2 = A_y \qquad \hat{\mathfrak{x}}_2 = \hat{\mathbf{j}}$$
$$A_3 = A_z \qquad \hat{\mathfrak{x}}_3 = \hat{\mathbf{k}}$$

The three vectors $\hat{\mathbf{i}}$, $\hat{\mathbf{j}}$, and $\hat{\mathbf{k}}$ form a complete, linearly independent orthogonal set, in terms of which any vector $\mathbf{A}$ can be expressed.

---

problem 2-20. Prove that $\hat{\mathbf{i}}$, $\hat{\mathbf{j}}$, and $\hat{\mathbf{k}}$ are linearly independent.

The components A_x, A_y, and A_z are found by a method quite analogous to harmonic analysis, namely, by scalar multiplication of both sides of Eq. (2-41) by one of the unit vectors. We shall do this both in the conventional notation, and in the notation using the Σ symbol:

$$\mathbf{A} = \hat{\mathbf{i}}A_x + \hat{\mathbf{j}}A_y + \hat{\mathbf{k}}A_z$$

$$\hat{\mathbf{i}} \cdot \mathbf{A} = (\hat{\mathbf{i}} \cdot \hat{\mathbf{i}})A_x + (\hat{\mathbf{i}} \cdot \hat{\mathbf{j}})A_y + (\hat{\mathbf{i}} \cdot \hat{\mathbf{k}})A_z$$

However, $\hat{\mathbf{i}} \cdot \hat{\mathbf{i}} = 1$, $\hat{\mathbf{i}} \cdot \hat{\mathbf{j}} = 0$, $\hat{\mathbf{i}} \cdot \hat{\mathbf{k}} = 0$

Therefore $A_x = \hat{\mathbf{i}} \cdot \mathbf{A}$

Similarly $A_y = \hat{\mathbf{j}} \cdot \mathbf{A}$

$$A_z = \hat{\mathbf{k}} \cdot \mathbf{A}$$

$$\mathbf{A} = \sum_{n=1}^{3} A_n \hat{\mathfrak{x}}_n$$

$$\hat{\mathfrak{x}}_m \cdot \mathbf{A} = \sum_{n=1}^{3} A_n \hat{\mathfrak{x}}_m \cdot \hat{\mathfrak{x}}_n$$

However, $\hat{\mathfrak{x}}_m \cdot \hat{\mathfrak{x}}_n = 0$ when $m \neq n$

and $\hat{\mathfrak{x}}_m \cdot \hat{\mathfrak{x}}_m = 1$

Therefore $A_m = \hat{\mathfrak{x}}_m \cdot \mathbf{A}$

and in general $A_n = \hat{\mathfrak{x}}_n \cdot \mathbf{A}$

Thus, the orthogonality of the vectors $\hat{\mathbf{\imath}}$, $\hat{\mathbf{\jmath}}$, and $\hat{\mathbf{k}}$ is used in much the same way in finding the components of a vector, as the condition expressed by Eq. (2-40) is used to perform a harmonic analysis. It is well known in vector analysis that there are many orthogonal coordinate systems that can be used as a reference system; for instance, any cartesian system can be transformed into another one having the same origin by a rotation. This is equivalent to taking a linear combination of the original unit vectors. The two orthogonal sets of functions sin $(n\pi q/q_0)$ and cos $(n\pi q/q_0)$ on the one hand and exp $(in\pi q/q_0)$ on the other are similarly related, for each of the functions of the one set is a linear combination of some functions of the other set. Just as in the case of vector algebra, the choice of a coordinate system is determined by the nature of the problem; in the same way the choice of an orthogonal set of functions will be determined by the form of $g^2(\mathbf{q})$. The functions sin $(n\pi q/q_0)$, cos $(n\pi q/q_0)$, and exp $(in\pi q/q_0)$ are characteristic of the harmonic wave equation, which has $g^2(\mathbf{q}) = 0$. In general the functions $\chi_n(\mathbf{q})$ are related to the functions $g^2(\mathbf{q})$ of Eq. (2-35). For each form of the function $g^2(\mathbf{q})$ there exists a set of characteristic functions $\chi_n(\mathbf{q})$ that is used as a frame of reference. Instead of the term "characteristic" function the German equivalent "eigenfunction" is frequently used.

There corresponds to each solution χ_n of Eq. (2-35) a value of $(-K^2)$, denoted by $(-K_n{}^2)$. This value is called the "eigenvalue" of Eq. (2-15*a*) corresponding to the eigenfunction χ_n.

2-12 Transforms. The expansions in terms of stationary harmonics discussed in Sec. 2-10 originated with boundary constraints imposed at two points, $q = \pm\frac{1}{2}q_0$. It was these constraints that restricted the wave number and consequently the frequency to discrete values. The difference between the allowed values of the wave number was found to be inversely proportional to the distance between points where the boundary constraints were imposed. In the present section we allow the distance between these points to increase indefinitely, so that the quantized values of wave number approach each other. In that case, the points in Fig. 2-5 approach each other to form a continuous curve.

Since $\gamma_n = n\pi/q_0$, Eq. (2-38) can be rewritten

$$\phi_n = \frac{1}{2q_0}\int_{-q_0}^{+q_0} \exp\,(-i\gamma_n q)\Psi(q,0)\,dq$$

Since the quantized values of γ differ from each other by integral multiples of π/q_0, we define $\Delta\gamma = \pi/q_0$; the last equation then becomes

$$\phi_n = \frac{\Delta\gamma}{2\pi}\int_{-q_0}^{+q_0} \exp(-i\gamma_n q)\Psi(q,0)\,dq$$

When q_0 goes to infinity, $\Delta\gamma$ goes to zero, and the limits of the integral become minus infinity and plus infinity. Accordingly, we define

$$\phi(\gamma) \equiv \sqrt{(2\pi)}\lim_{q_0\to\infty}\frac{\phi_n}{\Delta\gamma} \tag{2-42}$$

assuming that this limit does in fact exist. It follows from this definition that

$$\phi(\gamma) = \frac{1}{\sqrt{2\pi}}\int_{-\infty}^{\infty} \exp(-i\gamma q)\Psi(q,0)\,dq \tag{2-43}$$

(The introduction of the factor $\sqrt{2\pi}$ into the definition of $\phi(\gamma)$ is as yet quite arbitrary, but will be justified presently on the basis of a symmetry argument.)

When q_0 goes to infinity, Eq. (2-36) becomes

$$\begin{aligned}\Psi(q,t) &= \lim_{q_0\to\infty}\sum_{n=-\infty}^{\infty}\phi_n \exp i(\gamma q - \omega t)\\ &= \frac{1}{\sqrt{2\pi}}\lim_{\Delta\gamma\to 0}\sum_{n=-\infty}^{\infty}\Delta\gamma\,\phi(\gamma)\exp i(\gamma q - \omega t)\end{aligned}$$

From the definition of an integral it follows that the last equation becomes

$$\Psi(q,t) = \frac{1}{\sqrt{2\pi}}\int_{-\infty}^{\infty}\exp[i(\gamma q - \omega t)]\phi(\gamma)\,d\gamma \tag{2-44}$$

and that, in particular

$$\Psi(q,0) = \frac{1}{\sqrt{2\pi}}\int_{-\infty}^{\infty}\exp(i\gamma q)\phi(\gamma)\,d\gamma \tag{2-45}$$

Equation (2-45) is a "Fourier transform"; it is a limiting expression for a Fourier series. Equation (2-43) is called an "inverse Fourier transform"; the symmetry between Eqs. (2-43) and (2-45) is striking and justifies the arbitrary introduction of the factor $\sqrt{(2\pi)}$.

Equation (2-44) can be interpreted as the superposition of an infinite number of harmonic waves with continuously varying wave numbers. $\Psi(q,t)$ as given by Eq. (2-44) represents a so-called "wave packet" whose components have the wave function $\phi(\gamma) \exp i(\gamma q - \omega t)$. The function $\phi(\gamma)$ then indicates the relative amount of admixture of each component in the wave packet, and is called the "distribution function." Wave packets will be discussed more extensively in Chap. 3.

2-13 General expansion in terms of orthogonal functions. Sections 2-8 to 2-12 have dealt principally with solutions of the harmonic wave equation. This section deals once more with the general wave equation. The most general solution of Eq. (2-7) is, for a single coordinate,

$$\Psi(q,t) = \sum_{n=-\infty}^{\infty} \phi_n \chi_n(q) \exp -i\omega_n t \tag{2-46}$$

where χ_n is any solution of the stationary wave equation, Eq. (2-15*a*),

$$\frac{d^2\chi_n}{dq^2} + g^2(q)\chi_n = -K_n{}^2\chi_n \tag{2-47}$$

the summation is carried out over *all* solutions of Eq. (2-47), and where ω_n is given by Eq. (2-18*a*):

$$-\omega_n{}^2 b - ia\omega_n = -K_n{}^2 \tag{2-18a}$$

As in the case of harmonic analysis, we can find the coefficients ϕ_n in terms of $\Psi(q,0)$ if the functions χ_n are orthogonal to each other. When all functions, χ_n, having different integer values of n are orthogonal to each other, these functions are called an "orthogonal set."

We shall now investigate under what conditions the solutions of the stationary wave equation, Eq. (2-47), form an orthogonal set. To do so, multiply both sides of this equation by χ_m^*, where $m \neq n$ and χ_m is a solution of Eq. (2-47),

$$\chi_m^* \frac{d^2\chi_n}{dq^2} + g^2(q)\chi_m^*\chi_n = -K_n{}^2\chi_m^*\chi_n \tag{2-48}$$

Since the function χ_m is itself a solution of Eq. (2-47),

$$\frac{d^2\chi_m}{dq^2} + g^2(q)\chi_m = -K_m{}^2\chi_m$$

If $g^2(q)$ and $K_m{}^2$ are real, then it follows by taking the complex conjugate of both sides of this last equation that

$$\frac{d^2\chi_m^*}{dq^2} + g^2(q)\chi_m^* = -K_m{}^2\chi_m^*$$

and hence

$$\chi_n \frac{d^2\chi_m^*}{dq^2} + g^2(q)\chi_n\chi_m^* = -K_m{}^2\chi_n\chi_m^* \tag{2-48a}$$

When Eq. (2-48a) is subtracted from Eq. (2-48), an equation results that is independent of $g^2(q)$:

$$\chi_m^* \frac{d^2\chi_n}{dq^2} - \chi_n \frac{d^2\chi_m^*}{dq^2} = (K_m{}^2 - K_n{}^2)\chi_m^*\chi_n$$

When the left-hand side of this equation is integrated by parts between two, as yet unspecified, limits $q = q_1$ and $q = q_2$, it becomes

$$\chi_m^* \frac{d\chi_n}{dq}\bigg|_{q_1}^{q_2} - \int_{q_1}^{q_2} \frac{d\chi_m^*}{dq}\frac{d\chi_n}{dq}\,dq - \chi_n \frac{d\chi_m^*}{dq}\bigg|_{q_1}^{q_2} + \int_{q_1}^{q_2} \frac{d\chi_n}{dq}\frac{d\chi_m^*}{dq}\,dq$$

and consequently

$$\left(\chi_m^* \frac{d\chi_n}{dq} - \chi_n \frac{d\chi_m^*}{dq}\right)\bigg|_{q_1}^{q_2} = (K_m{}^2 - K_n{}^2)\int_{q_1}^{q_2} \chi_m^*\chi_n\,dq \tag{2-49}$$

From Eq. (2-49) it follows that the integral $\int_{q_1}^{q_2} \chi_m^*\chi_n\,dq$ necessarily vanishes when both of the following conditions are valid:

$$\left(\chi_m^* \frac{d\chi_n}{dq} - \chi_n \frac{d\chi_m^*}{dq}\right)_{q=q_1} = \left(\chi_m^* \frac{d\chi_n}{dq} - \chi_n \frac{d\chi_m^*}{dq}\right)_{q=q_2} \tag{2-50}$$

and

$$K_m{}^2 \neq K_n{}^2$$

Under these conditions χ_m and χ_n are orthogonal over the interval $q_1 < q < q_2$. When Eq. (2-50) is valid, but $K_m{}^2 = K_n{}^2$, χ_m and χ_n may be orthogonal, but are not necessarily so. When $K_m{}^2$ equals $K_n{}^2$, the eigenfunctions χ_m and χ_n are called "degenerate."

---

problem 2-21. (a) Show that the functions $\chi_m = \sin(m\pi q/q_0)$ and $\chi_n = \sin(n\pi q/q_0)$ obey the condition imposed by Eq. (2-50) when $q_1 = -q_0$, and $q_2 = +q_0$.

(*b*) Determine whether these two functions are degenerate or nondegenerate eigenfunctions of the harmonic wave equation.

(*c*) Determine whether, according to the conditions just derived, these functions are necessarily orthogonal.

(*d*) Determine by direct integration whether these functions are in fact orthogonal.

(*e*) Show that the functions $\exp(in\pi q/q_0)$ and $\sin(n\pi q/q_0)$ are degenerate eigenfunctions of the harmonic wave equation.

(*f*) Show that the latter two functions satisfy Eq. (2-50).

(*g*) Show that, nevertheless, these functions are *not* orthogonal.

We have shown that nondegenerate eigenfunctions of the wave equation are necessarily orthogonal. Since the summation in Eq. (2-46) implies summation over *all* eigenfunctions, we should account for the degenerate eigenfunctions, as well, before solving for ϕ_n. For the time being, however, we shall assume that all eigenfunctions are orthogonal and postpone the treatment of degenerate eigenfunctions until Sec. 2-14.

To solve for ϕ_n in Eq. (2-46), set t equal to zero, multiply both sides of the resulting equation by χ_m^*, and integrate over the range of orthogonality of the set χ_n:

$$\int_{q_1}^{q_2} \chi_m^* \Psi(q,0)\, dq = \sum_{n=-\infty}^{\infty} \phi_n \int_{q_1}^{q_2} \chi_m^* \chi_n\, dq$$

As long as it is assumed that χ_m and χ_n are orthogonal, only one term remains in the summation, so that

$$\phi_n = \frac{\int_{q_1}^{q_2} \chi_n^* \Psi(q,0)\, dq}{\int_{q_1}^{q_2} \chi_n^* \chi_n\, dq} \tag{2-51}$$

Equation (2-51) is completely analogous to Eq. (2-38) for harmonic analysis; it can be similarly used to find a wave function at any time if the wave function is known at a particular time, and if all eigenfunctions of the wave equation are known. We have therefore shown that the method of Fourier analysis, which is so commonly used for media having g^2 independent of $\mathbf{q}$, can be generalized to include media having a g^2 that varies with $\mathbf{q}$. This generalization is very important in wave mechanics, because here g^2 usually varies strongly with $\mathbf{q}$.

We shall conclude this chapter with a discussion of degenerate eigenfunctions and of the integral

$$\int_{q_1}^{q_2} \chi_m^* \chi_n \, dq$$

---

problem 2-22. As an illustration of the use of the development in this section, let us consider the Legendre functions. These functions, given by the expression $P_n(x) = \frac{1}{2^n n!} \frac{d^n}{dx^n} (x^2 - 1)^n$, form an orthogonal set. Confirm this statement for the particular pair of functions having $n = 1$ and $n = 2$, and the interval $-1 < x < +1$.

---

problem 2-23. (*a*) Prove that the function $f(x) = x^2$ is orthogonal to all functions $P_n(x)$ defined in Prob. 2-22, except those having $n = 0$ and $n = 2$.

(*b*) Expand the function $f(x) = x^2$ for the range $-1 < x < +1$ in terms of the orthogonal set of functions $P_n(x)$. (*Hint:* Show that x^2 can be expressed as a linear combination of P_0 and P_2.)

2-14 Orthonormal sets; degenerate eigenfunctions. In Sec. 2-11 we pointed out the analogy between a set of orthogonal functions and the set of unit vectors defining an orthogonal coordinate system. While we have considered the analogy of Eq. (2-40) to the vector equation $\hat{\mathbf{i}} \cdot \hat{\mathbf{j}} = 0$, we have not considered the analog of the vector equation $\hat{\mathbf{i}} \cdot \hat{\mathbf{i}} = 1$, an equation defining the "unit length" of the unit vector. This analog would be Eq. (2-52):

$$\int_{q_1}^{q_2} w^*(q)w(q) \, dq = 1 \tag{2-52}$$

Since we always consider functions that are solutions of linear, homogeneous equations, these functions may be multiplied by an arbitrary constant and remain solutions of the same equations. Therefore Eq. (2-52) does not impose a very serious constraint on wave functions, beyond the fact that the integral in Eq. (2-52) actually exists. When a function obeys Eq. (2-52), it is said to be "normalized" over the interval $q_1 < q < q_2$; when each function in an orthogonal set is normalized, the set is called "orthonormal." We shall denote the symbol $\int_{q_1}^{q_2}$, where $q_1 < q < q_2$ is the interval of orthogonality, by the abbreviation $\int_{\text{orth}}$.

---

problem 2-24. Normalize the functions $\sin(n\pi q/q_0)$, $\cos(n\pi q/q_0)$, and $\exp(in\pi q/q_0)$ over the interval $-q_0 < q < q_0$.

We have now established a set of functions χ_n that serve as a reference frame for the wave function $\Psi(q,t)$; this wave function may be thought of as a multidimensional vector whose components are ϕ_n. The inversion of Eq. (2-46), that is, the expression of ϕ_n in terms of $\Psi(q,0)$ can be accomplished if it is known that the χ_n's form an orthonormal set. The one doubt that remains about this last condition occurs in the case of degenerate eigenfunctions. To resolve this problem, we once more refer to the vector analogy. In Fig. 2-6 it is shown that the

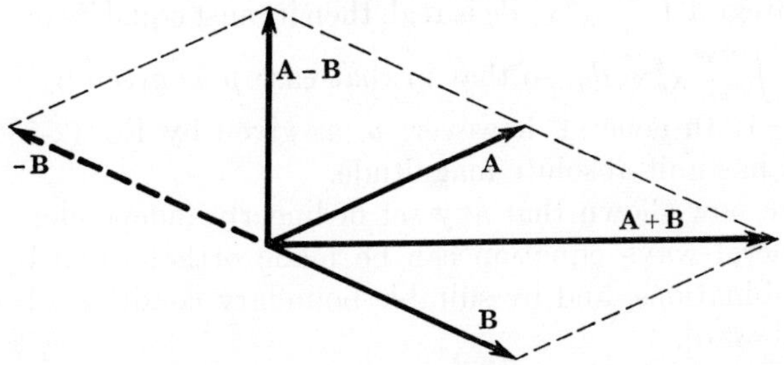

fig. 2-6 linear combination of an oblique pair of vectors into an orthogonal pair

sum and differences of two vectors of equal length are orthogonal to each other: the product $[\mathbf{A} + \mathbf{B}] \cdot [\mathbf{A} - \mathbf{B}]$ equals $[A]^2 - [B]^2$, which vanishes if $|A| = |B|$. By analogy, let us take two degenerate normalized eigenfunctions χ_m and χ_n that are not orthogonal to each other. Let us form the two linear combinations $(\chi_m + \chi_n)$ and $(\chi_m + p\chi_n)$, and determine p such that these two new functions are orthogonal. From the analogous vector representation it might be concluded that p equals -1, but we shall see that the imaginary nature of our functions does not make this generally true.

---

problem 2-25. Show that the functions $(\chi_m + \chi_n)$ and $(\chi_m + p\chi_n)$ have the same eigenvalues as do χ_m and χ_n, if the latter two are degenerate.

If $(\chi_m + \chi_n)$ and $(\chi_m + p\chi_n)$ are to be orthogonal over the interval $-q_0 < q < q_0$, then

$$0 = \int_{-q_0}^{+q_0} (\chi_m + \chi_n)^*(\chi_m + p\chi_n)\, dq =$$
$$= 1 + p + p\int_{-q_0}^{+q_0} \chi_n\chi_m^*\, dq + \int_{-q_0}^{+q_0} \chi_m\chi_n^*\, dq$$

If χ_m and χ_n were orthogonal, then $\int_{-q_0}^{+q_0} \chi_n^*\chi_m\, dq$ and $\int_{-q_0}^{+q_0} \chi_m^*\chi_n\, dq$ would vanish, so that p in this case equals minus unity. If, however, χ_n and χ_m are not orthogonal, then

$$p = -\frac{1 + \int_{-q_0}^{+q_0} \chi_n^*\chi_m\, dq}{1 + \int_{-q_0}^{+q_0} \chi_m^*\chi_n\, dq} \tag{2-53}$$

If the integral $\int_{-q_0}^{+q_0} \chi_n^*\chi_m\, dq$ is real, then it must equal its own complex conjugate $\int_{-q_0}^{+q_0} \chi_m^*\chi_n\, dq$, so that in that case p as given by Eq. (2-53), becomes -1. In general, however, p, as given by Eq. (2-53) is imaginary, but has unit absolute magnitude.

We have now shown that any set of linearly independent solutions of the general wave equation can be made orthonormal by suitable linear combinations, and by suitable boundary conditions [Eq. (2-50) must be obeyed].

---

problem 2-26. Show that all pairs of degenerate eigenfunctions of the wave equation obey Eq. (2-50), whether or not they are orthogonal.

---

problem 2-27. In Prob. 2-21*g*, it was shown that the pair of degenerate functions $\exp(in\pi q/q_0)$ and $\sin(n\pi q/q_0)$ is not an orthogonal pair. Using Eq. (2-53), find two linear combinations of these two functions that are orthogonal to each other. [Remember that χ_n and χ_m in Eq. (2-53) are assumed to be normalized.]

2-15 Summary. We have presented, by the examples of harmonic waves and by extension to solutions of the general wave equation, some of the concepts of wave theory that are basic to wave mechanics.

The relation of quantization to the imposition of boundary constraints has been emphasized, and expansion in terms of quantized stationary wave functions discussed in detail. In the next chapter we shall deal principally with nonquantized waves, and with wave packets and their mathematical description. We shall be particularly concerned with the change of shape of packets as time progresses.

wave packets and the uncertainty principle

chapter

3

3-1 Introduction. Chapter 2 has dealt principally with waves that are composed of a discrete set of eigenfunctions of the wave equation. The present chapter deals with harmonic waves having continuous distribution functions, whose wave function is

$$\Psi(q,t) = \frac{1}{\sqrt{2\pi}} \int_{-\infty}^{\infty} \exp\,[i(\gamma q - \omega t)]\phi(\gamma)\,d\gamma \qquad (2\text{-}44)$$

where

$$\phi(\gamma) = \frac{1}{\sqrt{2\pi}} \int_{-\infty}^{\infty} \exp\,(-i\gamma q)\Psi(q,0)\,dq \qquad (2\text{-}43)$$

Frequently the component waves reinforce each other at one point and partially cancel each other elsewhere, so that the contour of the resulting wave has a maximum magnitude for a certain value of q and decreases on both sides of this maximum. Such a wave is called a wave packet. It is important that we have an understanding of wave packets since in the next chapter we shall find it helpful to associate a wave packet with a moving electron.

3-2 Distribution functions of some wave packets. As an example, we shall find the distribution function associated with a wave packet whose profile is gaussian, as shown by Fig. 3-1. Let us suppose then that at time $t = 0$ the wave packet has its maximum amplitude at the point $q = 0$, so that its normalized wave function is

$$\Psi(q,0) = \left(\frac{2\alpha^2}{\pi}\right)^{1/4} \exp -\alpha^2 q^2 \tag{3-1}$$

The maximum value of the amplitude of this wave packet is $(2\alpha^2/\pi)^{1/4}$: the amplitude drops to $1/e$ of this maximum value at the points

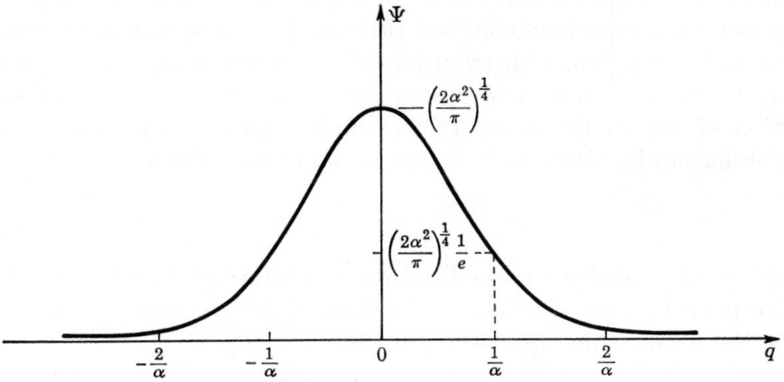

fig. 3-1 a gaussian wave function

$q = \pm 1/\alpha$. When α is large, the maximum is high, and the amplitude drops off steeply, while for small α the maximum is low and the amplitude decreases gently from the maximum. The distance $1/\alpha$ is a measure of the width of the wave packet and is called the "half width" of the packet. (Half width is sometimes defined using $\frac{1}{2}$ or $\sqrt{\frac{1}{2}}$ instead of $1/e$; the various definitions lead to different numerical values but to the same order of magnitude for the half width.) The distribution function for the gaussian wave packet is found by substituting Eq. (3-1) into Eq. (2-43):

$$\begin{aligned}\phi(\gamma) &= \frac{\alpha}{2\pi}\int_{-\infty}^{\infty} \exp(-i\gamma q - \alpha^2 q^2)\, dq \\ &= \frac{\alpha}{2\pi}\int_{-\infty}^{\infty} \cos\gamma q \exp(-\alpha^2 q^2)\, dq - \frac{i\alpha}{2\pi}\int_{-\infty}^{\infty} \sin\gamma q \exp(-\alpha^2 q^2)\, dq\end{aligned}$$

Since the function $\sin \gamma q$ is odd in q and the function $\exp -\alpha^2 q^2$ is even in q, the integrand in the second integral on the right-hand side is odd, so that the second integral vanishes. Therefore

$$\phi(\gamma) = \frac{1}{2\sqrt{\pi}} \exp \frac{-\gamma^2}{4\alpha^2} \tag{3-2}$$

The resulting distribution function is therefore gaussian also; it is a characteristic property of a gaussian function that its Fourier transform is again gaussian. The half width of the distribution function is seen to be 2α. Therefore, a narrow wave packet (large α) has a very broad distribution function, while a very narrow function gives rise to a very broad wave packet. When α approaches zero, the distribution function becomes a sharp peak, while the wave packet becomes very flat. The conclusion, derived here for a gaussian wave packet, is generally true: wave packets confined principally to a very narrow region contain a very broad distribution of harmonic waves, while wave packets spread over a very wide region contain a very narrow distribution of harmonic waves. In the limit, monochromatic radiation, which has an infinitely wide Ψ, has an infinitely narrow ϕ.

---

problem 3-1. Find the normalized wave function at time $t = 0$ for the wave packet whose distribution function is $\phi(\gamma) = \exp -\beta^2\gamma^2$. Compare the result with Eqs. (3-1) and (3-2).

We shall consider a second example to illustrate this important relation between the widths of Ψ and ϕ. Suppose that a traveling harmonic wave whose wave function is $\Psi(q,t) = \exp i(\gamma_0 q - \omega_0 t)$ were incident on a shutter located at $q = 0$ that is open only during the interval $-\Delta t \leq t \leq 0$. The passage of the transmitted wave is illustrated by Fig. 3-2. It is seen that a portion of the incident wave is

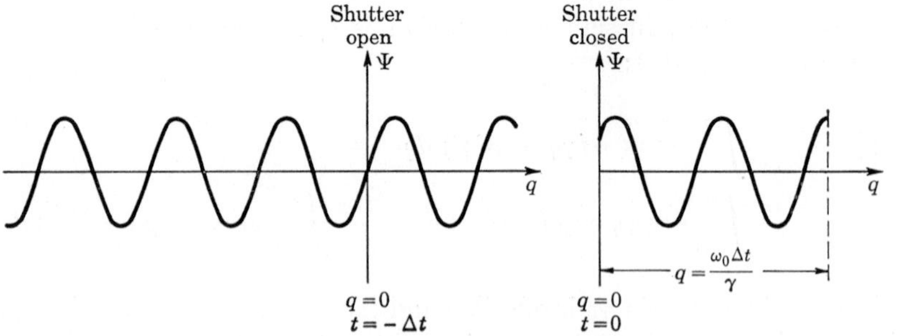

fig. 3-2 monochromatic wave passing through a shutter

clipped off, whose length equals the velocity of the wave ω_0/γ_0 multiplied by the time Δt. We shall concern ourselves only with the clipped-off wave packet, whose wave function at time $t = 0$ is given by

$$\Psi(q,0) = \begin{cases} 0 & \text{for } q < 0 \\ \exp i\gamma_0 q & \text{for } 0 \le q \le \dfrac{\omega_0\,\Delta t}{\gamma_0} \\ 0 & \text{for } \dfrac{\omega_0\,\Delta t}{\gamma_0} < q \end{cases} \tag{3-3}$$

At time $t = 0$, the clipped-off wave is limited to the region $0 \le q \le \omega_0\,\Delta t/\gamma_0$; this limitation gives rise to a distribution function different from the distribution which exists in the original monochromatic wave. The original harmonic wave had a distribution function with a sharp peak at $\gamma = \gamma_0$ but vanishing elsewhere. To find the distribution function of the clipped wave, substitute Eq. (3-3) into Eq. (2-43):

$$\begin{aligned}\phi(\gamma) &= \frac{1}{\sqrt{2\pi}} \int_0^{\omega_0\,\Delta t/\gamma_0} \exp(-i\gamma q)\exp(i\gamma_0 q)\,dq \\ &= \frac{1}{\sqrt{2\pi}} \frac{\exp i(\gamma_0 - \gamma)q}{i(\gamma_0 - \gamma)}\Bigg|_0^{q=\omega_0\,\Delta t/\gamma_0} \\ &= \frac{\exp\left(i\,\dfrac{\gamma_0 - \gamma}{\gamma_0}\,\omega_0\,\Delta t\right) - 1}{(-2\pi)^{1/2}(\gamma_0 - \gamma)}\end{aligned}$$

The real and imaginary parts of this distribution function are plotted in Fig. 3-3; the function vanishes whenever

$$\exp\left(i\,\frac{\gamma_0 - \gamma}{\gamma_0}\,\omega_0\,\Delta t\right) = 1 \qquad \text{and} \qquad \gamma \ne \gamma_0$$

that is, when $[(\gamma_0 - \gamma)/\gamma_0]\omega_0\,\Delta t = -2n\pi$; hence when

$$\gamma = \gamma_0 + \frac{2n\pi\gamma_0}{\omega_0\,\Delta t},\ n \ne 0$$

When γ approaches γ_0,

$$\exp\left(i\,\frac{\gamma_0 - \gamma}{\gamma_0}\,\omega_0\,\Delta t\right) \cong 1 + i\,\frac{\gamma_0 - \gamma}{\gamma_0}\,\omega_0\,\Delta t$$

so that $\phi(\gamma = \gamma_0) = \dfrac{\omega_0\,\Delta t}{\sqrt{2\pi}\,\gamma_0}$.

The half width of the distribution function can be characterized by the distance from the peak to the nearest intersection of its real part with the axis of the abscissa, $\pi\gamma_0/(\omega_0\,\Delta t)$. When the shutter is opened for a long time, Δt is large, and the distribution function has a high,

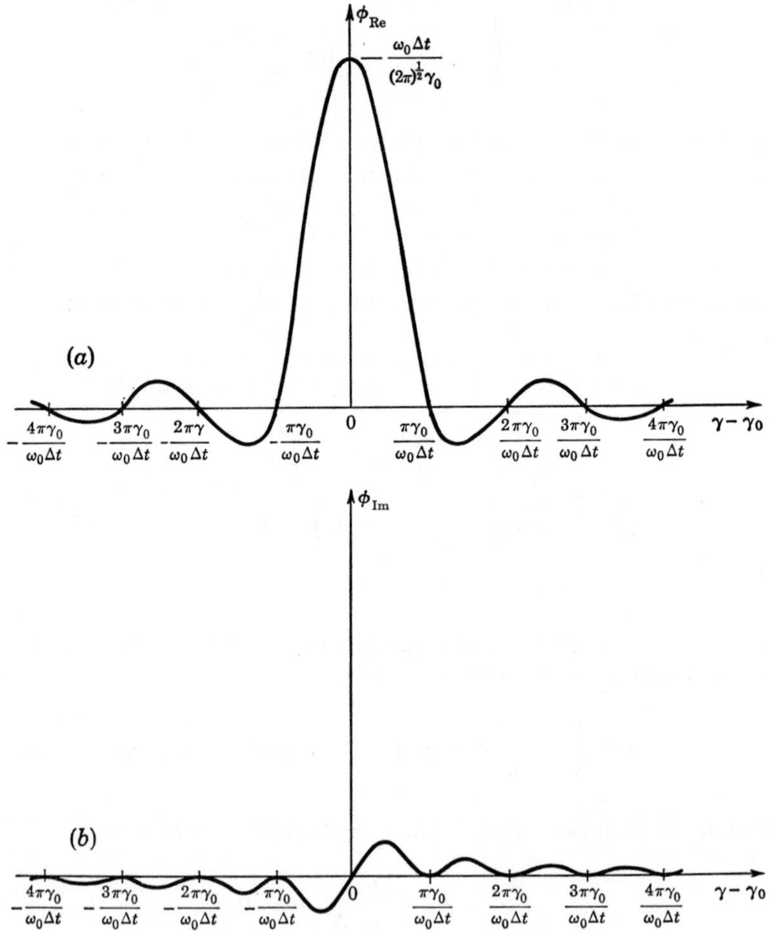

fig. 3-3 real and imaginary parts of $\phi(\gamma) = \dfrac{\exp\left(i\,\dfrac{\gamma_0-\gamma}{\gamma_0}\,\omega_0\,\Delta t\right) - 1}{(-2\pi)^{1/2}(\gamma_0-\gamma)}$

sharp peak at $\gamma = \gamma_0$. When Δt becomes infinite, the entire monochromatic beam passes through the shutter and remains monochromatic. When, on the other hand, the shutter is opened for only a very short time, the clipped-off wave packet is very short and the distribution function is very broad. The uncertainty in the position of the wave packet is its length $\omega_0 \, \Delta t/\gamma_0$; the uncertainty in the wave number for the packet is the width of its distribution function, $2\pi\gamma_0/\omega_0 \, \Delta t$; the product of these two is constant just as in the case of the gaussian wave packet.

---

problem 3-2. Find the distribution function for the wave packet produced by clipping off a portion of the monochromatic wave whose wave function is $\Psi = \sin(\gamma_0 q - \omega_0 t)$ by means of a shutter that is open during the period $-\frac{1}{2}\,\Delta t \leq t \leq \frac{1}{2}\,\Delta t$.

3-3 The uncertainty principle. A wave packet has neither an exact location nor an exact wave number; the center of the gaussian wave packet, for instance, can be exactly located, but its amplitude falls exponentially, and yet remains finite at all finite distances from the center. It was shown that such a wave packet is built up out of a large number of monochromatic harmonic waves, each with its own wave number, so that the wave number of a wave packet is not exactly determinable. It is, therefore, not realistic to speak about "the" wave number and "the" location of a packet, for both are to a certain extent indeterminate. The two examples in Sec. 3-2 demonstrate that the indeterminacy in position and wave number are reciprocally related. This is actually true for all wave packets, and is summarized in the uncertainty principle or indeterminacy principle: the indeterminacy in position and wave number of a wave packet are reciprocally related. The uncertainty principle has important applications in wave mechanics, as will be seen in Chap. 6; actually it applies to all wave phenomena, and is equally important in determining the resolution of optical equipment and in the design of antennae. The uncertainty principle is expressed

$$\Delta q \cdot \Delta\gamma \gtrsim 1 \tag{3-4}$$

where Δq and $\Delta\gamma$ are the respective uncertainties in position and wave number.

---

problem 3-3. The wave function of a certain traveling wave packet is

$$\Psi(q,t) = \frac{\alpha}{\sqrt{2\pi}} \exp\left[-\alpha^2\left(q - \frac{\omega_0 t}{\gamma_0}\right)^2 + i(\gamma_0 q - \omega_0 t)\right]$$

(*a*) Sketch the profile of the real and imaginary parts of this wave packet at time $t = 0$, and express the number of wavelengths within the width of the packet in terms of α and γ_0.

(*b*) Find the distribution function for this packet, and sketch it as a function of γ. Where does the maximum of this wave packet lie?

(*c*) Check the uncertainty principle by estimating Δq and $\Delta\gamma$ for following values of α: $1A^{-1}$; 1 micron^{-1}; 1 cm^{-1}.

(*d*) Determine the number of oscillations of the wave function within the half width of the wave packets for the following values of the ratio γ_0/α: 3000; 50; 6.

3-4 Dispersion of wave packets. In this section we shall study the change of contour of wave packets as time progresses. In Chap. 2 it was shown that a monochromatic harmonic wave travels with a velocity $v = \omega/\gamma$. It was also shown that any harmonic wave obtained by the superposition of several monochromatic waves only preserves its contour if each component wave travels with the same velocity.

A traveling monochromatic harmonic wave has the wave function $\Psi = \phi \exp i(\gamma q - \omega t) = \phi \exp i\gamma(q - vt)$. When a traveling wave packet is constructed out of such monochromatic waves, the resulting wave function is

$$\Psi(q,t) = \frac{1}{\sqrt{2\pi}} \int_{-\infty}^{\infty} \exp i\gamma[q - v(\gamma)t]\phi(\gamma)\, d\gamma \tag{3-5}$$

where $v(\gamma)$ indicates the dependence on the wave number of the velocity of each component wave, and $\phi(\gamma)$ is the distribution function.

If v is independent of γ, then the wave packet propagates without change of profile, while if $v(\gamma)$ changes with γ, the wave packet has a changing profile. The dependence of $v(\gamma)$ on γ is a property of the medium through which the wave is propagated. For instance, white light, having a very broad spectral distribution, is propagated as a compact wave packet in vacuum, but is dispersed in a prism, with all monochromatic components traveling with different velocities. From Eq. (2-43),

$$\phi(\gamma) = \frac{1}{\sqrt{2\pi}} \int_{-\infty}^{\infty} \exp(-i\gamma q)\Psi(q,0)\, dq$$

While the variable q occurs in the integral, $\phi(\gamma)$ is not a function of q, since the integral is definite. When we substitute $\phi(\gamma)$ into Eq.

(3-5), it is multiplied by a factor which does depend on q; without affecting $\phi(\gamma)$, we may label the q in the expression for $\phi(\gamma)$ with a prime and rewrite the expression:

$$\phi(\gamma) = \frac{1}{\sqrt{2\pi}} \int_{-\infty}^{\infty} \exp\,(-i\gamma q')\Psi(q',0)\, dq'$$

The symbol used for the variable of integration in a definite integral does not affect the value of the integral; this variable is therefore often called a "dummy" variable. Substitution of the last expression for $\phi(\gamma)$ into Eq. (3-5) gives

$$\Psi(q,t) = \frac{1}{2\pi} \int_{-\infty}^{\infty} \exp\, i\gamma[q - v(\gamma)t] \int_{-\infty}^{\infty} \exp\,(-i\gamma q')\Psi(q',0)\, dq'\, d\gamma$$

Since we have been careful to distinguish between q and q', we can interchange the order of integration:

$$\Psi(q,t) = \frac{1}{2\pi} \int_{-\infty}^{\infty} \left\{ \int_{-\infty}^{\infty} \exp\, i\gamma[q - q' - v(\gamma)t]\, d\gamma \right\} \Psi(q',0)\, dq' \qquad (3\text{-}6)$$

Equation (3-6) expresses the wave function at any time t in terms of the wave function at time $t = 0$. If $v(\gamma)$ is known as a function of γ, then $\Psi(q,t)$ can be found explicitly in terms of $\Psi(q,0)$.

Consider first the case where $v(\gamma)$ is independent of γ. Then the inner integral vanishes for all values of q' except $q' = q - vt$, in which case it becomes infinite.

The behavior of the integral $\int_{-\infty}^{\infty} \exp\, i\gamma(q - q' - vt)\, d\gamma$ is better understood when it is considered as the limit of the integral $\int_{-\Gamma}^{\Gamma} \exp\, i\gamma(q - q' - vt)\, d\gamma$, as Γ becomes infinite:

$$\begin{aligned} \int_{-\Gamma}^{\Gamma} \exp\, i\gamma(q - q' - vt)\, d\gamma &= \int_{-\Gamma}^{\Gamma} \cos \gamma(q - q' - vt)\, d\gamma \\ &\qquad + i \int_{-\Gamma}^{\Gamma} \sin \gamma(q - q' - vt)\, d\gamma \\ &= \frac{2 \sin \Gamma(q - q' - vt)}{q - q' - vt} \end{aligned}$$

This function has a maximum of height (2Γ) at $q = q' + vt$, and vanishes whenever $q - q' - vt = n\pi/\Gamma$, where n is an integer. As Γ increases indefinitely, the function becomes a spike of infinite height at $q' = q - vt$ and zero elsewhere. It is then called a "delta function" or "impulse function." Equation (3-6) can now be rewritten

$$\Psi(q,t) = \frac{1}{2\pi} \lim_{\Gamma\to\infty} \int_{-\infty}^{\infty} \frac{2 \sin \Gamma(q - q' - vt)}{q - q' - vt} \Psi(q',0)\, dq'$$

As Γ approaches infinity the integrand becomes zero everywhere except in the immediate vicinity of the point $q' = q - vt$; we can assume that in that vicinity the function $\Psi(q',0)$ equals $\Psi(q - vt, 0)$, and does not appreciably change with q' in that vicinity. Therefore, when Γ is sufficiently large,

$$\Psi(q,t) = \frac{1}{2\pi} \Psi(q - vt, 0) \lim_{\Gamma\to\infty} \int_{-\infty}^{\infty} \frac{2 \sin \Gamma(q - q' - vt)}{q - q' - vt}\, dq'$$

The integral is seen to be independent of Γ, so that

$$\Psi(q,t) = \frac{1}{2\pi} \Psi(q - vt, 0) \cdot 2\pi = \Psi(q - vt, 0)$$

This means that the function Ψ has the same value at time t at the point q that it had at the point $q - vt$, at time $t = 0$, so that it travels with a speed v without change of contour. This confirms the observation that no dispersion occurs when v is independent of γ.

Next we investigate the dispersion of the wave packet due to a linear dependence of v on γ. We shall see in Sec. 4-5 that this is just the way in which v varies with γ in the wave packet associated with an electron traveling at a constant velocity in vacuum. Let us write $v(\gamma) = A\gamma + B$, where A and B are independent of γ; then Eq. (3-6) becomes

$$\Psi(q,t) = \frac{1}{2\pi} \int_{-\infty}^{\infty} \left\{ \int_{-\infty}^{\infty} \exp i[(q - q' - Bt)\gamma - At\gamma^2]\, d\gamma \right\} \Psi(q',0)\, dq'$$

The inner integral can be evaluated by completing the square of the exponent:

$$(q - q' - Bt)\gamma - At\gamma^2 = -At\left(\gamma - \frac{q - q' - Bt}{2At}\right)^2 + \frac{(q - q' - Bt)^2}{4At}$$

Therefore

$$\int_{-\infty}^{\infty} \exp i[(q - q' - Bt)\gamma - At\gamma^2]\, d\gamma$$
$$= \exp\left[i\,\frac{(q - q' - Bt)^2}{4At}\right] \int_{-\infty}^{\infty} \exp\left[-iAt\left(\gamma - \frac{q - q' - Bt}{2At}\right)^2\right] d\gamma =$$

(changing variable)

$$= \frac{1}{(At)^{1/2}} \exp\left[i\frac{(q-q'-Bt)^2}{4At}\right]\int_{-\infty}^{\infty}\exp(-ix^2)\,dx$$

$$= \left(\frac{\pi}{2At}\right)^{1/2}(1-i)\exp i\,\frac{(q-q'-Bt)^2}{4At}$$

and $$\Psi(q,t) = \frac{1-i}{(8\pi At)^{1/2}}\int_{-\infty}^{\infty}\exp\left[i\frac{(q-q'-Bt)^2}{4At}\right]\Psi(q',0)\,dq' \quad (3\text{-}7)$$

Equation (3-7) expresses a wave function at any time in terms of the wave function at time $t = 0$ if the velocity of propagation is a linear function of the wave number. This equation will now be applied to the wave packet produced by clipping off a portion of a monochromatic wave by means of a shutter, as discussed in Sec. 3-2. The wave function at time $t = 0$ is given by Eq. (3-3); therefore

$$\Psi(q,t) = \frac{1-i}{(8\pi At)^{1/2}}\int_0^{\omega_0\,\Delta t/\gamma_0}\exp\left\{i\left[\gamma_0 q' + \frac{(q-q'-Bt)^2}{4At}\right]\right\}dq'$$

The last integral cannot be evaluated analytically; we shall make an approximation for the limiting case of a pulse produced by opening the shutter for a very short time only. When $\omega_0\,\Delta t/\gamma_0$ is sufficiently small, the integrand may be assumed to be constant over the interval of integration and to have the same value throughout the interval that it has at $q' = 0$. In that case,

$$\Psi(q,t) = \frac{1-i}{(8\pi At)^{1/2}}\exp\left[i\frac{(q-Bt)^2}{4At}\right]\frac{\omega_0\,\Delta t}{\gamma_0}$$

$$= \frac{\omega_0\,\Delta t}{2\gamma_0(\pi At)^{1/2}}\exp i\left[\frac{(q-Bt)^2}{4At}-\frac{\pi}{4}\right] \quad (3\text{-}8)$$

Equation (3-8) represents a wave packet that changes its shape as time progresses. This change of shape is described quantitatively by the dependence on time of the following quantities:

1. Velocity of propagation
2. Maximum amplitude
3. Dimension along the direction of propagation

The first of these, the velocity of propagation of the wave packet, is properly the velocity with which the center of the packet travels. Since the wave function given by Eq. (3-8) is an even function of $(q - Bt)$, the center of the packet occurs at $q = Bt$, which means that the packet travels with a velocity B. The maximum amplitude of the packet becomes attenuated at a rate inversely proportional to the square root of the time. The dimension along the direction of propagation can be determined as a function of time by directing one's attention on the positions where the real part of the wave function vanishes, and by following the separation between these positions as a function of time.

The real part of the wave function given by Eq. (3-8) vanishes whenever

$$\frac{(q - Bt)^2}{4At} - \frac{\pi}{4} = (n + \tfrac{1}{2})\pi \qquad n \text{ being an integer}$$

hence when $q = Bt \pm [(4n + 3)\pi At]^{\frac{1}{2}}$. The first term represents the position of the center of the packet; the second term the distance

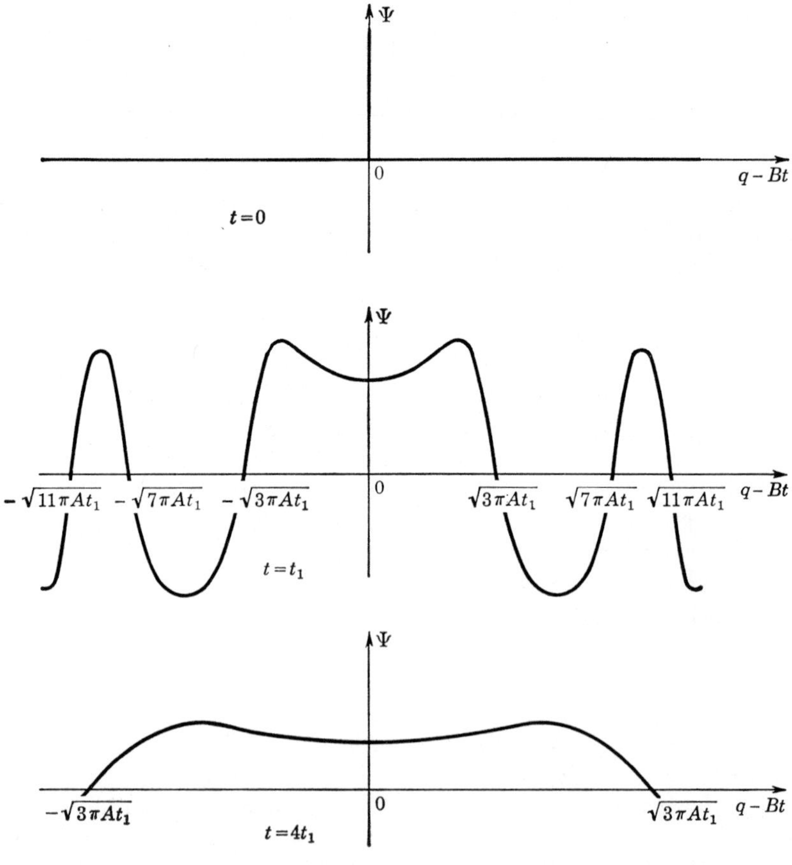

fig. 3-4 change in contour of an impulse due to dispersion as time progresses

from the center to the various nodes of the real part of the wave. For instance, the distance from the center to the first node is found by setting $n = 0$, and hence equals $(3\pi At)^{1/2}$. The rate at which the first node moves away from the center, as time progresses, is a good indication of the rate of spreading of the packet. We can say, therefore, that the wave packet spreads at a rate proportional to the square root of the time and that the dispersion is also determined by the magnitude of A, the dispersion coefficient. In Fig. 3-4 we demonstrate the attenuation and spreading of the real part of the packet given by Eq. (3-8) by plotting the real part of the wave function at various times. For each plot the center of the packet is chosen as the origin; the coordinate system is therefore chosen such that it moves along with the center of the packet.

---

problem 3-4. How does the wave packet whose wave function is given in Prob. (3-3) behave in a medium characterized by the equation $v(\gamma) = A\gamma + B$, as time progresses?

3-5 Summary. We have shown that there is a reciprocal relation between the dimension of a wave packet and the width of its spectral distribution. Furthermore, we have shown that with the passing of time a wave packet tends to spread in a dispersive medium. Any attempt to localize a wave packet in a dispersive medium will only be successful for a relatively short time. Here we have only discussed waves in an abstract sense; in the next chapter we shall apply the conclusions reached here to particle waves.

de Broglie's hypotheses applied to electron beams

chapter

4

4-1 Introduction. In Chap. 1 experiments were described demonstrating the wave properties associated with electron beams. Here we shall discuss de Broglie's hypotheses, which provide a quantitative relation between the wave characteristics and the dynamic parameters (energy and momentum) of electrons moving without acceleration. Later we shall extend these hypotheses to particles subject to potential gradients.

4-2 de Broglie's hypotheses. The experiments of Davisson and Germer, which confirmed de Broglie's hypotheses, were made with a beam of electrons having a certain energy E and linear momentum $\mathbf{p}$. The following relations result for the wave associated with such a beam:

$$E = h\nu = \frac{h\omega}{2\pi} = \hbar\omega \qquad \omega = \frac{E}{\hbar} \tag{4-1}$$

$$p = \frac{h}{\lambda} = \frac{h\gamma}{2\pi} = \hbar\gamma \qquad \gamma = \frac{p}{\hbar} \tag{4-2}$$

When the interference pattern, obtained by Davisson and Germer from the interaction of an electron beam with a nickel crystal, was analyzed on the basis of wave theory, the parameters corresponded to the values given by Eqs. (4-1) and (4-2). Since a beam of electrons may be assumed to extend indefinitely in its direction of motion, its wave properties may be compared to those of a simple harmonic wave, the wave function of which extends indefinitely in the direction of propagation.

According to Eqs. (4-1) and (4-2) the wave function associated with an electron beam becomes

$$\Psi = \phi \exp i\hbar^{-1}(pq - Et) \tag{4-3}$$

The speed of propagation of such a wave is ω/γ which here becomes E/p. Since the electrons move in a field-free region, all their energy is kinetic, so that the E in Eq. (4-3) is equal to $p^2/2m$, and E/p, the speed of propagation of the wave, becomes $p/2m$. The electrons composing the beam have a momentum p, so that the particle velocity is p/m. The particle velocity of the electrons is therefore twice as large as the propagation velocity; even so, this wave will not separate from the particle since the wave representing the monoenergetic beam of electrons may be considered to have an infinite length. The momentum and energy of the electron beam can be expressed explicitly in terms of the wave function Ψ by partial differentiation of Eq. (4-3):

$$\frac{\partial \Psi}{\partial q} = i\hbar^{-1}p\phi \exp i\hbar^{-1}(pq - Et) = i\hbar^{-1}p\Psi$$

Therefore $$p = -i\hbar \frac{\partial}{\partial q} (\ln \Psi)$$

Because p is obtained from Ψ by use of the operation $-i\hbar(\partial/\partial q)$, we call $-i\hbar(\partial/\partial q)$ the momentum operator, and denote it by the symbol $\mathcal{P}$. The last two relations can then be written in symbolic form:

$$p = \mathcal{P}(\ln \Psi)$$

or $$\mathcal{P}\Psi = p\Psi \tag{4-4}$$

When these equations are valid, we say that Ψ is an eigenfunction of the operator $\mathcal{P}$ with eigenvalue p. Similarly, we can extract the value of energy:

$$\frac{\partial \Psi}{\partial t} = -i\hbar^{-1}E\phi \exp i\hbar^{-1}(pq - Et) = -i\hbar^{-1}E\Psi$$

Therefore $$E = i\hbar \frac{\partial \ln \Psi}{\partial t}$$

If we denote $i\hbar(\partial/\partial t)$ by $\mathcal{E}$, then

$$E = \mathcal{E} \ln \Psi$$

or $$\mathcal{E}\Psi = E\Psi \tag{4-5}$$

Thus Ψ is an eigenfunction of the operator $\mathcal{E}$, with eigenvalue E. In general, if the effect of an operator $\mathfrak{F}$, operating on a function, is to multiply that function by a constant f, that is, if $\mathfrak{F}\Psi = f\Psi$, then that function is called an eigenfunction of the operator $\mathfrak{F}$ with corresponding eigenvalue f.

Neither $\phi \cos [\hbar^{-1}(pq - Et)]$ nor $\phi \sin [\hbar^{-1}(pq - Et)]$ is an eigenfunction of the momentum and energy operator. Furthermore, these cosine and sine functions are not stationary functions, since they do not factor into a space-independent and time-independent term. In principle there is no objection to nonstationary wave functions; it has been pointed out, however, that every nonstationary wave function can be expressed in terms of a complete set of stationary wave functions. For this reason we shall generally first look for the stationary wave functions of a system. Consequently, neither $\phi \cos \hbar^{-1}(pq - Et)$ nor $\phi \sin \hbar^{-1}(pq - Et)$ can be considered as suitable for wave functions as $\phi \exp i\hbar^{-1}(pq - Et)$.

It is easily proved that every eigenfunction of the energy operator is a stationary function. If Ψ_n is an eigenfunction of $\mathcal{E}$, then $\mathcal{E}\Psi_n = E_n\Psi_n$; that is, $i\hbar(\partial \ln \Psi_n/\partial t) = E_n$ from which $\ln \Psi_n = \ln \psi_n - i\hbar^{-1}E_n$, where ψ_n is independent of time, so that

$$\Psi_n = \psi_n \exp -i\hbar^{-1}E_nt \tag{4-6}$$

Note that when t in the exponent is increased by h/E, then Ψ is unchanged in value ($\exp -2\pi i = 1$), so that $E/\hbar = \omega = 2\pi\nu$ and relation (4-1) is satisfied. Equation (4-6) represents a stationary wave function because it is factored into time-independent and space-independent terms.

4-3 The wave equation for free-electron beams. It was noted in Sec. 4-2 that functions such as $\cos \gamma q$ and $\sin \gamma q$ are not eigenfunctions of the momentum operator, $\mathcal{P}$. Such functions are, however, eigenfunctions of the $\mathcal{P}^2$ operator, for

$$\mathcal{P}(\cos \gamma q) = -i\hbar \frac{\partial}{dq} \cos \gamma q = i\gamma\hbar \sin \gamma q$$

$$\mathcal{P}^2(\cos \gamma q) = \mathcal{P}[\mathcal{P}(\cos \gamma q)] = -i\hbar \frac{\partial}{\partial q} (i\gamma\hbar \sin \gamma q) = \gamma^2\hbar^2(\cos \gamma q)$$

Thus by double differentiation the relation $p^2 = \gamma^2\hbar^2$ can be extracted from the function $\cos \gamma q$. Such a procedure permits only the magnitude of p to be determined, but not its sign. For free particles the energy is related to the momentum and mass:

$$E = \frac{p^2}{2m} \tag{4-7}$$

Since $E = \dfrac{i\hbar}{\Psi}\dfrac{\partial \Psi}{\partial t}$ and $p^2 = -\dfrac{\hbar^2}{\Psi}\dfrac{\partial^2 \Psi}{\partial q^2}$, Eq. (4-7) can be put into operator form:

$$\frac{i\hbar}{\Psi}\frac{\partial \Psi}{\partial t} = -\frac{\hbar^2}{2m\Psi}\frac{\partial^2 \Psi}{\partial q^2}$$

or

$$\frac{\partial^2 \Psi}{\partial q^2} = -\frac{2im}{\hbar}\frac{\partial \Psi}{\partial t} \tag{4-8}$$

Equation (4-7) represents the conservation of energy for free particles; Eq. (4-8) is the equivalent equation in operator form. Equation (4-8) is a special case of the general wave equation, in which the coefficient of the second time derivative is zero and in which the coefficient of the first time derivative is imaginary. It was shown in Chap. 2 that the solutions of Eq. (4-8) are harmonic wave functions. Thus de Broglie's hypotheses have led to the wave equation for a free-particle beam.

4-4 Solutions of the wave equation for the free-particle beam. Equation (4-8) has two linearly independent solutions:

$$\Psi_+ = \phi_+ \exp i(\gamma q - \omega t)$$

and

$$\Psi_- = \phi_- \exp i(-\gamma q - \omega t)$$

where ϕ_+ and ϕ_- are independent of q and t. By applying the momentum operator to Ψ_+ and Ψ_-, we can determine the momentum corresponding to each of the wave functions:

$$\mathcal{P}\Psi_+ = -i\hbar\frac{\partial \Psi_+}{\partial q} = \gamma\hbar\phi_+ \exp i(\gamma q - \omega t) = \gamma\hbar\Psi_+$$

$$\mathcal{P}\Psi_- = -i\hbar\frac{\partial \Psi_-}{\partial q} = -\gamma\hbar\phi_- \exp i(-\gamma q - \omega t) = -\gamma\hbar\Psi_-$$

Thus a beam whose wave function is Ψ_+ has a momentum of $(+\gamma\hbar)$, while the one with wave function Ψ_- has a momentum of $(-\gamma\hbar)$. The functions Ψ_+ and Ψ_- therefore represent beams of electrons traveling with equal speeds but in opposite directions. In the light of this interpretation it might be interesting to consider the wave functions $\Psi_c = \phi_c \cos \gamma q \exp -i\omega t$ and $\Psi_s = \phi_s \sin \gamma q \exp -i\omega t$. When $\phi_+ = \phi_- = \phi_c = \phi_s$, Ψ_+ and Ψ_- are related to Ψ_c and Ψ_s:

$$\Psi_c = \tfrac{1}{2}(\Psi_+ + \Psi_-) \qquad \text{and} \qquad \Psi_s = -\tfrac{1}{2}i(\Psi_+ - \Psi_-)$$

Both Ψ_c and Ψ_s are therefore linear combinations of the wave functions of beams traveling in opposite directions; they represent the superposition of two traveling waves. This is consistent with the observation made in Sec. 4-3 that for such wave functions, the magnitude but not the direction of the momentum can be determined, for both Ψ_c and Ψ_s represent the superposition of beams traveling in opposite directions with equal speeds. In this interpretation we have assumed that when particle beams are superimposed, the associated waves are superimposed and that conversely the superposition of wave functions implies the superposition of the associated particle beams. This assumption is one of the most important hypotheses made in the interpretation of wave mechanics; it implies that the particle and wave nature of mechanical systems exist simultaneously and are inseparable.

4-5 Attempted isolation of an electron from a beam. In Sec. 3-2 an experiment was described in which a portion of a wave train was "chopped off" by means of a shutter. Let us consider now the feasibility of isolating an electron from a stream of monoenergetic electrons by use of such a shutter. Extending the classical concept of particle behavior to electrons, one should be able to isolate an electron from a beam of electrons by opening the shutter for a very short period of time. However, we are equally convinced that a beam of particles has associated with it a wave so that we may apply the results obtained for a chopped-off wave packet.

In Sec. 3-4 it was shown that the rate at which the wave packet becomes attenuated depends on the relation between propagation velocity and wave numbers of the waves constituting the packet. For the propagation of electromagnetic waves in vacuum, $\omega = c\gamma$; the velocity of propagation of any wave equals $v = \omega/\gamma = c$, a constant, independent of γ. The maximum amplitude and width of a representative packet composed of such waves do not change with time. For waves associated with particles, however, the propagation velocity is proportional to the wave number:

$$v = \frac{\omega}{\gamma} = \frac{E}{\hbar}\frac{1}{\gamma} = \frac{p^2}{2m}\frac{1}{\hbar\gamma} = \frac{\gamma^2\hbar^2}{2m}\frac{1}{\hbar\gamma} = \frac{\gamma\hbar}{2m} \tag{4-9}$$

so that the velocities of the component waves of a packet representing the chopped-off electric charge will differ from one another. Such behavior is also characteristic of a packet composed of a group of waves, such as light waves, when they pass through a dispersive medium. Thus, it may be said that the wave packet representing the chopped-off *particle* beam will be dispersed, even *in vacuo*. The amount of dispersion depends on the magnitude of the coefficient of γ in Eq. (4-9); for an electron beam this coefficient is appreciable. Therefore, the wave packet representing the chopped-off electron will be diffused rapidly. Since the association of a particle with a packet only makes sense if the particle and wave packet are located approximately in the same small region of space, the conclusion must be that the isolation of a single electron from an electron beam is not possible and that the attempt to localize the little bit of matter taken from the electron beam cannot be permanently successful.

4-6 The effect of mass on the dispersion. The linear dependence of v on γ, $v = A\gamma + B$, that was chosen as an example in Sec. 3-4 is shown by Eq. (4-9) to be applicable to particle beams. The constant of proportionality A, which is a measure of the dispersion, has been shown to equal $\hbar/2m$, so that the dispersion of a particle wave packet is inversely proportional to the mass of the particles composing the beam. For heavy particles the dispersion may be negligible, as will be demonstrated in Prob. 4-4.

---

problem 4-1. Demonstrate whether or not the relation

$$v_g = v_w - \lambda_w \frac{dv_w}{d\lambda_w}$$

is valid for the wave associated with an electron beam in a vacuum.

v_g (group velocity) is the velocity with which energy is transmitted by a wave train.

v_w (wave velocity) is the propagation velocity for the wave.

λ_w is the wavelength for the wave with velocity v_w. Compare your answer with the discussion in Sec. 4-2.

---

problem 4-2. An attempt is made to isolate a single electron from a very narrow beam of electrons by opening and closing a shutter just long enough to clip from the beam a quantity of electricity equal to the charge on a single electron. All the electrons in the beam have the same velocity, having been accelerated through a potential difference of 54 volts.

(*a*) Give the wave function of the wave packet clipped off.

(*b*) Estimate the *time* that must elapse until the *distance* from the center peak to the first node of the wave packet is

(1) 1 angstrom
(2) 1 micron
(3) 1 centimeter

[*Hint:* Recall from Sec. 3-4 that in a dispersive medium the distance from the center peak to the nearest node of the wave packet under consideration equals $(3\pi At)^{1/2}$.]

---

problem 4-3. Consider a nucleus of a lead atom moving with the same momentum as the electron in Prob. 4-2:

(*a*) Calculate the wave number γ associated with this particle.

(*b*) Calculate the dispersion coefficient A of this wave.

(*c*) Estimate the time for this wave packet to spread, as was done in Prob. 4-2*b*.

---

problem 4-4. Consider a lead bullet 1 cm long, 0.5 cm in diameter, and moving with a velocity 400 m/sec:

(*a*) Calculate the wave number γ associated with this particle.

(*b*) Calculate the dispersion coefficient A of this wave packet.

(*c*) Assuming that a beam consisting of a train of more than 1000 wavelengths is essentially monochromatic, give your conclusion about the spreading of the wave packet associated with the moving lead bullet.

Problems 4-2 to 4-4 illustrate the rate of spreading of waves associated with three different types of particles. Of the three types, the electron has associated with it the wave packet that diffuses most rapidly. The wave packet associated with the bullet is found not to disperse noticeably because of the large size of the bullet compared with its associated wavelength; therefore, we can "track" the moving bullet. The wave packet associated with the lead nucleus was found to spread much less rapidly than the wave packet associated with the electron because of its much larger mass, so that we would also expect to be able to track this nucleus.

Having considered a lightweight small particle, a heavy small particle, and a much heavier larger particle, we conclude that the dispersion of the associated wave packet is appreciable only for the first particle. It is possible to track accurately a particle having either a large mass or large size, or both. The location of a single electron cannot be determined accurately. It is characteristic of wave mechanics that while many variables are found to have only discrete values, the location of electrons in atomic and molecular systems is very diffuse. The wave model of matter, first hypothesized for a beam of electrons, deals with large numbers of particles and can only yield statistical information about individual particles. The statistical description of systems and the manner in which information can be obtained from this description are formulated in the postulates which follow in the next chapter.

4-7 Summary. We have examined some of the implications of de Broglie's hypotheses regarding particle beams in field-free regions. These implications are essentially the consequences of the wave nature of particles, namely, the uncertainty in location due to the dispersion as time progresses. It should be stressed again that the wave packets representing particles, in contrast to those representing electromagnetic waves, are dispersed in a vacuum.

In order to extend the wave theory of particles to regions in which the particles are subjected to fields, we shall in the next chapter extend de Broglie's hypotheses.

the postulates of wave mechanics

chapter

5

5-1 Introduction. In Chap. 4 it was shown that the behavior of individual lightweight particles can only be inferred from the behavior of an assembly of large numbers of such particles. This means that many variables of individual particles can only be determined subject to statistical fluctuations rather than with absolute certainty. In the present chapter we shall extend the treatment of free particles to include particles subject to external fields.

Let us now consider the postulates upon which wave mechanics is based. These postulates cannot be proved or derived; they are accepted as long as they lead to results that are in agreement with experiments. The foregoing chapters serve to make the postulates more plausible and to review those aspects of wave theory that are of prime importance in the application of the postulates.

5-2 The first postulate of wave mechanics. According to the first postulate, information about the properties of a system of particles is contained in a function of all coordinates and time that is called the "wave function." This information may be determinate, or it may be in statistical form.

There are certain restrictions to which the wave functions must conform; these restrictions are called the rules for proper behavior of the functions. In order to be an acceptable wave function, a function should go to zero at infinity, it should be single-valued, and the square of its absolute magnitude should be integrable over all coordinates. The last requirement implies that the function should be continuous everywhere, except at a discrete number of points where those singularities are permitted that do not violate the integrability requirement. Details of the proper behavior will be discussed at appropriate times.

5-3 The second postulate. The second postulate defines the operators by means of which information regarding any physical variable of a system of particles can be extracted. These operators are listed in Table 5-1.

5-4 Schroedinger's wave equation. The fundamental equation of classical mechanics, namely, the equality of the Hamiltonian H and the energy E is retained in wave mechanics, with the proviso that the Hamiltonian and the energy are replaced by their operators as defined in the second postulate. Since the Hamiltonian is a function of coordinates, momentum and time, each of these independent variables must be replaced by its appropriate operator in forming the Hamiltonian operator $\mathcal{H}$. By multiplying both sides of the fundamental equation of classical mechanics (in operator form) by the wave function Ψ, we obtain the fundamental equation of wave mechanics:

$$\mathcal{H}\left(q_1, q_2, \ldots, q_k, -i\hbar\frac{\partial}{\partial q_1}, -i\hbar\frac{\partial}{\partial q_2}, \ldots, -i\hbar\frac{\partial}{\partial q_k}, t\right)\Psi = \mathcal{E}\Psi \tag{5-1}$$

For a conservative system the Hamiltonian is the sum of the kinetic and the potential energy, expressed in terms of coordinates and momenta. In terms of cartesian coordinates Eq. (5-1) then becomes for a single particle of mass μ

$$-\frac{\hbar^2}{2\mu}\left(\frac{\partial^2}{\partial x^2} + \frac{\partial^2}{\partial y^2} + \frac{\partial^2}{\partial z^2}\right)\Psi + V(x,y,z)\Psi = i\hbar\frac{\partial\Psi}{\partial t} \tag{5-2}$$

Equations (5-1) and (5-2) are both forms of Schroedinger's wave equation. de Broglie's hypotheses follow from Schroedinger's theory for the special case of linear motion with potential energy independent of position. In this case Eq. (5-2) corresponds to the harmonic wave equation, whose solutions are harmonic wave functions. Schroedinger's wave equation can be solved analytically only for certain special forms of the potential function; some of these special cases will be discussed in detail in succeeding chapters. Usually approximate methods must be resorted to for solving Schroedinger's wave equation.

table 5-1

operators used in wave mechanics

variable	classical symbol	operator symbol	operation
Coordinate	$q_1, \ldots, q_k$	$\mathcal{Q}_1, \ldots, \mathcal{Q}_k$	Multiply by q_k
Linear momentum	$p_1, \ldots, p_k$	$\mathcal{P}_1, \ldots, \mathcal{P}_k$	$-i\hbar \frac{\partial}{\partial q_1}, \ldots, -i\hbar \frac{\partial}{\partial q_k}$
Time	t	τ	Multiply by t
Energy	E	$\mathcal{E}$	$+i\hbar \frac{\partial}{\partial t}$
Any function of coordinate momentum and time	$F(q_1, \ldots, q_k, p_1, \ldots, p_k, t)$	$\mathfrak{F}$	$f\left(q_1, \ldots, q_k, -i\hbar \frac{\partial}{\partial q_1}, \ldots, -i\hbar \frac{\partial}{\partial q_k}, \ldots, t\right)$
Potential energy	$V(q_1, \ldots, q_k, t)$	V	Multiplication by V

Schroedinger's equation will be solved by first finding all its stationary solutions, and then expanding the general solution as a linear combination of these stationary functions, as was done for the general wave equation in Chap. 2. Before doing this, however, we shall first discuss the rules for extracting information from wave functions.

5-5 Proper behavior of operators. In wave mechanics the operators, like the wave functions, must conform to certain rules of proper behavior. The operators defined in Sec. 5-4 have the following characteristics:

A. They are linear:

$$\mathfrak{F}(a\Psi_a + b\Psi_b) = a\mathfrak{F}\Psi_a + b\mathfrak{F}\Psi_b$$

where a and b are constants.

---

problem 5-1. Determine which of the following operators are linear:

(*a*) $\sqrt{\ }$
(*b*) sin
(*c*) $\dfrac{d}{dx}$
(*e*) exp
(*f*) x
(*g*) $(\ )^2$

B. They follow the law of indices:

$$\mathfrak{F} \cdot \mathfrak{F} = \mathfrak{F}^2 \qquad \text{and} \qquad \mathfrak{F}^m\mathfrak{F}^n = \mathfrak{F}^{m+n}$$

C. They obey the associative law:

$$\mathfrak{F}(\mathfrak{G}\Psi) = (\mathfrak{F}\mathfrak{G})(\Psi)$$

D. They do not necessarily commute:
For every Ψ,†

$$\mathfrak{F}\mathfrak{G}\Psi = \mathfrak{G}\mathfrak{F}\Psi \text{ only if } \mathfrak{F} \text{ and } \mathfrak{G} \text{ commute}$$
$$\mathfrak{F}\mathfrak{G}\Psi \neq \mathfrak{G}\mathfrak{F}\Psi \text{ when } \mathfrak{F} \text{ and } \mathfrak{G} \text{ do not commute}$$

† Note that if a particular function u exists such that $\mathfrak{F}\mathfrak{G}u = \mathfrak{G}\mathfrak{F}u$, this does not necessarily mean that $\mathfrak{F}$ and $\mathfrak{G}$ commute. $\mathfrak{F}$ and $\mathfrak{G}$ commute only if $\mathfrak{F}\mathfrak{G}\Psi = \mathfrak{G}\mathfrak{F}\Psi$ for any Ψ whatsoever, and if *any* function v exists such that $\mathfrak{F}\mathfrak{G}v \neq \mathfrak{G}\mathfrak{F}v$, then $\mathfrak{F}$ and $\mathfrak{G}$ do not commute.

problem 5-2. Determine which pairs among the following operators commute:

$$(a)\ \frac{\partial}{\partial x};\quad (b)\ \frac{\partial}{\partial t};\quad (c)\ x;\quad (d)\ t$$

problem 5-3. (*a*) Prove that the Hamiltonian operator and the energy operator commute.

(*b*) Determine whether the Hamiltonian and momentum operators commute.

5-6 The third postulate. The third postulate gives the rules for extracting information from the wave function. The expectation value of a variable f of a system whose wave function is Ψ, is

$$\bar{f} = \frac{\oint \Psi^* \mathfrak{F} \Psi \, dq + \oint \Psi \mathfrak{F}^* \Psi^* \, dq}{2 \oint \Psi^* \Psi \, dq} \tag{5-3}$$

Here the symbol $\oint \ldots dq$ indicates integration over *all* values of *all* coordinates. The expectation value represents the arithmetic average over a large number of simultaneous experiments; in general, wave mechanics admits a fluctuation in these measurements, while in classical mechanics it is assumed that every variable is in principle absolutely determinate. Such fluctuation necessarily is connected with the association of waves with particles and is not due to human frailties, as was assumed in classical mechanics. The expectation value $\bar{f}$ given by Eq. (5-3) corresponds to what, in classical mechanics, is called the observed value of f.

Since the second term of the numerator in the right-hand side of Eq. (5-3) is just the complex conjugate of the first term, the expectation value is always real, as it must be because it corresponds to an observable. We shall show in the next section that many wave mechanical operators are Hermitian, in which case Eq. (5-3) assumes the simpler form

$$\bar{f} = \frac{\oint \Psi^* \mathfrak{F} \Psi \, dq}{\oint \Psi^* \Psi \, dq} \tag{5-3a}$$

5-7 Hermitian conjugation and Hermitian operators. Consider the expression

$$I = \oint u(q)\mathfrak{F}v(q)\,dq$$

where $u(q)$ and $v(q)$ are any two functions that obey the rules of proper behavior imposed on wave functions. We define the Hermitian conjugate of I by interchanging u and v and taking the complex conjugate of $\mathfrak{F}$:

$$I^\dagger = \oint v(q)\mathfrak{F}^*u(q)\,dq$$

As an example consider the operator $\mathcal{P}$:

$$I = \oint u\mathcal{P}v\,dq = -i\hbar\oint u\frac{\partial v}{\partial q}\,dq$$

$$I^\dagger = \oint v\mathcal{P}^*u\,dq = i\hbar\oint v\frac{\partial u}{\partial q}\,dq$$

By integrating I by parts, we show that in this particular case $I = I^\dagger$:

$$I = -i\hbar\oint u\frac{\partial v}{\partial q}\,dq = -i\hbar\left(uv\oint - \oint v\frac{\partial u}{\partial q}\,dq\right)$$

Because of their proper behavior, the functions u and v vanish at both limits of the integration. Therefore

$$I = i\hbar\oint v\frac{\partial u}{\partial q}\,dq = I^\dagger$$

This relation is due to the special character of the operator $\mathcal{P}$; we say that $\mathcal{P}$ is a Hermitian operator. In general, an operator $\mathfrak{F}$ is called Hermitian if

$$\oint u(q)\mathfrak{F}v(q)\,dq = \oint v(q)\mathfrak{F}^*u(q)\,dq \tag{5-4}$$

where u and v are properly behaved functions.

If we set $u = \Psi^*$ and $v = \Psi$ in Eq. (5-4), we find that for a Hermitian operator

$$\oint \Psi^*\mathfrak{F}\Psi\,dq = \oint \Psi\mathfrak{F}^*\Psi^*\,dq$$

Therefore Eq. (5-3) reduces to Eq. (5-3*a*) whenever $\mathfrak{F}$ is Hermitian.

---

problem 5-4. Below is a list of properties of a system. Determine which properties are associated with Hermitian operators:

(*a*) Position (coordinate)
(*b*) Potential energy
(*c*) Product of coordinate, and momentum parallel to coordinate
(*d*) Product of coordinate, and momentum perpendicular to coordinate (angular momentum)
(*e*) Hamiltonian
(*f*) Energy (use Schroedinger's equation)

---

problem 5-5. (*a*) If $\mathfrak{F}$ and $\mathfrak{G}$ are two Hermitian operators that commute with each other, is the operator $\mathfrak{F}\mathfrak{G}$ Hermitian?
(*b*) Prove that the operator $\mathfrak{F}^2$ is Hermitian if $\mathfrak{F}$ is Hermitian.

5-8 Applications of the three postulates. As an example of the application of the first three postulates, consider the following wave function:

$$\Psi = \frac{(k\mu)^{1/8}}{(\pi\hbar)^{1/4}} \exp\left[-\frac{(k\mu)^{1/2}q^2}{2\hbar} - \tfrac{1}{2}i\left(\frac{k}{\mu}\right)^{1/2} t\right] \tag{5-5}$$

where k and μ are independent of q and t.

We can learn a great deal about the system represented by this wave function by applying the second and third postulates. Substitution of Eq. (5-5) into Schroedinger's equation gives the potential energy:

$$\frac{\partial\Psi}{\partial q} = -\frac{(k\mu)^{1/2}q}{\hbar}\Psi; \qquad \frac{\partial^2\Psi}{\partial q^2} = -\frac{(k\mu)^{1/2}}{\hbar}\Psi\left[1 - \frac{(k\mu)^{1/2}}{\hbar}q^2\right]$$

$$\frac{\partial\Psi}{\partial t} = -\tfrac{1}{2}i\left(\frac{k}{\mu}\right)^{1/2}\Psi$$

therefore $$\tfrac{1}{2}\hbar\left(\frac{k}{\mu}\right)^{1/2}\Psi\left[1 - \frac{(k\mu)^{1/2}}{\hbar}q^2\right] + V\Psi = \tfrac{1}{2}\hbar\left(\frac{k}{\mu}\right)^{1/2}\Psi$$

so that $$V = \tfrac{1}{2}kq^2$$

We recognize this potential function as that of a linear harmonic oscillator whose displacement from equilibrium is given by q and whose restoring-force constant is given by k. Equation (5-5) therefore represents a wave function of a linear harmonic oscillator. Let us apply the third postulate to this oscillator to find the expectation value of its displacement from equilibrium. Keeping in mind that $\mathcal{Q}$ is a Hermitian operator (see Prob. 5-4), we find that

$$\bar{q} = \frac{\int_{-\infty}^{+\infty} \Psi^* q \Psi \, dq}{\int_{-\infty}^{+\infty} \Psi^* \Psi \, dq}$$

The wave function given by Eq. (5-5) is even in q, so that the integrand of the numerator in the last equation is odd. When such an integrand is integrated from $-\infty$ to $+\infty$, the result is zero; therefore the expectation value of the displacement q is zero. This means that the displacement is as likely to be positive as negative.

---

problem 5-6. Prove that the expectation value of linear momentum for the linear harmonic oscillator whose wave function is given by Eq. (5-5) equals zero. (*Hint:* The derivative of an even function is odd.)

In the process of finding V we also found that $\mathcal{E}\Psi = \frac{1}{2}\hbar(k/\mu)^{\frac{1}{2}}\Psi$. This result can be used here to find the expectation value of the energy

$$\bar{E} = \frac{\int_{-\infty}^{+\infty} \Psi^* \mathcal{E} \Psi \, dq}{\int_{-\infty}^{+\infty} \Psi^* \Psi \, dq} = \frac{1}{2}\hbar \left(\frac{k}{\mu}\right)^{\frac{1}{2}} \frac{\int_{-\infty}^{+\infty} \Psi^* \Psi \, dq}{\int_{-\infty}^{+\infty} \Psi^* \Psi \, dq} = \frac{1}{2}\hbar \left(\frac{k}{\mu}\right)^{\frac{1}{2}}$$

Since the expression $(k/\mu)^{\frac{1}{2}}$ represents the natural frequency ω_0 of the oscillator, we find that $\bar{E} = \frac{1}{2}\hbar\omega_0$ for the oscillator whose wave function is given by Eq. (5-5). Since we have found that the potential energy function has the form $\frac{1}{2}kq^2$, we can find the expectation value of the potential energy as follows, keeping in mind that V is Hermitian.

$$\bar{V} = \frac{\oint \Psi^* (\frac{1}{2}kq^2) \Psi \, dq}{\oint \Psi^* \Psi \, dq} = \frac{1}{2}k \frac{\oint \Psi^* q^2 \Psi \, dq}{\oint \Psi^* \Psi \, dq}$$

According to the third postulate this means that

$$\bar{V} = \frac{1}{2}k\overline{(q^2)}$$

Similarly the expectation value of the kinetic energy is

$$\overline{\text{KE}} = \frac{\oint \Psi^* \mathcal{P}^2 \Psi \, dq}{2\mu \oint \Psi^* \Psi \, dq} = \frac{1}{2\mu} \overline{(p^2)}$$

To find $\overline{(q^2)}$ and $\overline{(p^2)}$, the following results are used:

$$\oint \Psi^* \Psi \, dq = 1$$

$$\oint \Psi^* q^2 \Psi \, dq = \frac{\hbar}{2(k\mu)^{1/2}}$$

From these expressions it follows directly that

$$\overline{(q^2)} = \frac{\hbar}{2(k\mu)^{1/2}}$$

and hence $\bar{V} = \frac{1}{4}\hbar(k/\mu)^{1/2} \equiv \frac{1}{4}\hbar\omega_0 = \frac{1}{2}\bar{E}$.

The same integrals can also be used to find $\overline{(p^2)}$ by making use of the Hermitian character of the operator $\mathcal{P}^2$.

$$\overline{(p^2)} = \frac{\oint \Psi^* \mathcal{P}^2 \Psi \, dq}{\oint \Psi^* \Psi \, dq} = \frac{\oint \Psi^* \mathcal{P}(\mathcal{P}\Psi) \, dq}{1}$$
$$= \oint \mathcal{P}\Psi \mathcal{P}^* \Psi^* \, dq = \oint |\mathcal{P}\Psi|^2 \, dq$$

We have already found that for this linear harmonic oscillator,

$$\mathcal{P}\Psi = i(k\mu)^{1/2} q \Psi$$

so that $$\overline{(p^2)} = k\mu \oint \Psi^* q^2 \Psi \, dq = k\mu \overline{(q^2)} = \tfrac{1}{2}\hbar(k\mu)^{1/2}$$

and hence $$\overline{\text{KE}} = \tfrac{1}{4}\hbar \left(\frac{k}{\mu}\right)^{1/2} = \tfrac{1}{4}\hbar\omega_0 = \tfrac{1}{2}\bar{E} = \bar{V}$$

Since $H = \text{KE} + V = E$, we have confirmed that the expectation value of the Hamiltonian equals the expectation value of the energy. We have furthermore established that the expectation values of kinetic and potential energies equal each other. The evaluation of the expectation values of these energies has yielded additional interesting results. Although $\bar{p} = 0$ and $\bar{q} = 0$, we have just found that $\overline{(p^2)} \neq 0$ and $\overline{(q^2)} \neq 0$. Thus $(\bar{p})^2 \neq \overline{(p^2)}$, and $(\bar{q})^2 \neq \overline{(q^2)}$; in other words, the operations of squaring and taking the mean do *not* commute. A physical insight into these mathematical results is easily gained when one realizes that p and q can have negative as well as positive values, and hence could easily average to zero. The quantities p^2 and q^2, however, are never negative, so that they could only average to zero if they equaled zero everywhere. Therefore *any* deviation from zero in either p or q, whether in the positive or negative direction, would give rise to a *positive* energy.

5-9 Fluctuations. In Sec. 5-8 we found that the kinetic energy of the harmonic oscillator whose state is described by the wave function of Eq. (5-5) is positive, in spite of the fact that the expectation value of momentum is zero. This positive value of kinetic energy was shown to be due to deviations of the momentum from its zero expectation value. Such deviations from an expectation value must be interpreted in the light of what has been said in Chap. 4, namely, that it is impossible to isolate lightweight particles and track them for an appreciable time. Wave mechanics is essentially a statistical science, dealing with large ensembles of atoms or molecules. This statistical nature is intrinsic in the formulation of the third postulate, which deals with expectation values, that is, average values for the large ensemble of atoms or molecules. Individual atoms or molecules in the ensemble do not exactly conform to the average behavior. We have just seen in the example considered in Sec. 5-8 that certain variables of a system, such as kinetic energy, depend on the deviations of other variables, such as momentum, from their expectation value.

Experiments give only the average of a property for all atoms or molecules in the ensemble. Since some variables depend on the fluctuations in other variables, it should be possible to make at least an indirect determination of these fluctuations. For instance, in the example of the harmonic oscillator, knowledge of the kinetic energy enables us to determine the magnitude of the fluctuation of momentum around its expectation value.

When in general we consider the fluctuation of a variable f from its expectation value $\bar{f}$ as a property of a system whose wave function is Ψ, then the expectation value of this fluctuation is, according to postulate 3,

$$\overline{(f-\bar{f})} = \frac{\oint \Psi^*(\mathfrak{F}-\bar{f})\Psi\,dq + \oint \Psi(\mathfrak{F}^*-\bar{f})\Psi^*\,dq}{2\oint \Psi^*\Psi\,dq}$$

$$= \frac{\oint \Psi^*\mathfrak{F}\Psi\,dq + \oint \Psi\mathfrak{F}^*\Psi^*\,dq}{2\oint \Psi^*\Psi\,dq} - \bar{f} = \bar{f} - \bar{f} = 0$$

This indicates that the fluctuation is as often positive as negative, and hence averages to zero. Such a definition does not distinguish between small and large deviations. For our purpose it will be more useful to express the fluctuation in terms of its root mean square or standard deviation rather than its average value.

$$\text{Standard deviation} = \Delta f = \overline{[(f - \bar{f})^2]}^{1/2}$$

Therefore

$$(\Delta f)^2 = \overline{(f - \bar{f})^2} = \overline{[f^2 - 2f\bar{f} + (\bar{f})^2]} = \overline{f^2} - 2\bar{f} \cdot \bar{f} + (\bar{f})^2 = \overline{f^2} - (\bar{f})^2$$

---

problem 5-7. Show that $\overline{(f\bar{f})} = (\bar{f})^2$.

The mean-square deviation is just the difference between the mean of the square and the square of the mean. It was pointed out above that the operations of squaring and taking the mean do not commute, so that generally the mean-square deviation is not zero.

We can now summarize the results obtained for the linear harmonic oscillator in Sec. 5-8:

Since $\bar{q} = 0$,

$$\Delta q = \overline{(q^2)}^{1/2} = \left[\frac{\hbar}{2(k\mu)^{1/2}}\right]^{1/2}$$

and since $\bar{p} = 0$,

$$\Delta p = \overline{(p^2)}^{1/2} = [\tfrac{1}{2}\hbar(k\mu)^{1/2}]^{1/2}$$

The standard deviations in displacement and momentum are reciprocally related for the linear harmonic oscillator:

$$\Delta p \cdot \Delta q = \tfrac{1}{2}\hbar \tag{5-6}$$

If we accept the standard deviations as expressions representing the uncertainties in determining the values of the variables of a system, then Eq. (5-6) illustrates the uncertainty principle, for any attempt to reduce the standard deviation in p (for instance, by reducing k or μ) will result in an increase in the standard deviation in q.

In Sec. 5-8 we found that

$$\bar{E} = \bar{H} = \overline{\text{KE}} + \bar{V} = \tfrac{1}{2}\mu^{-1/2}(\Delta p)^2 + \tfrac{1}{2}k(\Delta q)^2$$

Let us now find the standard deviation of the energy from its expectation value:

$$(\Delta E)^2 = \overline{E^2} - (\bar{E})^2$$

In Sec. 5-8 we found $\bar{E} = \frac{1}{2}\hbar(k/\mu)^{\frac{1}{2}}$; application of the energy operator on the wave function of Eq. (5-5) gives

$$\mathcal{E}^2\Psi = -\hbar^2 \frac{\partial^2\Psi}{\partial t^2} = -\hbar^2 \frac{k\Psi}{4\mu}$$

and hence $$\overline{E^2} = \frac{\hbar^2 k}{4\mu}$$

Therefore, $\overline{E^2} = (\bar{E})^2$, and $\Delta E = 0$.

We find that in this special case the mean square of the energy just equals the square of the mean energy, so that the standard deviation of the energy is zero. This means that the energy is in this case determinate. In Sec. 5-10 we shall give a general rule for determining directly from the wave function whether a property of a given system is determinate.

---

problem 5-8. Find whether the potential and kinetic energies are separately determinate for the system whose wave function is given by Eq. (5-5).

$$[\textit{Hint: } (\Delta V)^2 = (\overline{V^2}) - (\bar{V})^2 = \tfrac{1}{4}k^2[\overline{q^4} - (\overline{q^2})^2]$$

5-10 Eigenstates. In Sec. 5-9 a system was studied whose energy is determinate, that is, has zero standard deviation. The wave function for this system as given by Eq. (5-5) is stationary.

In general, the standard deviation is zero when

$$\overline{(f^2)} = (\bar{f})^2$$

According to the third postulate, this means that for a Hermitian operator $\mathfrak{F}$

$$\frac{\oint \Psi^*\mathfrak{F}^2\Psi\, dq}{\oint \Psi^*\Psi\, dq} = (\bar{f})^2$$

or $$\oint \Psi^*\mathfrak{F}^2\Psi\, dq = (\bar{f})^2 \oint \Psi^*\Psi\, dq \qquad (5\text{-}7)$$

Equation (5-7) is certainly satisfied if the result of operating on Ψ with operator $\mathfrak{F}$ is simply the multiplication of Ψ by the quantity $\bar{f}$:

$$\mathfrak{F}\Psi = \bar{f}\Psi \tag{5-8}$$

for then

$$\mathfrak{F}^2\Psi = \bar{f}\mathfrak{F}\Psi = (\bar{f})^2\Psi$$

and

$$\oint \Psi^*\mathfrak{F}^2\Psi\, dq = (\bar{f})^2 \oint \Psi^*\Psi\, dq$$

so that the variable f of a system is determinate whenever the wave function of the system is an eigenfunction of the operator $\mathfrak{F}$. In this case the expectation value of f just equals the eigenvalue of the operator $\mathfrak{F}$. We say that the system is in an "eigenstate" of the variable f.

Since Eq. (5-5) describes an eigenfunction of the energy operator, it is not surprising that it corresponds to a system with determinate energy. On the other hand, Eq. (5-5) does not represent an eigenfunction of either $\mathcal{Q}$ or $\mathcal{P}$, for the application of each of these operators leads to a multiplication of the function by q. Since q is not independent of coordinates, it does not satisfy the requirements of Eq. (5-8). Therefore it is not surprising that p and q are not determinate for the linear harmonic oscillator.

---

problem 5-9. Below are three wave functions describing three different systems. Determine which of the following variables is determinate: momentum, potential energy, kinetic energy, total energy, for each of the three wave functions:

$$(a)\ \Psi = \sqrt{\frac{2}{a}} \sin\frac{n\pi x}{a} \exp -\frac{i\pi^2 n^2 \hbar t}{2\mu a^2} \qquad \text{for } 0 \le x \le a$$

$$= 0 \qquad \text{for } x \le 0 \text{ and } x \ge a, \text{ where } n \text{ is an integer}$$

$$(b)\ \Psi = \phi \exp i(\gamma q - \omega t)$$

$$(c)\ \Psi = \sqrt{\frac{2}{q_0}}\left[\exp i\left(\frac{\pi q}{q_0} - \frac{\pi^2\hbar t}{2\mu q_0^2}\right) + \exp i\left(-\frac{2\pi q}{q_0} - \frac{2\pi^2\hbar t}{\mu q_0^2}\right)\right]$$

---

problem 5-10. The wave function for a particle of mass μ moving freely along coordinate x, but constrained between the points $x = 0$ and $x = a$, is given in Prob. 5-9a.

(a) Prove that this wave function is a solution of Schroedinger's equation.

(b) Find the potential energy function $V(x)$, for this system.

(*c*) Find the expectation values and the standard deviations of the following properties of the particle:

(1) Position
(2) Momentum
(3) Potential energy
(4) Kinetic energy
(5) Total energy

(Note particularly the dependence of the standard deviations upon the distance a and the dependence of the expectation values on n.)

---

problem 5-11. (*a*) Find the wave function for a system having determinate linear momentum.

(*b*) Expand the wave function of Prob. 5-9*a* in terms of eigenfunctions of the momentum operator.

(*c*) For each term of the expansion found in part (*b*), find the eigenvalue of momentum.

(*d*) Compare the result of (*c*) with the expectation value for momentum found in Prob. 5-10*c*.

5-11 Expansion in terms of eigenfunctions. Let us review the distinction between wave functions and eigenfunctions. *Wave functions* were defined in the first postulate as carriers of information about a system of particles. *Eigenfunctions* are functions linked to *operators* by Eq. (5-8); an eigenfunction is never an isolated entity, but always belongs to an operator or a differential equation. In wave mechanics all wave functions are eigenfunctions of Schroedinger's wave equation [Eqs. (5-1) and (5-2)]. When a system is described by a wave function that happens to be an eigenfunction of a given operator $\mathfrak{F}$, then the system is in an eigenstate of the variable f, which is then determinate.

In Chap. 2 we showed that the eigenfunctions of the general wave equation may be used as an orthonormal "frame of reference" for expanding any wave function. We shall now show that not only the nondegenerate eigenfunctions of the stationary wave equation, but in fact the nondegenerate eigenfunctions of any Hermitian operator form an orthogonal set. (Nondegenerate eigenfunctions of a Hermitian operator are those eigenfunctions that do not have the same eigenvalues.) For the proof, consider any pair of normalized eigenfunctions of the Hermitian operator $\mathfrak{F}$, for instance, χ_m and χ_n. Then

$$\mathfrak{F}\chi_m = \bar{\bar{f}}_m\chi_m \quad (5\text{-}9m)$$
$$\mathfrak{F}\chi_n = \bar{\bar{f}}_n\chi_n \quad (5\text{-}9n)$$

where $\bar{\bar{f}}_m$ and $\bar{\bar{f}}_n$ are the respective eigenvalues. As long as χ_m and χ_n are nondegenerate, $\bar{\bar{f}}_m \neq \bar{\bar{f}}_n$. From Eq. (5-9$m$) it follows by the usual procedure that

$$\oint \chi_n^* \mathfrak{F}\chi_m \, dq = \bar{\bar{f}}_m \oint \chi_n^* \chi_m \, dq \quad (5\text{-}10)$$

and from Eq. (5-9n) that

$$\oint \chi_m \mathfrak{F}^* \chi_n^* \, dq = \bar{\bar{f}}_n \oint \chi_n^* \chi_m \, dq \quad (5\text{-}11)$$

[It is recalled that eigenvalues, being special cases of expectation values, are always real; hence $(\bar{\bar{f}}_n)^* = \bar{\bar{f}}_n$.] When $\mathfrak{F}$ is Hermitian, the left-hand sides of Eqs. (5-10) and (5-11) equal each other; therefore the right-hand sides of these equations also equal each other. Thus

$$\bar{\bar{f}}_m \oint \chi_n^* \chi_m \, dq = \bar{\bar{f}}_n \oint \chi_n^* \chi_m \, dq$$

Since $\bar{\bar{f}}_m \neq \bar{\bar{f}}_n$, the last equation can be true only if $\oint \chi_n^* \chi_m \, dq = 0$, so that χ_n and χ_m are orthogonal.

Degenerate eigenfunctions of a Hermitian operator are not necessarily orthogonal; however, such functions may be linearly combined into orthogonal eigenfunctions by the procedure given in Chap. 2. We can therefore express any wave function Ψ as a linear combination of the *complete* normalized set of eigenfunctions χ_n of a Hermitian operator $\mathfrak{F}$:

$$\Psi(q,t) = \sum_n \phi_n \chi_n(q,t) \quad (5\text{-}12)$$

where

$$\phi_n = \int_{orth} \Psi(t = 0)\chi_n^*(t = 0) \, dq \quad (5\text{-}13)$$

The coefficients ϕ_n are called "distribution coefficients"; they are independent of coordinates and time.

5-12 Stationary states. An important Hermitian operator is the energy operator $\mathcal{E}$. Its eigenfunctions obey the differential equation

$$i\hbar \frac{\partial \chi_n}{\partial t} = E_n \chi_n$$

hence all have the form

$$\chi_n = \psi_n \exp -i\hbar^{-1}E_n t \tag{5-14}$$

where ψ_n is independent of time. The wave function for the linear harmonic oscillator given by Eq. (5-5) is such an eigenfunction of the energy operator, so that the system described by Eq. (5-5) has determinate energy. It is observed from Eq. (5-14) that all eigenfunctions of the energy operator are stationary wave functions. When Eq. (5-14) is substituted in Eq. (5-2), the so-called stationary Schroedinger equation is obtained:

$$-\tfrac{1}{2}\hbar^2 \sum_k \frac{1}{\mu_k}\frac{\partial^2\psi_n}{\partial q_k{}^2} = [E_n - V(q_1, q_2, \ldots, q_k)]\psi_n \tag{5-15}$$

or symbolically

$$\mathcal{H}\psi_n = E_n\psi_n$$

When all solutions ψ_n and all eigenvalues of energy E_n are found, then the most general solution that can be found is a linear combination of the stationary wave functions

$$\Psi(q_1, q_2, \ldots, q_k, t) = \sum_n \phi_n\psi_n \exp -i\hbar^{-1}E_n t \tag{5-16}$$

where

$$\phi_n = \int_{orth} \Psi(q_1, q_2, \ldots, q_k, t = 0)\psi_n^* \, dq \tag{5-17}$$

and ψ_n is assumed to be normalized. Observe that Eq. (5-17) is equivalent to Eq. (2-51). If Ψ is known at any given time, and the set ψ_n and the set E_n are known, then Ψ can be found at any time. As we shall see later, the orthogonal set of eigenfunctions of energy is very frequently used as a frame of reference; for this reason we usually find first the stationary wave functions of a system and then expand the general solution in terms of these. While the energy of each of these stationary wave functions is determinate, this does not imply that the energy of a system is generally determinate. This is illustrated in the following section.

5-13 An example of a nonstationary state. Let us suppose that χ_1 and χ_2 are two nondegenerate eigenfunctions of the energy operator:

$$\chi_1 = \psi_1 \exp -i\hbar^{-1}E_1 t \tag{5-18}$$

$$\chi_2 = \psi_2 \exp -i\hbar^{-1}E_2 t \tag{5-19}$$

where ψ_1 and ψ_2 are normalized functions independent of t and $E_2 > E_1$.

Suppose that a system is in a state described:

$$\Psi = \frac{1}{\sqrt{2}}(\chi_1 + \chi_2) \tag{5-20}$$

Since χ_1 and χ_2 are nondegenerate, the system described by Ψ is not in a stationary state. We shall examine here two variables of this system to illustrate the behavior of nonstationary systems, namely, position q and energy E.

The expectation value of position is given by

$$\begin{aligned}\bar{q} &= \tfrac{1}{2}\oint(\chi_1^* + \chi_2^*)q(\chi_1 + \chi_2)\,dq \\ &= \tfrac{1}{2}\oint\psi_1^* q\psi_1\,dq + \tfrac{1}{2}\oint\psi_2^* q\psi_2\,dq + \\ &\quad + \tfrac{1}{2}\exp[-i\hbar^{-1}(E_2 - E_1)t]\oint\psi_1^* q\psi_2\,dq + \\ &\quad + \tfrac{1}{2}\exp[i\hbar^{-1}(E_2 - E_1)t]\oint\psi_1 q\psi_2^*\,dq\end{aligned}$$

The last two terms of this equation can be simplified by remembering the polar notation for complex numbers. If we define

$$\oint\psi_1^* q\psi_2\,dq \equiv A\exp -i\alpha$$

where A and α are real,

then $\qquad \oint\psi_1 q\psi_2^*\,dq = A\exp i\alpha$

and $\qquad |\oint\psi_1^* q\psi_2\,dq| = |\oint\psi_1 q\psi_2^*\,dq| = A$

Therefore

$$\begin{aligned}\bar{q} &= \tfrac{1}{2}\oint\psi_1^* q\psi_1\,dq + \tfrac{1}{2}\oint\psi_2^* q\psi_2\,dq + \\ &\quad + |\oint\psi_1^* q\psi_2\,dq|\cos[\hbar^{-1}(E_2 - E_1)t + \alpha]\end{aligned} \tag{5-21}$$

Of the three terms in $\bar{q}$ the first two are independent of time, whereas the third one oscillates in time.

Equation (5-21) may be used for representation of the expectation value of the dipole moment, $e\bar{q}_x$, of an atomic (or molecular) system; e is the net electric charge and q_x is the distance between the + and − charges along the x direction. The time-dependent term of Eq. (5-21) gives the frequency of oscillation of the dipole moment, which is seen to be $\hbar^{-1}(E_2 - E_1)$. According to classical electromagnetic theory, the interaction of radiation of this frequency with the system would cause the electric charges to resonate, and hence radiation of this frequency would be observed. Equation (5-21) is a useful relation to account for the occurrence of spectral lines. Bohr, in setting up his orbital quantum model, had postulated that electrons can abruptly change orbits on absorbing or emitting radiation of just the frequency $\nu = (E_2 - E_1)/h$. We see that the superposition of two stationary states leads to the same result as did Bohr's hypothesis; a term value $(-E/h)$ may be assigned each stationary state and each absorption and emission line corresponds to the "beat frequency" $|\Delta E/h|$, where ΔE is the difference in energies of the stationary states.

One important result that follows from Eq. (5-21) is that if the magnitude of the integral $\oint \psi_1^* q \psi_2 \, dq$ vanishes, then there is no oscillation in $e\bar{q}$, and no spectral line appears. It has indeed been observed that a great many lines that might be expected actually do not appear in atomic spectra, and in each such case it turns out that the integral $\oint \psi_1^* q \psi_2 \, dq$ does vanish for each potential spectral line. Given the wave functions of some particular system, we can predict (by evaluating this integral) which transitions in the Bohr model will occur. Thus we can derive the so-called selection rules for these systems.

---

problem 5-12. Prove that no spectral lines can result from transitions between two stationary states whose wave functions have the same parity, i.e., are both even or both odd in all coordinates.

We shall now examine the energy of the system whose wave function is given by Eq. (5-20):

$$\begin{aligned}\bar{E} &= \tfrac{1}{2}\oint (\chi_1^* + \chi_2^*)\mathcal{E}(\chi_1 + \chi_2)\, dq \\ &= \tfrac{1}{2}\left(E_1 \oint \chi_1^*\chi_1\, dq + E_2 \oint \chi_1^*\chi_2\, dq + E_1 \oint \chi_2^*\chi_1\, dq + E_2 \oint \chi_2^*\chi_2\, dq\right)\end{aligned}$$

Since χ_1 and χ_2 are nondegenerate, they are orthogonal; therefore the second and third terms in this expression for $\bar{E}$ vanish. It has furthermore been postulated that χ_1 and χ_2 are normalized, so that

$$\bar{E} = \tfrac{1}{2}(E_1 + E_2) \tag{5-22}$$

Thus we have shown that when two stationary states are admixed *equally* to form a nonstationary state, the expectation value of energy is just the *arithmetic* mean of the stationary-state energies. We are also interested in the standard deviation of energy from its expectation value. We can find in a manner completely analogous to the derivation of Eq. (5-22) that

$$\overline{(E^2)} = \tfrac{1}{2}(E_1^2 + E_2^2) \tag{5-23}$$

Using Eqs. (5-22) and (5-23), we find that

$$\begin{aligned}(\Delta E)^2 &= \overline{(E^2)} - (\bar{E})^2 = \tfrac{1}{2}(E_1^2 + E_2^2) - \tfrac{1}{4}(E_1 + E_2)^2 \\ &= \tfrac{1}{4}(E_1^2 + E_2^2 - 2E_1E_2) = [\tfrac{1}{2}(E_1 - E_2)]^2\end{aligned}$$

Therefore the standard deviation is just one-half the difference between the two stationary-state energies. We conclude, accordingly, that for this combination of stationary states the expectation value of energy lies just halfway between the two stationary-state energies, but that it may fluctuate anywhere between these energies.

---

problem 5-13. If a system is described by the wave function $\Psi = \phi_1\chi_1 + \phi_2\chi_2$, where χ_1 and χ_2 are normalized eigenfunctions of the energy operator with respective eigenvalues E_1 and E_2, find the expectation value and standard deviation of energy for this system. What condition should ϕ_1 and ϕ_2 obey so that Ψ would be normalized?

5-14 Summary. We have extended de Broglie's hypotheses to particles subjected to an external field. The postulates of wave mechanics have been stated in terms of wave functions and operators, and it was shown that wave functions can be expanded as linear combinations of eigenfunctions of Hermitian operators. The statistical nature of wave mechanics has been emphasized. We have used the third postulate not only for finding the expectation value of a physical variable, but also for finding the standard deviation from this expectation value. It was shown that if the wave function describing a system is an eigenfunction of an operator corresponding to a given variable of the system, then that variable is determinate. In conclusion we showed that eigenfunctions of the energy operator are always stationary and that the energy of a nonstationary state is not determinate, but fluctuates over a continuous range of values. The uncertainty principle was derived here from the third postulate in the particular case of a linear harmonic oscillator. In the next chapter we shall discuss the uncertainty principle in more general terms.

the uncertainty principle†

chapter

6

6-1 Introduction. In Chap. 3, it was shown that any attempt to localize a wave packet in space results in a spectrum with a wide distribution of wave numbers. Similarly we observed that when a monochromatic wave passes through a shutter that is open for only a finite time, the wave transmitted by the shutter is of finite length, hence it is no longer monochromatic. The shutter experiment implies that the accuracy of any spectroscopic experiment is limited by the time of observation. We have noted that the energy values of the different stationary states of a system can be determined by studying its absorption or emission spectra. The accuracy with which the values of these energies can be determined is thus limited by the accuracy with which the frequency or wave number of the spectral lines can be measured, and hence by the duration of the experiment. One might therefore infer that one could increase the accuracy indefinitely by sufficiently increasing the time of observation in such measurements.

In practice, however, the excited atoms and molecules under observation are not isolated, but interact with each other and with their environment. As a consequence, these atoms and molecules do not remain in stationary states indefinitely, but have a finite lifetime. It is pointless to extend the time of observation beyond the

† First proposed by W. Heisenberg in 1927, *Z. Physik,* **43,** 172 (1927).

lifetime of the state in question. Therefore, the lifetime limits the accuracy with which energy can be determined.

A general relation between the standard deviations from expectation values of any pair of variables, for instance, of momentum and position, and of frequency and time, will be derived here from the postulates of wave mechanics.

6-2 Derivation of the general uncertainty relation. Consider any two variables a and b, with respective Hermitian operators $\mathcal{A}$ and $\mathcal{B}$. The product of the squares of the standard deviations of these two variables is found from the third postulate

$$(\Delta a)^2(\Delta b)^2 = \oint \Psi^*(\mathcal{A} - \bar{a})^2\Psi\, dq \oint \Psi^*(\mathcal{B} - \bar{b})^2\Psi\, dq$$

where Ψ is normalized.

It follows from Prob. 5-5b that $(\mathcal{A} - \bar{a})^2$ and $(\mathcal{B} - \bar{b})^2$ are Hermitian, so that

$$\begin{aligned}(\Delta a)^2(\Delta b)^2 &= \oint (\mathcal{A} - \bar{a})^*\Psi^*(\mathcal{A} - \bar{a})\Psi\, dq \oint (\mathcal{B} - \bar{b})^*\Psi^*(\mathcal{B} - \bar{b})\Psi\, dq \\ &= \oint |(\mathcal{A} - \bar{a})\Psi|^2\, dq \oint |(\mathcal{B} - \bar{b})\Psi|^2\, dq \qquad (6\text{-}1)\end{aligned}$$

This relation can be put into a more useful form by means of Schwarz's inequality. To derive this inequality in the form most useful for our purpose, consider the function

$$\lambda(\mathcal{A} - \bar{a})\Psi + i(\mathcal{B} - \bar{b})\Psi$$

where λ is a real parameter, independent of coordinates.

The square of the absolute magnitude, that is, the product of this function and its complex conjugate, is always positive or zero. Therefore

$$\lambda^2|(\mathcal{A} - \bar{a})\Psi|^2 + i\lambda[(\mathcal{A}^* - \bar{a})\Psi^*(\mathcal{B} - \bar{b})\Psi - (\mathcal{A} - \bar{a})\Psi(\mathcal{B}^* - \bar{b})\Psi^*] + \\ + |(\mathcal{B} - \bar{b})\Psi|^2 \geq 0$$

The integral of this expression over all values of all coordinates must also be nonnegative:

$$[\oint |(\mathcal{A} - \bar{a})\Psi|^2\, dq]\lambda^2 + i[\oint (\mathcal{A}^* - \bar{a})\Psi^*(\mathcal{B} - \bar{b})\Psi\, dq + \\ - \oint (\mathcal{A} - \bar{a})\Psi(\mathcal{B}^* - \bar{b})\Psi^*\, dq]\lambda + \\ + \oint |(\mathcal{B} - \bar{b})\Psi|^2\, dq \geq 0 \qquad \text{[inequality (6-1)]}$$

The left-hand side of this last inequality is a quadratic in λ (λ has already been defined as a real number). According to elementary theory of equations such a quadratic can have negative values only if it has two real roots; if it has no root, or at most one (double) root, it is limited to positive or zero values. Therefore inequality (6-1) is valid only if there is no more than one real root. Again, according to elementary theory of equations, a quadratic has two real roots if its discriminant is positive, has one double real root if its discriminant is zero, and has no real roots if the discriminant is negative. Inequality (6-1) can therefore be valid only if the discriminant of the left-hand side is zero or negative, that is, if

$$4\oint|(\mathcal{A} - \bar{a})\Psi|^2\,dq \oint|(\mathcal{B} - \bar{b})\Psi|^2\,dq \geq -[\oint(\mathcal{A}^* - \bar{a})\Psi^*(\mathcal{B} - \bar{b})\Psi\,dq + \\ - \oint(\mathcal{A} - \bar{a})\Psi(\mathcal{B}^* - \bar{b})\Psi^*\,dq]^2 \qquad \text{[inequality (6-2)]}$$

When Eq. (6-1) is substituted into inequality (6-2),

$$(\Delta a)^2(\Delta b)^2 \geq -\tfrac{1}{4}[\oint(\mathcal{A}^* - \bar{a})\Psi^*(\mathcal{B} - \bar{b})\Psi\,dq + \\ - \oint(\mathcal{A} - \bar{a})\Psi(\mathcal{B}^* - \bar{b})\Psi^*\,dq]^2 \qquad \text{[inequality (6-3)]}$$

Since Ψ is normalized, and since $\oint\Psi^*\mathcal{A}\Psi\,dq = \bar{a}$, and $\oint\Psi^*\mathcal{B}\Psi\,dq = \bar{b}$,

$$\oint(\mathcal{A}^* - \bar{a})\Psi^*(\mathcal{B} - \bar{b})\Psi\,dq = \oint\mathcal{A}^*\Psi^*\mathcal{B}\Psi\,dq - \overline{ab} \qquad (6\text{-}2)$$

Taking the complex conjugates of both sides of Eq. (6-2),

$$\oint(\mathcal{A} - \bar{a})\Psi(\mathcal{B}^* - \bar{b})\Psi^*\,dq = \oint\mathcal{A}\Psi\mathcal{B}^*\Psi^*\,dq - \overline{ab} \qquad (6\text{-}3)$$

When Eqs. (6-2) and (6-3) are substituted into inequality (6-3),

$$|\Delta a|^2|\Delta b|^2 \geq -\tfrac{1}{4}[\oint\mathcal{A}^*\Psi^*\mathcal{B}\Psi\,dq - \oint\mathcal{A}\Psi\mathcal{B}^*\Psi^*\,dq]^2$$

and since $\mathcal{A}$ and $\mathcal{B}$ are Hermitian,

$$|\Delta a|\,|\Delta b| \geq |\oint\Psi^*[\tfrac{1}{2}i(\mathcal{A}\mathcal{B} - \mathcal{B}\mathcal{A})]\Psi\,dq| \qquad \text{[inequality (6-4)]}$$

Inequality (6-4) is the general expression for the *uncertainty principle.*

---

problem 6-1. Show that the right-hand side of inequality (6-4) vanishes if Ψ is an eigenfunction of both $\mathcal{A}$ and $\mathcal{B}$.

problem 6-2. From inequality (6-4) find a lower limit for the following products:

(*a*) $|\Delta p|\,|\Delta q|$; (*c*) $|\Delta p|\,|\Delta t|$; (*e*) $|\Delta p|\,|\Delta E|$
(*b*) $|\Delta E|\,|\Delta t|$; (*d*) $|\Delta E|\,|\Delta q|$; (*f*) $|\Delta q|\,|\Delta t|$

If the operators $\mathcal{A}$ and $\mathcal{B}$ commute, then the right-hand side of inequality (6-4) vanishes for any wave function Ψ; in this case there is no limit to the accuracy with which a and b can be determined simultaneously. On the other hand, when $\mathcal{A}$ and $\mathcal{B}$ do not commute, then the right-hand side of inequality (6-4) does not generally vanish, so that Δa and Δb are reciprocally related. This means that great accuracy in the determination of a implies a large lower limit in the uncertainty with which b can be determined, and vice versa.

Pairs of variables in which the accuracy in the determination of one variable places a lower limit on the accuracy with which the other variable may be determined are called "conjugate" variables. Therefore, variables whose operators do not commute are conjugate variables.

6-3 Application of the general uncertainty relation. As an example, we consider linear momentum, and position, p and q, for *any* wave function Ψ; we shall then compare the result with that obtained earlier for the particular case of the linear harmonic oscillator (Sec. 5-8). From inequality (6-4) we conclude that, for *any* normalized function Ψ that is not an eigenfunction of either $\mathcal{P}$ or $\mathcal{Q}$,

$$|\Delta p|\,|\Delta q| \geq \tfrac{1}{2}\hbar \oint \Psi^* \left[\frac{\partial}{\partial q}(q\Psi) - q\frac{\partial \Psi}{\partial q}\right] dq$$

Since $(\partial/\partial q)(q\Psi) - q\partial\Psi/\partial q = \Psi$ and since $\oint \Psi^*\Psi\, dq = 1$,

$$|\Delta p|\,|\Delta q| \geq \tfrac{1}{2}\hbar$$

When this result is compared with that obtained for the example of the linear harmonic oscillator, it is observed that in that example the uncertainty has the smallest value allowed by the uncertainty principle.

problem 6-3. (*a*) Show that for a stationary state the time is completely indeterminate. (*Hint:* First find ΔE; then apply the uncertainty principle to find Δt.)

(*b*) Estimate the lower limit of the accuracy with which the energy can be determined of the state of a system having a lifetime of 10^{-10} sec. Repeat the estimate for lifetimes 10^{-13} sec and 10^{-7} sec.

6-4 Conjugate variables and their eigenfunctions. Having shown that two conjugate variables cannot be simultaneously determinate, we shall now show that two variables whose operators commute may be simultaneously determinate. Specifically, we shall show that all *nondegenerate* eigenfunctions of a given operator are also eigenfunctions of all operators that commute with the given operator. Therefore a system that is in a nondegenerate eigenstate of a given operator will be shown to be in an eigenstate of all operators that commute with the given operator. For the proof of this statement consider a function χ that is an eigenfunction of $\mathcal{A}$:

$$\mathcal{A}\chi = \bar{\bar{a}}\chi \tag{6-4}$$

Let $\mathcal{B}$ operate on both sides of Eq. (6-4):

$$\mathcal{B}\mathcal{A}\chi = \mathcal{B}(\bar{\bar{a}}\chi) = \bar{\bar{a}}\mathcal{B}\chi$$

If $\mathcal{B}$ commutes with $\mathcal{A}$, then

$$\mathcal{B}\mathcal{A}\chi = \mathcal{A}\mathcal{B}\chi$$

so that

$$\mathcal{A}\mathcal{B}\chi = \bar{\bar{a}}\mathcal{B}\chi$$

Therefore, if $\mathcal{A}$ and $\mathcal{B}$ commute and if χ is an eigenfunction of $\mathcal{A}$ with eigenvalue $\bar{\bar{a}}$, then $\mathcal{B}\chi$ is also an eigenfunction of $\mathcal{A}$ with eigenvalue $\bar{\bar{a}}$. There are two conditions under which both χ and $(\mathcal{B}\chi)$ may be eigenfunctions of $\mathcal{A}$ with eigenvalue $\bar{\bar{a}}$:

1. χ and $(\mathcal{B}\chi)$ are linearly independent, and are two degenerate eigenfunctions of $\mathcal{A}$.
2. χ is a nondegenerate eigenfunction of $\mathcal{A}$ and $(\mathcal{B}\chi)$ is simply proportional to χ; in other words, χ is an eigenfunction of $\mathcal{B}$.

If χ is nondegenerate, the first of these possibilities is eliminated; in that case, the second one is the only one allowed, so that χ is an eigenfunction of $\mathcal{B}$. Therefore if $\mathcal{A}$ and $\mathcal{B}$ commute and χ is a nondegenerate eigenfunction of $\mathcal{A}$, then χ is necessarily an eigenfunction of $\mathcal{B}$.

These relations between the eigenfunctions of various operators are illustrated by the use of some elementary set theory. A "set" is defined as a collection of members; we are interested here in sets of eigenfunctions of wave-mechanical operators. If we denote the set of all eigenfunctions of $\mathcal{A}$ by A and the set of all eigenfunctions $\mathcal{B}$ by B, then we say that B is a subset of A if and only if every eigenfunction of $\mathcal{B}$ is also an eigenfunction of $\mathcal{A}$. Figure 6-1 denotes that B is a subset of A; the entire area of B is also part of A but A contains members that are not members of B.

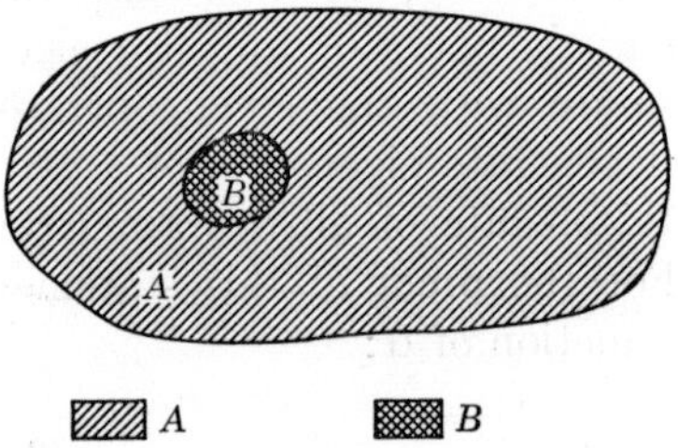

fig. 6-1 B is a subset of A

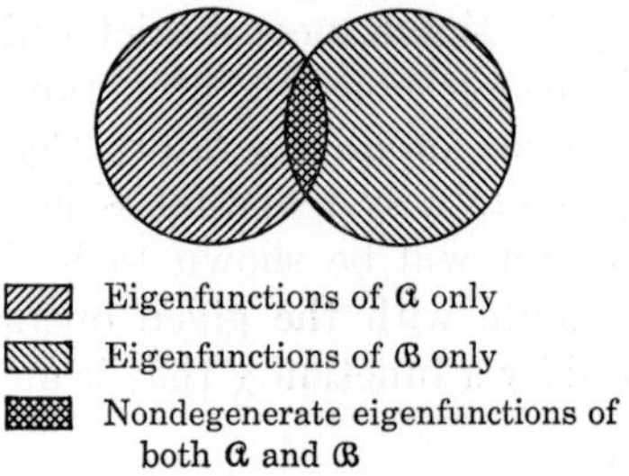

fig. 6-2 nondegenerate sets of eigenfunctions of commuting operators

We showed above that all *nondegenerate* eigenfunctions of $\mathcal{A}$ are also eigenfunctions of $\mathcal{B}$ if $\mathcal{A}$ and $\mathcal{B}$ commute; conversely, all *nondegenerate* eigenfunctions of $\mathcal{B}$ are also eigenfunctions of $\mathcal{A}$ if $\mathcal{A}$ and $\mathcal{B}$ commute. However, there may be *degenerate* eigenfunctions of $\mathcal{A}$ that are not eigenfunctions of $\mathcal{B}$, and vice versa. Therefore, all *nondegenerate* eigenfunctions form a subset of both A and B, for they certainly belong to both set A and B, but they do not necessarily occupy all of either A or B. This is illustrated by Fig. 6-2.

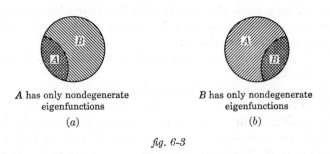

A has only nondegenerate eigenfunctions

(*a*)

B has only nondegenerate eigenfunctions

(*b*)

fig. 6-3

In the special case that $\mathcal{A}$ has *only nondegenerate* eigenfunctions, Fig. 6-2 reduces to Fig. 6-3*a*, while if $\mathcal{B}$ has only nondegenerate eigenfunctions, then Fig. 6-3*b* is produced; in the former case A is a subset of B, in the latter B is a subset of A.

If both $\mathcal{A}$ and $\mathcal{B}$ have only nondegenerate eigenfunctions, and, of course, $\mathcal{A}$ and $\mathcal{B}$ commute, then the sets A and B have all their elements in common; in such a case we say that A equals B (see Fig. 6-4).

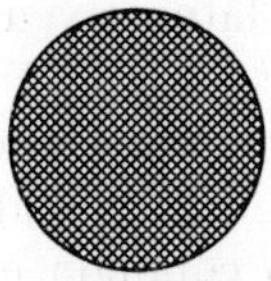

A and *B* have a common set of eigenfunctions

fig. 6-4 A = B

As examples, consider the operators $\mathcal{P}$ and $\mathcal{H}$, first for a free particle, and afterward for the linear harmonic oscillator. In the case of a free particle,

$$\mathcal{H} = \frac{1}{2\mu}\,\mathcal{P}^2$$

therefore

$$\mathcal{P}\mathcal{H} = \frac{1}{2\mu}\,\mathcal{P}^3 = \mathcal{H}\mathcal{P}$$

For the free particle, therefore, $\mathcal{P}$ and $\mathcal{H}$ commute. The eigenfunctions of $\mathcal{P}$ are $\exp \pm i\hbar^{-1}pq$, which are nondegenerate. Therefore all eigenfunctions of $\mathcal{P}$ are also eigenfunctions of $\mathcal{H}$, and P is a subset of H. There are also many additional eigenfunctions of $\mathcal{H}$, for example, $\cos \hbar^{-1}pq$ and $\sin \hbar^{-1}pq$, that are not eigenfunctions of $\mathcal{P}$; therefore H is not a subset of P. Note that $\cos \hbar^{-1}pq$ and $\sin \hbar^{-1}pq$ are degenerate eigenfunctions of $\mathcal{H}$, so that this is an illustration of a case where condition 1, above, is valid.

For the linear harmonic oscillator,

$$\mathcal{H} = \frac{1}{2\mu}\,\mathcal{P}^2 + \tfrac{1}{2}kq^2$$

$$\mathcal{P}\mathcal{H} = \frac{1}{2\mu}\,\mathcal{P}^3 - \tfrac{1}{2}ik\hbar\,\frac{\partial}{\partial q}\,(q^2\,\cdot\,)$$

$$\mathcal{H}\mathcal{P} = \frac{1}{2\mu}\,\mathcal{P}^3 - \tfrac{1}{2}ik\hbar q^2\,\frac{\partial}{\partial q}$$

Therefore

$$\mathcal{P}\mathcal{H} - \mathcal{H}\mathcal{P} = -ik\hbar q$$

Since $\mathcal{P}$ and $\mathcal{H}$ do not commute here, they do not necessarily have *any* eigenfunctions in common.† Inequality (6-4) tells us that

$$|\Delta p|\,|\Delta H| \geq \tfrac{1}{2}k\hbar \oint \Psi^* q \Psi \, dq \qquad \text{[inequality (6-5)]}$$

For the state of the oscillator given by Eq. (5-5), Ψ is an even function of q. Therefore the integrand in the right-hand side of inequality (6-5) is odd, so that the right-hand side of the inequality vanishes. In spite of the fact that $\mathcal{H}$ and $\mathcal{P}$ do not commute here, and as a matter of fact have no common eigenfunctions, the product of Δp and ΔH nevertheless happens to be zero for this example. Therefore there is no lower limit to the accuracy with which H and p could in principle be determined simultaneously.

6-5 Summary. We have derived the general uncertainty relation, and have shown that a high accuracy in the determination of a particular variable of a system may impose a lower limit on the accuracy with which all other variables of the same system can be determined. We have also shown that two variables whose operators commute may both, in principle, be determined simultaneously without limit in accuracy. Furthermore, when two operators do not commute, then their corresponding variables have standard deviations that are reciprocally related, though in special cases both variables may be determinate. Inequality (6-4), together with the second postulate, can in each case be used to estimate the accuracy with which a variable may be determined.

---

† See footnote Sec. 5-5.

a physical interpretation of the wave and distribution functions

chapter

7

7-1 Introduction. In Chap. 5 we defined the wave function as a carrier of information, and we expanded wave functions in terms of orthonormal sets of eigenfunctions. In the present chapter we shall examine some properties of the wave functions and of the coefficients of the expansion in terms of eigenfunctions, and on the basis of these properties we shall give these functions a more physical interpretation.

The expectation value of a property of a single atom is determined by performing an experiment on an ensemble of a great many atoms. We infer a model for an atom by imagining what properties the individual atoms might have, so that when many of them are assembled, the ensemble will give the measured result. Since these properties fluctuate, the superposition of the individual atoms may yield a fuzzy model, such as is often produced by a time exposure of photographic film. We shall see that this fuzzy model behaves in some ways like the model used for the study of macroscopic flow of fluids.

7-2 The distribution coefficients. The statistical nature of wave mechanics allows for the distribution of atoms or molecules over the different eigenstates of any variable: in Eq. (7-1)† the wave function Ψ is expanded in terms of an orthogonal set of eigenfunctions χ_n of an

† This equation is identical with Eq. (5-12).

operator $\mathfrak{F}$:

$$\Psi = \sum_n \phi_n \chi_n \tag{7-1}$$

The coefficients ϕ_n denote the contribution of each eigenfunction into the wave function Ψ; since Ψ depends on time, and ϕ_n does not, χ_n is generally time-dependent.

---

problem 7-1 (*a*) Show that multiplication of an eigenfunction of the momentum operator by an arbitrary function of time that is independent of coordinates, produces another eigenfunction of the momentum operator.

(*b*) Expand the wave function of Prob. 5-9*a* in terms of eigenfunctions of the momentum operator.

---

problem 7-2. (*a*) Expand the wave function of Prob. 5-9*c* in terms of a set of eigenfunctions of energy.

(*b*) Expand the same wave function in terms of the same eigenfunctions of momentum that were used in Prob. 7-1.

We give the coefficients ϕ_n a physical interpretation by expressing the expectation value of a variable f in terms of the orthogonal set of eigenfunctions χ_n of the corresponding operator $\mathfrak{F}$. If we assume $\mathfrak{F}$ to be Hermitian,

$$\bar{f} = \frac{\oint \Psi^* \mathfrak{F} \Psi \, dq}{\oint \Psi^* \Psi \, dq} = \frac{\oint \left(\sum_n \phi_n^* \chi_n^*\right) \mathfrak{F} \left(\sum_n \phi_n \chi_n\right) dq}{\oint \left(\sum_n \phi_n^* \chi_n^*\right)\left(\sum_n \phi_n \chi_n\right) dq}$$

$$= \frac{\oint \left(\sum_n \phi_n^* \chi_n^*\right)\left(\sum \phi_n \bar{\bar{f}}_n \chi_n\right) dq}{\oint \left(\sum_n \phi_n^* \chi_n^*\right)\left(\sum_n \phi_n \chi_n\right) dq} \tag{7-2}$$

The summations in the integrands are written out explicitly as follows:

$$\sum_n \phi_n^* \chi_n^* = \cdots + \phi_{-j}^* \chi_{-j}^* + \cdots + \phi_{-1}^* \chi_{-1}^* + \phi_0^* \chi_0^* + \phi_1^* \chi_1^* + \\ + \cdots + \phi_j^* \chi_j^* + \cdots$$

$$\sum_n \phi_n \bar{\bar{f}}_n \chi_n = \cdots + \phi_{-j}\bar{\bar{f}}_{-j}\chi_{-j} + \cdots + \phi_{-1}\bar{\bar{f}}_{-1}\chi_{-1} + \phi_0\bar{\bar{f}}_0\chi_0 + \\ + \phi_1\bar{\bar{f}}_1\chi_1 + \cdots + \phi_j\bar{\bar{f}}_j\chi_j + \cdots$$

$$\sum_n \phi_n \chi_n = \cdots + \phi_{-j}\chi_{-j} + \cdots + \phi_{-1}\chi_{-1} + \phi_0\chi_0 + \phi_1\chi_1 + \\ + \cdots + \phi_j\chi_j + \cdots$$

When these sums are multiplied together, double sums are obtained; a typical term in the numerator of Eq. (7-2) can be represented by $\phi_m^*\chi_m^*\bar{\bar{f}}_n\phi_n\chi_n$, where, in general, $m \neq n$. Similarly, a typical term in the denominator is $\phi_m^*\chi_m^*\phi_n\chi_n$. When the double sums are integrated term by term, the typical numerator term is $\phi_m^*\phi_n\bar{\bar{f}}_n\oint\chi_m^*\chi_n\,dq$, and the typical denominator term $\phi_m^*\phi_n\oint\chi_m^*\chi_n\,dq$. Since the set χ_n is orthonormal, all integrals vanish except $\oint\chi_n^*\chi_n\,dq$; in other words those where the subscripts m and n have equal values. Since the non-vanishing integrals equal unity, Eq. (7-2) becomes

$$\bar{f} = \frac{\sum_n \phi_n^*\phi_n\bar{\bar{f}}_n}{\sum_n \phi_n^*\phi_n} \tag{7-3}$$

Equation (7-3) lends itself conveniently to physical interpretation when it is recognized that it represents a weighted average of all eigenvalues $\bar{\bar{f}}_n$, the weighting factor being $(\phi_n^*\phi_n)$. We know that in the special case when f is determinate, Ψ equals one of the eigenfunctions of $\mathfrak{F}$, say χ_m, so that in that case all ϕ_n's equal zero, except ϕ_m. Then, of course, $\bar{f} = \bar{\bar{f}}_m$. In general, however, f is not determinate; then the wave function is a linear combination of eigenfunctions, each eigenfunction being admixed with a coefficient ϕ_n, and the expectation value is a weighted average of eigenvalues, each eigenvalue being weighted by the coefficient $|\phi_n|^2$. Without going into mathematical detail, we point out that the same interpretation can be given the distribution function $\phi(\gamma)$ in the Fourier transform.

---

problem 7-3. (*a*) Prove that Ψ, as given by Eq. (7-1), is normalized if $\sum_n |\phi_n|^2 = 1$ and if the χ_n's are normalized.

(*b*) By analogy show that the vector **A** has unit length if its cartesian coordinates obey the condition $A_x^2 + A_y^2 + A_z^2 = 1$.

(*c*) The distribution coefficients for the normalized eigenfunctions of the energy operator for a system are

$$\phi_1:\phi_2:\phi_3:\phi_4:\phi_5: = 2:4:6:5:3: \quad \text{all other } \phi\text{'s are negligibly small.}$$

Find $\bar{E}$ in terms of E_1, E_2, E_3, E_4, and E_5.

---

problem 7-4. Use Eq. (7-3) to find the expectation value and rms deviation of momentum for a system whose wave function is

$$\Psi = \sin\frac{\pi x}{a}\exp\left(-i\frac{\pi^2\hbar}{2\mu a^2}t\right) + \sin\frac{3\pi x}{a}\exp\left(-i\frac{9\pi^2\hbar}{2\mu a^2}t\right)$$

for $0 \leq x \leq a$, and $\Psi = 0$ for $x \leq 0$ and $x \geq a$.

7-3 The probability density. In Chap. 5 the wave function was defined as a function of coordinates $q_1, q_2 \ldots, q_k$ and the time t; in the examples considered thus far only a single coordinate was considered. Let us consider here a point charge whose location is described by a vector $\mathbf{r}$ from the origin of a given coordinate system. The cartesian components of the vector $\mathbf{r}$ are the coordinates x, y, and z of this particle. The expectation value of the position of the particle is then given by Eq. (7-4).

$$\bar{\mathbf{r}} = \frac{\int_{-\infty}^{\infty}\int_{-\infty}^{\infty}\int_{-\infty}^{\infty}\Psi^*(\hat{\mathbf{i}}x + \hat{\mathbf{j}}y + \hat{\mathbf{k}}z)\Psi\,dx\,dy\,dz}{\int_{-\infty}^{\infty}\int_{-\infty}^{\infty}\int_{-\infty}^{\infty}\Psi^*\Psi\,dx\,dy\,dz} \tag{7-4}$$

Equation (7-4) can be compared with the classical equation for the center of mass of a body whose density varies with location, and is given by the function $\rho(x,y,z)$:

$$\bar{\mathbf{r}} = \frac{\int_{-\infty}^{\infty}\int_{-\infty}^{\infty}\int_{-\infty}^{\infty}\rho(x,y,z)(\hat{\mathbf{i}}x + \hat{\mathbf{j}}y + \hat{\mathbf{k}}z)\,dx\,dy\,dz}{\int_{-\infty}^{\infty}\int_{-\infty}^{\infty}\int_{-\infty}^{\infty}\rho(x,y,z)\,dx\,dy\,dz} \tag{7-5}$$

It is seen that Eqs. (7-4) and (7-5) are identical if we set $\Psi^*\Psi = \rho$. Thus the "fuzzy" model referred to in the introduction to this chapter which resulted from the superposition of a great many identical systems with fluctuating characteristics, can be thought of as consisting of a fluid or cloud whose local density is given by $|\Psi|^2$. This interpretation of the wave function is a simple consequence of the third postulate; it should be emphasized that it is merely an interpretation and that the wave function of an ensemble of particles cannot be determined directly but may only be inferred from the measurement of several properties such as those manifested by its spectrum and magnetic characteristics. Perhaps the experiments that come closest to a direct determination of the wave function are the scattering of X rays and electron beams by matter, for these phenomena depend directly on the location of electrons and their fluctuations, and therefore give a measure of the "probability density" $|\Psi|^2$. With the aid of the third postulate, we can find the standard deviation for the vector $\mathbf{r}$ from its expectation value:

$$(\Delta r)^2 = \overline{[\mathbf{r} - (\mathbf{r})]^2} = \overline{(x - \bar{x})^2} + \overline{(y - \bar{y})^2} + \overline{[z - \bar{z})^2}$$
$$= \frac{\int_{-\infty}^{\infty}\int_{-\infty}^{\infty}\int_{-\infty}^{\infty} \Psi^*[(x - \bar{x})^2 + (y - \bar{y})^2 + (z - \bar{z})^2]\Psi\, dx\, dy\, dz}{\int_{-\infty}^{\infty}\int_{-\infty}^{\infty}\int_{-\infty}^{\infty} \Psi^*\Psi\, dx\, dy\, dz}$$

Hence

$$(\Delta r)^2 \left(\int_{-\infty}^{\infty}\int_{-\infty}^{\infty}\int_{-\infty}^{\infty} \Psi^*\Psi\, dx\, dy\, dz\right)$$
$$= \int_{-\infty}^{\infty}\int_{-\infty}^{\infty}\int_{-\infty}^{\infty} \Psi^*[(x - \bar{x})^2 + (y - \bar{y})^2 + (z - \bar{z})^2]\Psi\, dx\, dy\, dz \tag{7-6}$$

Now $\int_{-\infty}^{\infty}\int_{-\infty}^{\infty}\int_{-\infty}^{\infty} \Psi^*\Psi\, dx\, dy\, dz$ represents a mass if $\Psi^*\Psi$ is considered analogous to a density. (The requirement that $\Psi^*\Psi$ be integrable can then be interpreted as a requirement that the "mass" or total amount of matter in a system be finite.) Then Δr, as given by Eq. (7-6), is analogous to a radius of gyration as defined in the classical mechanics of bodies of finite size. The expression $\Psi^*\Psi\, dx\, dy\, dz$ is proportional to the probability of finding an electron in the volume element $dx\, dy\, dz$. The radius of gyration of the fluid with respect to a given position corresponds to the standard deviation from that position. Accordingly, we often speak of an "electron cloud" to denote the result of superimposing the electrons of many identical systems.

7-4 The probability current. Having interpreted the square of the absolute magnitude of the wave function as a probability density, we should like to find its behavior as a function of time. In the first place we note that the stationary wave functions of the form

$$\Psi = \psi \exp -i\hbar^{-1}Et$$

have probability densities given by $\Psi^*\Psi = \psi\psi^*$, so that $\partial(\Psi^*\Psi)/\partial t = 0$. Therefore the probability of finding an electron in a small volume element of a system does not change with time if that system is in a stationary state.

For nonstationary wave functions,

$$\frac{\partial(\Psi^*\Psi)}{\partial t} = \Psi^* \frac{\partial \Psi}{\partial t} + \Psi \frac{\partial \Psi^*}{\partial t}$$

According to Schroedinger's equation,

$$\frac{\partial \Psi}{\partial t} = -i\hbar^{-1}\mathcal{H}\Psi \qquad \text{and hence} \qquad \frac{\partial \Psi^*}{\partial t} = i\hbar^{-1}\mathcal{H}^*\Psi^*$$

Therefore $$\frac{\partial(\Psi^*\Psi)}{\partial t} = -i\hbar^{-1}(\Psi^*\mathcal{H}\Psi - \Psi\mathcal{H}^*\Psi^*) \qquad (7\text{-}7)$$

---

problem 7-5. (*a*) A certain state of the hydrogen atom is described by the wave function $\Psi = \phi \exp(-r/a_0 - i\hbar^{-1}Et)$, where r is the proton-electron distance and where a_0 and E are real. Find both the most probable values and the expectation value of the electron-proton distance, in terms of the parameter a_0.

(*b*) Repeat part (*a*) for the wave function

$$\Psi = \phi(1 - br)\exp(-br - i\hbar^{-1}E't)$$

where b and E' are real. (*Hint:* $dq = 4\pi r^2\, dr$.)

In terms of many coordinates the Hamiltonian operator becomes

$$\mathcal{H} = \frac{1}{2}\sum_k \frac{\mathcal{P}_k{}^2}{\mu_k} + V(q_1, q_2, \ldots, q_k, \ldots)$$

For a single particle in cartesian coordinates,

$$\begin{aligned}\mathcal{H} &= \frac{1}{2\mu}(\mathcal{P}_x{}^2 + \mathcal{P}_y{}^2 + \mathcal{P}_z{}^2) + V(x,y,z) \\ &= -\frac{\hbar^2}{2\mu}\left(\frac{\partial^2}{\partial x^2} + \frac{\partial^2}{\partial y^2} + \frac{\partial^2}{\partial z^2}\right) + V(x,y,z) \\ &= -\frac{\hbar^2}{2\mu}\nabla^2 + V(x,y,z)\end{aligned}$$

Therefore $\mathcal{H}\Psi = -(\hbar^2/2\mu)\nabla^2\Psi + V\Psi$ and, since V is real,

$$\mathcal{H}^*\Psi^* = -(\hbar^2/2\mu)\nabla^2\Psi^* + V\Psi^*$$

Therefore Eq. (7-7) becomes

$$\frac{\partial}{\partial t}(\Psi^*\Psi) = \tfrac{1}{2} i \frac{\hbar}{\mu}(\Psi^*\nabla^2\Psi - \Psi\nabla^2\Psi^*) \tag{7-8}$$

It should be observed that Eq. (7-8) is independent of the potential function, so that everything that follows is true for any form that the potential function may have. We can write

$$\Psi^*\nabla^2\Psi = \nabla\cdot(\Psi^*\nabla\Psi) - \nabla\Psi^*\cdot\nabla\Psi$$

and

$$\Psi\nabla^2\Psi^* = \nabla\cdot(\Psi\nabla\Psi^*) - \nabla\Psi\cdot\nabla\Psi^*$$

Subtraction of the latter from the former equation gives

$$\Psi^*\nabla^2\Psi - \Psi\nabla^2\Psi^* = \nabla\cdot(\Psi^*\nabla\Psi - \Psi\,\nabla\Psi^*)$$

Therefore

$$\frac{\partial}{\partial t}(\Psi^*\Psi) = -\nabla\cdot\left\{\frac{1}{2\mu}[\Psi^*(-i\hbar\,\nabla\Psi) + \Psi(+i\hbar\,\nabla\Psi^*)]\right\}$$

The operator $-i\hbar\nabla$ can be written as

$$-i\hbar\nabla = -i\hbar\left(\hat{\mathbf{i}}\frac{\partial}{\partial x} + \hat{\mathbf{j}}\frac{\partial}{\partial y} + \hat{\mathbf{k}}\frac{\partial}{\partial z}\right) = \hat{\mathbf{i}}\mathcal{P}_x + \hat{\mathbf{j}}\mathcal{P}_y + \hat{\mathbf{k}}\mathcal{P}_z = \boldsymbol{\mathcal{P}}$$

Then

$$\frac{\partial}{\partial t}(\Psi^*\Psi) = -\nabla\cdot\left[\frac{1}{2\mu}(\Psi^*\boldsymbol{\mathcal{P}}\Psi + \Psi\boldsymbol{\mathcal{P}}^*\Psi^*)\right] \tag{7-9}$$

If we interpret $\Psi^*\Psi$ as a probability density, then Eq. (7-9) calls to mind the following equation in fluid mechanics:

$$\frac{\partial\rho}{\partial t} = -\nabla\cdot(\rho\mathbf{v}) \tag{7-10}$$

where ρ represents the density of the fluid, $\mathbf{v}$ its velocity, and $(\rho\mathbf{v})$ represents a current. Thus the interpretation of $\Psi^*\Psi$ together with Eq. (7-9) implies that the expression $(1/2\mu)[\Psi^*\boldsymbol{\mathcal{P}}\Psi + \Psi(\boldsymbol{\mathcal{P}}\Psi)^*]$ represents a probability current, and the expression $[\Psi^*\boldsymbol{\mathcal{P}}\Psi + \Psi(\boldsymbol{\mathcal{P}}\Psi)^*]/2\mu\Psi^*\Psi$ represents a local velocity. Just as Eq. (7-10) is called the continuity equation of fluid mechanics, Eq. (7-9) is called the continuity equation of wave mechanics. The continuity equation expresses the fact that in a given differential volume element the density increases at a rate proportional to the current flow into that volume element. Since for stationary states $\partial(\Psi^*\Psi)/\partial t$ equals zero, the current for such states is divergenceless, though not necessarily zero. (For one-dimensional flow this means that the current may be finite, but that its magnitude does not change along the direction of flow.)

$$\mathbf{v} = \frac{\Psi^*\mathcal{P}\Psi + \Psi(\mathcal{P}\Psi)^*}{2\mu\Psi^*\Psi} = \frac{\Psi^*\mathcal{P}\Psi - \Psi\mathcal{P}\Psi^*}{2\mu\Psi^*\Psi} \tag{7-11}$$

For stationary wave functions $\Psi = \psi \exp -i\hbar^{-1}Et$, and

$$\mathbf{v} = \frac{\psi^*\mathcal{P}\psi - \psi\mathcal{P}\psi^*}{2\mu\psi^*\psi} = \frac{1}{2\mu}\mathcal{P}\left(\ln\frac{\psi}{\psi^*}\right)$$

It is observed that $\mathbf{v}$ vanishes when $\psi^* = \psi$, i.o.w., when ψ is real. Thus a stationary state whose time-independent wave function is real has zero probability velocity and zero probability current associated with it. An example of such a state is the state of the harmonic oscillator discussed in Chap. 5. It will be seen later that the wave functions associated with some atoms are complex, while others are real; the complex wave functions describe those states in which there is a net current, and hence a magnetic dipole. Such complex wave functions are encountered in the study of magnetic phenomena.

From the third postulate of wave mechanics and Eq. (7-11), we can relate the expectation value of momentum to the probability velocity $\mathbf{v}$:

$$\bar{\mathbf{p}} = \frac{\oint(\Psi^*\mathcal{P}\Psi + \Psi\mathcal{P}^*\Psi^*)\,dq}{2\oint\Psi^*\Psi\,dq} = \frac{\oint\mu\mathbf{v}\Psi^*\Psi\,dq}{\oint\Psi^*\Psi\,dq} \tag{7-12}$$

Thus the expectation value of momentum is just the mass times the weighted average of the velocity, the average being taken over all space weighted by the density distribution. Equation (7-12) therefore gives an interpretation to the third postulate for the case of momentum.

7-5 Superposition of densities and currents. Having shown in Sec. 5-11 that every wave function can be expanded as a linear combination of eigenfunctions of any Hermitian operator we shall now consider how the linear superposition of eigenfunctions affect the probability density and velocity. For simplicity consider two eigenstates of a given operator $\mathcal{F}$, described by the respective wave functions Ψ_1 and

Ψ_2. The probability density for each of these states is given by

$$\rho_1 = |\Psi_1|^2; \qquad \rho_2 = |\Psi_2|^2$$

The probability velocities are given by

$$\mathbf{v}_1 = \frac{\Psi_1^* \mathcal{P} \Psi_1 + \Psi_1 (\mathcal{P} \Psi_1)^*}{2\mu \Psi_1^* \Psi_1}$$
$$\mathbf{v}_2 = \frac{\Psi_2^* \mathcal{P} \Psi_2 + \Psi_2 (\mathcal{P} \Psi_2)^*}{2\mu \Psi_2^* \Psi_2}$$

When the two wave functions Ψ_1 and Ψ_2 are linearly combined to form a new wave function Ψ, according to Eq. (7-13),

$$\Psi = \phi_1 \Psi_1 + \phi_2 \Psi_2 \tag{7-13}$$

then the probability density for the new state is given by

$$\begin{aligned} \rho = \Psi^* \Psi &= |\phi_1|^2 |\Psi_1|^2 + |\phi_2|^2 |\Psi_2|^2 + \phi_1^* \phi_2 \Psi_1^* \Psi_2 + \phi_1 \phi_2^* \Psi_1 \Psi_2^* \\ &= |\phi_1|^2 \rho_1 + |\phi_2|^2 \rho_2 + \phi_1^* \phi_2 \Psi_1^* \Psi_2 + \phi_1 \phi_2^* \Psi_1 \Psi_2^* \end{aligned}$$

Therefore the probability density ρ, corresponding to Ψ, is *not* a linear combination of the densities ρ_1 and ρ_2; superposition of wave functions generally does not lead to superposition of densities.

The current associated with the wave function given by Eq. (7-13) is found as follows:

$$\begin{aligned} \rho \mathbf{v} &= \frac{1}{2\mu} [(\phi_1 \Psi_1 + \phi_2 \Psi_2)^* \mathcal{P} (\phi_1 \Psi_1 + \phi_2 \Psi_2) \\ &\qquad + (\phi_1 \Psi_1 + \phi_2 \Psi_2)(\mathcal{P})^* (\phi_1 \Psi_1 + \phi_2 \Psi_2)^*] \\ &= \rho_1 \mathbf{v}_1 + \rho_2 \mathbf{v}_2 + \frac{1}{2\mu} \{\phi_1^* \phi_2 [\Psi_1^* \mathcal{P} \Psi_2 + \Psi_2 (\mathcal{P} \Psi_1)^*] \\ &\qquad + \phi_1 \phi_2^* [\Psi_1 (\mathcal{P} \Psi_2)^* + \Psi_2^* \mathcal{P} \Psi_1]\} \end{aligned} \tag{7-14}$$

Therefore neither probability currents nor probability velocities are linearly superimposed when the corresponding wave functions are. This fact is illustrated by Prob. 7.6.

An interesting consequence of Eq. (7-14) is observed when one considers the linear superposition of two real functions. We have seen above that zero current and zero velocity are associated with real functions. Therefore, if Ψ_1 and Ψ_2 are real,

$$\rho \mathbf{v} = \frac{1}{2\mu} (\phi_1^* \phi_2 - \phi_1 \phi_2^*)(\Psi_1 \mathcal{P} \Psi_2 - \Psi_2 \mathcal{P} \Psi_1)$$

If ϕ_1 and ϕ_2 are real, then Ψ is real, and $\rho\mathbf{v}$ is zero. Generally, however, ϕ_1 and ϕ_2 are not real, so that Ψ is complex, and $\rho\mathbf{v}$ is not zero. Therefore a current is associated with superimposed real wave functions as long as the superposition coefficients are imaginary. An example of such superposition is the current penetrating classically inaccessible regions that is discussed in Chap. 8.

---

problem 7-6. Find the probability velocity and probability current associated with the following wave functions:

(*a*) $\phi_+ \exp(i\gamma q - i\omega t)$
(*b*) $\phi_- \exp(-i\gamma q - i\omega t)$
(*c*) The sum of (*a*) and (*b*)
(*d*) The difference of (*a*) and (*b*)
(*e*) $\exp i\phi$, where ϕ is the angle measured about the Z axis in cylindrical coordinates

---

7-6 Summary. We have given interpretations to the distribution coefficients ϕ_n and the wave function Ψ. We have shown that when simultaneous measurements are made on a great many identical systems, then the fluctuation of the properties from system to system causes an uncertainty in the determination of the properties of the ensemble. A model has been studied which consists of a superposition of all the systems in the ensemble; this model consists of a fluid or cloud, which moves according to the laws of fluid mechanics; its density is everywhere proportional to the probability of finding a particle anywhere, and the time rate of change of the density is proportional to the divergence of the current of the fluid. Stationary states have divergenceless flow, and wave functions whose time-independent factor is real have no current associated with them. The linear superposition of wave functions, which is justified because of the linearity of the wave equation, does not generally give rise to a linear superposition of density and of current; this phenomenon is analogous to the linear superposition of amplitudes and the nonlinear superposition of intensities in optics. In optics we describe the nonlinear superposition of intensities as being due to interference effects; in wave mechanics we can trace such nonclassical effects as the penetration of classically inaccessible barriers, chemical bonding, and the coupling of magnetic dipoles, to similar nonlinear superposition.

trapped and traveling electrons

chapter

8

8-1 Introduction. In Chap. 4 the motion of free electrons was discussed, and it was pointed out that de Broglie's hypotheses are applicable to such electrons, but that the presence of an external field necessitates more elaborate postulates. Three such postulates were presented in Chap. 5, and interpreted in Chaps. 5, 6, and 7. In the present chapter we shall apply some of the postulates and in particular the concept of a probability current. The examples chosen are idealizations of physical systems; they serve to demonstrate the behavior of electrons under various circumstances. In later chapters we shall deal with the mathematical complexities of more realistic systems, but presently we limit ourselves to potential functions having zero derivatives everywhere except at a discrete set of points where the potential is discontinuous.

The idealized systems considered in this chapter represent the behavior of particles under the following conditions:

1. Electrons and other lightweight particles impinging on a potential barrier (see Fig. 8-1*a* and *b*); this might represent, for instance, electrons inside but near the surface of a metal.
2. Electrons and other lightweight particles trapped in a potential well (see Fig. 8-1*c*); this might represent the behavior of electrons in atoms, or α particles in nuclei.
3. Electrons in a series of adjacent potential wells (see Fig. 8-5); this might represent the behavior of electrons in crystals.

8-2 Discontinuities in the potential-energy function. Consider Schroedinger's stationary equation in the form

$$\frac{d^2\psi}{dq^2} = -\frac{2m}{\hbar^2}(E - V)\psi \tag{8-1}$$

where m is the mass of the traveling particle, and the potential energy

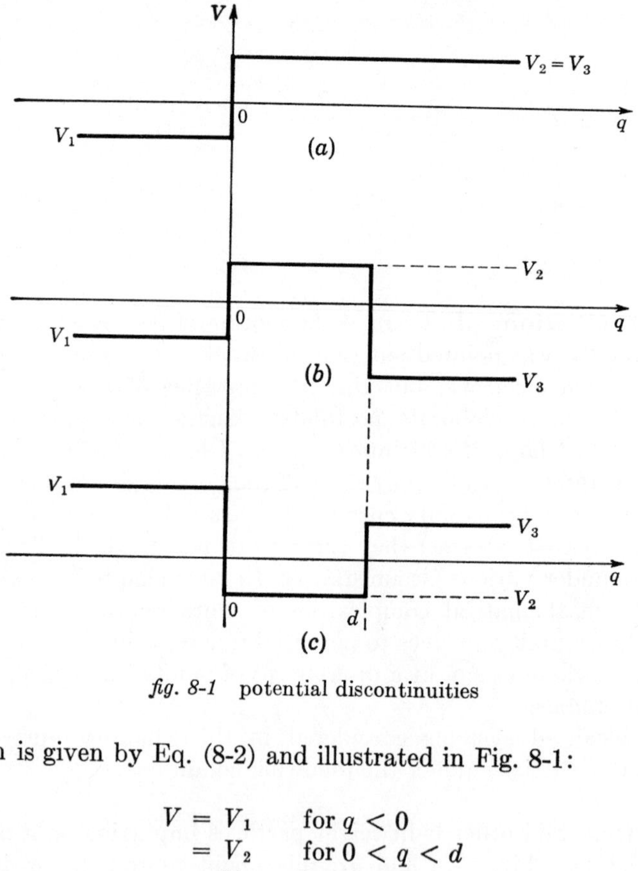

fig. 8-1 potential discontinuities

function is given by Eq. (8-2) and illustrated in Fig. 8-1:

$$\begin{aligned} V &= V_1 \qquad \text{for } q < 0 \\ &= V_2 \qquad \text{for } 0 < q < d \\ &= V_3 \qquad \text{for } d < q \end{aligned} \tag{8-2}$$

The general solution of Eq. (8-1), with V independent of q is

$$\psi = \phi_+ \exp i\hbar^{-1}pq + \phi_- \exp -i\hbar^{-1}pq \tag{8-3}$$

where ϕ_+ and ϕ_- are independent of q, and $p = [2m(E - V)]^{1/2}$ A.

solution of the type of Eq. (8-3) applies to each of the three regions $q < 0$, $0 < q < d$, and $d < q$. The requirement of proper behavior imposes the restriction that these solutions be "spliced" at the points $q = 0$ and $q = d$ in such a manner that the wave functions be continuous at $q = 0$ and at $q = d$. We shall now show that, while the requirement of proper behavior has *not* dealt with the derivatives of the wave function, the first derivative of the wave function with respect to the coordinate must necessarily be continuous everywhere except possibly where there is an infinite discontinuity in V.

To prove the continuity of the derivative, consider a potential function such as sketched in Fig. 8-2. This potential energy equals V_1 for $q < (q_0 - \epsilon)$, equals V_2 for $(q_0 + \epsilon) < q$, and is continuous in the region $(q_0 - \epsilon) < q < (q_0 + \epsilon)$. If we integrate both sides of Eq. (8-1),

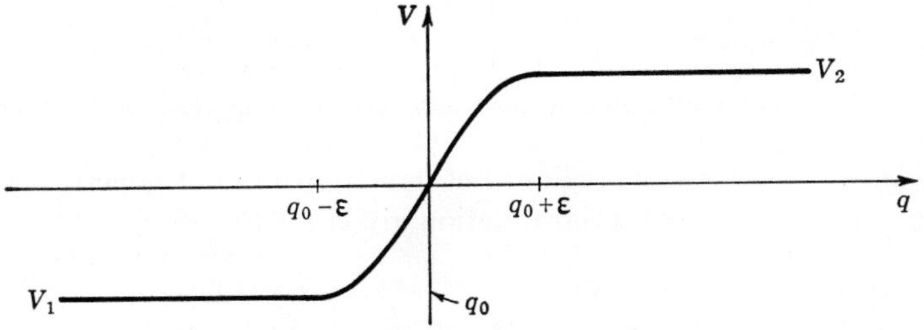

fig. 8-2 a continuous potential function

over the interval $(q_0 - \epsilon) < q < (q + \epsilon)$, using the potential function for V, shown in Fig. 8-2, we find that

$$\left(\frac{d\psi}{dq}\right)_{q=(q_0+\epsilon)} - \left(\frac{d\psi}{dq}\right)_{q=(q_0-\epsilon)} = -\frac{2m}{\hbar^2}\int_{(q_0-\epsilon)}^{(q_0+\epsilon)} (E - V)\psi \, dq \qquad (8\text{-}4)$$

The integrand of the right-hand side of this equation consists of two factors, $(E - V)$ and ψ, each of which is continuous. Therefore the integral approaches zero when ϵ is made to approach zero. When ϵ approaches zero, however, the potential function becomes discontinuous. On the other hand, since the right-hand side of Eq. (8-4) vanishes when ϵ does, the derivative of the wave function is continuous at $q = q_0$, even when ϵ vanishes. Thus we have proved the continuity of the derivative of ψ. When V has an infinite discontinuity at $q = q_0$, the integral in the right-hand side of Eq. (8-4) may or may not vanish; this depends on the order of the discontinuity in V. Therefore at those places where V has an infinite discontinuity, the first derivative of the wave function with respect to the coordinate is not necessarily continuous.

8-3 Splicing solutions at finite discontinuities in the potential. In Fig. 8-3 we show the splicing of the real part of a wave function in a classically inaccessible region to the real part of the wave function

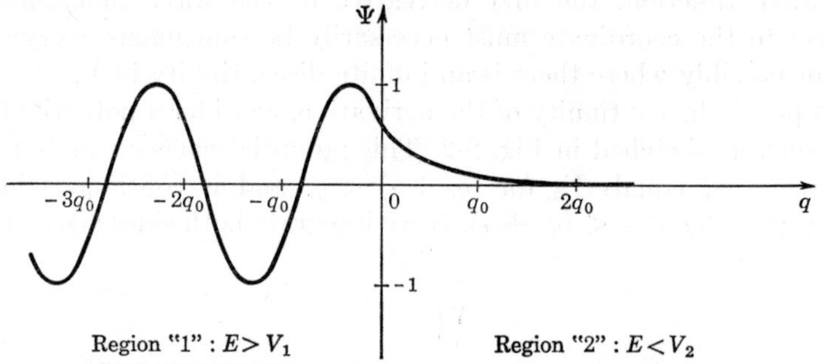

fig. 8-3 splicing of solutions in classically accessible and inaccessible regions

in a classically accessible region. Let us write the most general solution of Eq. (8-1) for the potential function given by Eq. (8-2):

For $q < 0$,

$$\psi = \phi_{1+} \exp i\hbar^{-1}p_1 q + \phi_{1-} \exp -i\hbar^{-1}p_1 q; \qquad p_1 = [2m(E - V_1)]^{1/2}$$

ϕ_{1+} and ϕ_{1-} independent of q

For $0 < q < d$,

$$\psi = \phi_{2+} \exp i\hbar^{-1}p_2 q + \phi_{2-} \exp -i\hbar^{-1}p_2 q; \qquad p_2 = [2m(E - V_2)]^{1/2}$$

ϕ_{2+} and ϕ_{2-} independent of q

For $d < q$,

$$\psi = \phi_{3+} \exp i\hbar^{-1}p_3 q + \phi_{3-} \exp -i\hbar^{-1}p_3 q; \qquad p_3 = [2m(E - V_3)]^{1/2}$$

ϕ_{3+} and ϕ_{3-} independent of q

The continuity of both ψ and $d\psi/dq$ at $q = 0$ and at $q = d$ therefore imposes the following restrictions on ϕ_{1+}, ϕ_{1-}, ϕ_{2+}, ϕ_{2-}, ϕ_{3+} and ϕ_{3-}:

At $q = 0$,

$$\phi_{1+} + \phi_{1-} = \phi_{2+} + \phi_{2-} \tag{8-5}$$

$$p_1(\phi_{1+} - \phi_{1-}) = p_2(\phi_{2+} - \phi_{2-}) \tag{8-6}$$

At $q = d$,

$$\phi_{2+} \exp i\hbar^{-1}p_2 d + \phi_{2-} \exp -i\hbar^{-1}p_2 d = \phi_{3+} \exp i\hbar^{-1}p_3 d + \phi_{3-} \exp -i\hbar^{-1}p_3 d \tag{8-7}$$

$$p_2(\phi_{2+} \exp i\hbar^{-1}p_2 d - \phi_{2-} \exp -i\hbar^{-1}p_2 d) = p_3(\phi_{3+} \exp i\hbar^{-1}p_3 d - \phi_{3-} \exp -i\hbar^{-1}p_3 d) \quad (8\text{-}8)$$

These four equations contain the six unknowns ϕ_{1+}, ϕ_{1-}, ϕ_{2+}, ϕ_{2-}, ϕ_{3+} and ϕ_{3-}. Two additional equations necessary for the evaluation of these six unknowns will be given in the next sections.

8-4 Classically accessible and classically inaccessible regions. In classical mechanics only those regions are accessible to particles for which $V < E$, or conversely, only those particles can penetrate a given region that have a total energy E larger than the potential energy V of that region. When V exceeds E, the momentum p becomes imaginary, and consequently the wave function $\exp i\hbar^{-1}pq$ becomes a real function in classically inaccessible regions. Therefore wave mechanics would permit a finite probability of finding an electron in a classically inaccessible region.

---

problem 8-1. (*a*) The wave function of electrons in a classically inaccessible region is given by $\psi = \phi \exp i\hbar^{-1}pq$, with p and ϕ independent of q. Estimate the relative probabilities of finding an electron at the following locations, if the potential energy in the region $q > 0$ exceeds the total energy by 0.25 ev.

(*a*) $q = 0$; (*b*) $q = 1$ A; (*c*) $q = 1$ micron (10^4 A)

(*b*) Find the standard deviation of the position of the electrons from $q = 0$ for the wave function of Prob. 8-1*a*. Interpret your result in the light of the uncertainty principle.

When classically inaccessible regions extend to infinity, proper behavior requires that the exponential wave functions vanish at infinity. For instance, if the region $q > d$ is classically inaccessible, then only the exponentially decreasing term in the wave function may be retained, for the exponentially increasing function would increase indefinitely with increasing q. When p is imaginary, $\exp i\hbar^{-1}p_3 q$ becomes an exponentially decreasing function. Therefore the term $\phi_{3-} \exp -i\hbar^{-1}p_3 q$ in the expression for the wave function in the region $q > d$, violates proper behavior; proper behavior can therefore only be maintained by equating ϕ_{3-} to zero. Similarly, if the region $q < 0$ is classically inaccessible, ϕ_{1+} must vanish. These conditions apply to the potential functions shown in Fig. 8-1*a* and *c*.

When the classically accessible regions extend to infinity, a problem arises with regard to the proper behavior of the wave function. The function exp $i\hbar^{-1}pq$ with p real, which has been used to describe a beam of electrons moving in the positive q direction in the absence of an external field, is not really properly behaved at all, for its absolute magnitude is unity everywhere, and hence does not vanish at infinity. Actually, such a beam cannot constitute a self-consistent system, for a source and a sink are implied. Since in nonrelativistic mechanics electrons cannot be created or destroyed, the electrons must be brought back by an external path from the sink to the source. This occurs in practice, for we know that no current flows through a normal conductor or a semiconductor without an emf closing the circuit. Therefore we cannot consider the electron beam without its associated electrodes; these electrodes may be very far from the potential discontinuities, but they are a finite distance apart. Between these electrodes, the wave function for the electron beam traveling in the positive q direction is $\phi_+ \exp i\hbar^{-1}pq$, but beyond the electrodes the wave function vanishes, and hence is properly behaved.

In the following sections we shall solve Eqs. (8-5) to (8-8) for the various potential functions shown in Fig. 8-1. We shall first consider two adjacent regions, as shown in Fig. 8-1*a*, of which the region $q < 0$ is classically accessible, while the region $q > 0$ may or may not be classically accessible. Next we shall consider two examples of three adjacent regions: the potential barrier Fig. 8-1*b* and the potential well Fig. 8-1*c*.

8-5 Reflection and transmission of electrons at a discontinuity in the potential. Consider first the potential function of Fig. 8-1*a*, with a source in the region $q < 0$ and a sink in the region $q > 0$. Assume that all electrons reaching the sink are eventually returned to the source by an external route, so that none are reflected from the sink. In that case, ϕ_{2-} vanishes, for the term $\phi_{2-} \exp -i\hbar^{-1}p_2q$ represents a beam of electrons traveling, in the region $q > 0$, in the negative q-direction. Equations (8-5) and (8-6) then become

$$\phi_{1+} + \phi_{1-} = \phi_{2+} \tag{8-9}$$
$$p_1(\phi_{1+} - \phi_{+1}) = p_2\phi_{2+} \tag{8-10}$$

We have here three unknowns (ϕ_{1+}, ϕ_{1-}, and ϕ_{2+}) and only two equations. Therefore we can only solve for two of the coefficients ϕ_{1+}, ϕ_{1-}, and ϕ_{2-}, in terms of the third. This leads to the expressions

$$\frac{\phi_{1-}}{\phi_{1+}} = \frac{p_1 - p_2}{p_1 + p_2} \tag{8-11}$$

$$\frac{\phi_{2+}}{\phi_{1+}} = \frac{2p_1}{p_1 + p_2} \tag{8-12}$$

In order to interpret Eqs. (8-11) and (8-12) physically, let us consider the probability currents associated with a wave function of the form given by Eq. (8-3). When p is real (classically accessible region),

$$\begin{aligned} \psi^* &= \phi_+^* \exp(-i\hbar^{-1}pq) + \phi_-^* \exp(i\hbar^{-1}pq) \\ \mathcal{P}\psi &= p[\phi_+ \exp(i\hbar^{-1}pq) - \phi_- \exp(-i\hbar^{-1}pq)] \end{aligned}$$

Therefore

$$\begin{aligned} \psi^*\mathcal{P}\psi &= p[|\phi_+|^2 - |\phi_-|^2 - \phi_+^*\phi_- \exp(-2i\hbar^{-1}pq) \\ &\qquad + \phi_+\phi_-^* \exp(2i\hbar^{-1}pq)] \\ \psi\mathcal{P}^*\psi^* &= p[|\phi_+|^2 - |\phi_-|^2 + \phi_+^*\phi_- \exp(-2i\hbar^{-1}pq) \\ &\qquad - \phi_+\phi_-^* \exp(2i\hbar^{-1}pq)] \end{aligned}$$

so that

$$\text{Current} = \frac{p(|\phi_+|^2 - |\phi_-|^2)}{m} \tag{8-13}$$

When, on the other hand, p is imaginary (classically inaccessible region), $p = i[2m(V - E)]^{1/2}$, and $p^* = -i[2m(V - E)]^{1/2} = -p$. Hence

$$\begin{aligned} \psi^*\mathcal{P}\psi &= p[|\phi_+|^2 \exp(2i\hbar^{-1}pq) - |\phi_-|^2 \exp(-2i\hbar^{-1}pq) \\ &\qquad + \phi_+\phi_-^* - \phi_+^*\phi_-] \\ \psi\mathcal{P}^*\psi^* &= -p[|\phi_+|^2 \exp(2i\hbar^{-1}pq) - |\phi_-|^2 \exp(-2i\hbar^{-1}pq) \\ &\qquad - \phi_+\phi_-^* + \phi_+^*\phi_-] \end{aligned}$$

and

$$\text{Current} = \frac{p(\phi_+\phi_-^* - \phi_+^*\phi_-)}{m} \tag{8-14}$$

From Eq. (8-13) it follows that in the example under consideration in this chapter the current in the region $q < 0$ is made up of the difference between two terms, of which the first is proportional to $p_1|\phi_{1+}|^2$ and represents a beam traveling to the right, the second is proportional to $p_1|\phi_{1-}|^2$ and represents a beam traveling to the left. The former of these beams we call the "incident beam," the latter the "reflected beam." In the region $q > 0$ there can only be one beam, since ϕ_{2-} has been set equal to zero. When p_2 is real, this beam, called the "transmitted beam," is proportional to $p_2|\phi_{2+}|^2$. When p is imaginary, Eq. (8-14) must be used for the transmittance. Since for proper behavior ϕ_{2-} was made to vanish, $\phi_{2-}^* = \phi_{2-} = 0$; hence the current is zero. The reflectance and transmittance at the potential discontinuity are defined as follows:

$$\text{Reflectance} \equiv \frac{\text{magnitude of reflected current}}{\text{magnitude of incident current}}$$

$$\text{Transmittance} \equiv \frac{\text{magnitude of transmitted current}}{\text{magnitude of incident current}}$$

Equations (8-11) and (8-12) are interpreted as follows:
When p_2 is real,

$$\text{Reflectance} = \frac{|\phi_{1-}|^2}{|\phi_{1+}|^2} = \frac{(p_1 - p_2)^2}{(p_1 + p_2)^2} \tag{8-15}$$

$$\text{Transmittance} = \frac{p_2|\phi_{2+}|^2}{p_1|\phi_{1+}|^2} = \frac{4p_1p_2}{(p_1 + p_2)^2} \tag{8-16}$$

When p_2 is imaginary, $p_2^* = -p_2$

$$\text{Reflectance} = \frac{(p_1 - p_2)(p_1 - p_2)^*}{(p_1 + p_2)(p_1 + p_2)^*} = \frac{(p_1 - p_2)(p_2 + p_2)}{(p_1 + p_2)(p_2 - p_2)} = 1 \tag{8-17}$$

$$\text{Transmittance} = 0 \tag{8-18}$$

Equations (8-15) and (8-16) are analogous to equations in physical optics, with p_1 and p_2 corresponding to the refractive indices of two adjacent media. From Eqs. (8-17) and (8-18) it follows that when the region $q > 0$ is classically inaccessible, no current can penetrate it in spite of the fact that there is a finite charge density ($\Psi\Psi^*$) within that region. In the following section it will be shown that classically inaccessible regions of finite width can indeed be penetrated by currents.

When E exceeds both V_1 and V_2, then Eqs. (8-15) and (8-16) are applicable; in terms of E and V, these become

$$\text{Reflectance} = \frac{\left[1 - \left(\dfrac{E - V_1}{E - V_2}\right)^{1/2}\right]^2}{\left[1 + \left(\dfrac{E - V_1}{E - V_2}\right)^{1/2}\right]^2} \tag{8-15a}$$

$$\text{Transmittance} = 1 - \text{reflectance}$$

Equation (8-15a) demonstrates that a fraction of all electrons incident on a potential discontinuity is reflected, even when the energy of these electrons everywhere exceeds the potential energy. The reflectance in this case depends on the ratio of the kinetic energies in the regions on both sides of the discontinuity. Table 8-1 lists the reflectance as a function of this kinetic-energy ratio; for convenience, the energies, as a function of both potentials for each value of the kinetic-energy ratio, are listed.

---

problem 8-2. If the zero point of energy is chosen as V_1, and if a beam of electrons impinges on an energy barrier of height 0.030 ev and of infinite width, find the fraction of electrons reflected at the barrier, if the energy of the impinging electrons is

(*a*) 0.025 ev
(*b*) 0.030 ev
(*c*) 0.040 ev
(*d*) 0.25 ev

8-6 Transmission and reflection at potential barriers of finite width. In this section we consider the potential sketched in Fig. 8-1b, in particular those cases where $V_1 < E$, $V_2 > E$, $V_3 < E$, in other words a classically inaccessible region separating two classically accessible regions. Again we assume a nonreflecting sink having a large positive value of q, so that ϕ_{3-} vanishes in Eqs. (8-7) and (8-8). To find the reflectance and transmittance of the potential barrier, we must

table 8-1

reflectance of barriers of infinite width as a function of total and potential energies

$\dfrac{E - V_2}{E - V_1}$	E	reflectance
0.0	V_2	1.00
0.2	$1.25V_2 - 0.25V_1$	0.16
0.4	$\frac{5}{3}V_2 - \frac{2}{3}V_1$	0.053
0.6	$2.5V_2 - 1.5V_1$	0.013
0.8	$5V_2 - 4V_1$	0.006
1.0	∞	0.000

solve Eqs. (8-5) to (8-8) for (ϕ_{1-}/ϕ_{1+}) and for (ϕ_{3+}/ϕ_{1+}). These equations can be rewritten as follows:

$$\frac{\phi_{1-}}{\phi_{1+}} - \frac{\phi_{2+}}{\phi_{1+}} - \frac{\phi_{2-}}{\phi_{1+}} = -1 \qquad (8\text{-}5a)$$

$$-p_1\frac{\phi_{1-}}{\phi_{1+}} - p_2\frac{\phi_{2+}}{\phi_{1+}} + p_2\frac{\phi_{2-}}{\phi_{1+}} = -p_1 \qquad (8\text{-}6a)$$

$$D\frac{\phi_{2+}}{\phi_{1+}} + D^{-1}\frac{\phi_{2-}}{\phi_{1+}} - \frac{\phi_{3+}}{\phi_{1+}}\exp i\hbar^{-1}p_3d = 0 \qquad (8\text{-}7a)$$

$$p_2D\frac{\phi_{2+}}{\phi_{1+}} - p_2D^{-1}\frac{\phi_{2-}}{\phi_{1+}} - p_3\frac{\phi_{3+}}{\phi_{1+}}\exp i\hbar^{-1}p_3d = 0 \qquad (8\text{-}8a)$$

where $D = \exp \hbar^{-1}(ip_2d)$.

$$\frac{\phi_{1-}}{\phi_{1+}} = \frac{p_2(p_1 - p_3)(D^{-1} + D) + (p_1p_3 - p_2^2)(D^{-1} - D)}{p_2(p_1 + p_3)(D^{-1} + D) + (p_1p_3 + p_2^2)(D^{-1} - D)}$$

and

$$\frac{\phi_{3+}}{\phi_{1+}}\exp i\hbar^{-1}p_3d = \frac{4p_1p_2}{p_2(p_1 + p_3)(D^{-1} + D) + (p_1p_3 + p_2^2)(D^{-1} - D)}$$

Therefore, the reflectance of the barrier is

$$\begin{aligned} R &= \frac{|\phi_{1-}|^2}{|\phi_{1+}|^2} = \frac{|p_2(p_1 - p_3)(D^{-1} + D) + (p_1p_3 - p_2^2)(D^{-1} - D)|^2}{|p_2(p_1 + p_3)(D^{-1} + D) + (p_1p_3 + p_2^2)(D^{-1} - D)|^2} \\ &= \frac{(p_1p_3 - p_2^2)^2 \tanh^2 \hbar^{-1}(ip_2)d - p_2^2(p_1 - p_3)^2}{(p_1p_3 + p_2^2)^2 \tanh^2 \hbar^{-1}(ip_2)d - p_2^2(p_1 + p_3)^2} \end{aligned} \qquad (8\text{-}19)$$

Similarly

$$T = \frac{p_3|\phi_{3+}|^2}{p_1|\phi_{1+}|^2} = 1 - R = \frac{-4p_1p_2^2p_3 \operatorname{sech}^2 \hbar^{-1}(ip_2)d}{(p_1p_3 + p_2^2)^2 \tanh^2 \hbar^{-1}(ip_2)d - p_2^2(p_1 + p_3)^2} \qquad (8\text{-}20)$$

Since p_2^2 equals $2m(E - V_2)$, it is real. Since E and V_2 are real, and V_2 is larger than E, p_2 is pure imaginary and ip_2 is real. Therefore R and T, as given by Eqs. (8-19) and (8-20), are real. Two special cases are important. The first is the case of the vanishing barrier, with ip_2d equal to zero. In that case Eqs. (8-18) and (8-20) become

$$R = \frac{(p_1 - p_3)^2}{(p_1 + p_3)^2}; \qquad T = \frac{4p_1p_3}{(p_1 + p_3)^2}$$

These expressions agree with Eqs. (8-15) and (8-16) if p_3 is substituted for p_2. The other case is that of a very large barrier, i.e., one having $ip_2d \gg \hbar$. In that case (remember that ip_2 is negative and that p_2^2 is negative),

$$\tanh \hbar^{-1}(ip_2)d \doteq 1$$
$$\operatorname{sech} \hbar^{-1}(ip_2)d \doteq 2 \exp \hbar^{-1}(ip_2)d$$

so that

$$R \doteq \frac{(p_1p_3 - p_2^2)^2 - p_2^2(p_1 - p_3)^2}{(p_1p_3 + p_2^2)^2 - p_2^2(p_1 + p_3)^2} =$$
$$= \frac{p_1^2p_3^2 - 2p_1p_2^2p_3 + p_2^4 - p_1^2p_2^2 + 2p_1p_3p_2^2 - p_2^2p_3^2}{p_1^2p_3^2 + 2p_1p_2^2p_3 + p_2^4 - p_1^2p_2^2 - 2p_1p_3p_2^2 - p_2^2p_3^2} = 1$$

and

$$T \doteq \frac{-16p_1p_2^2p_3 \exp 2\hbar^{-1}(ip_2)d}{p_1^2p_3^2 - p_1^2p_2^2 - p_2^2p_3^2 + p_2^4} \tag{8-20a}$$

If the potential on both sides of the barrier is the same and equal to zero,

$$p_1 = p_3 = (2mE)^{1/2}$$
$$p_2^2 = 2m(E - V_2)$$

When these two expressions are substituted in Eq. (8-20*a*), the transmittance of high or wide barriers becomes

$$T = 16E(V_2 - E)V_2^{-2} \exp \{-2\hbar^{-1}[2m(V_2 - E)]^{1/2}d\}$$

---

problem 8-3. Calculate the probability of transmission for each of the designated particles through the indicated barriers:

(*a*) Electrons: $V_2 = 2$ ev; $E = 1$ ev; barrier width 1A

(*b*) Protons: $V_2 = 2$ ev; $E = 1$ ev; barrier width 1A

(*c*) α particles: $V_2 = 3.6 \times 10^6$ ev $E = 5 \times 10^6$ ev; barrier width 10^{-4}A

From Eq. (8-20*a*) it follows that practically all electrons are reflected from very high and/or very wide barriers; nevertheless a few electrons are transmitted. Since the transmittance of such barriers depends exponentially on the height and width of the barrier, a relatively small change in either V or d substantially affects the amount of current passed. The phenomenon of electrons passing through potential barriers is called the "tunnel effect"; this effect is especially important in thermionic and field emission.

8-7 Potential wells. Consider next a classically accessible region surrounded by two classically inaccessible regions, as illustrated by Fig. 8-1*c*. Such a system exemplifies the idealized behavior of electrons in atomic systems. In this case there is neither a sink nor a source; in the region $q < 0$ proper behavior demands an increasing exponential function, so that ϕ_{1+} vanishes, while ϕ_{3-} vanishes for the same reason in the region $q > d$. Equations (8-5) to (8-8) then become

$$\phi_{1-} = \phi_{2+} + \phi_{2-} \tag{8-21}$$

$$-p_1\phi_{1-} = p_2(\phi_{2+} - \phi_{2-}) \tag{8-22}$$

$$\phi_{2+} \exp i\hbar^{-1}p_2d + \phi_{2-} \exp -i\hbar^{-1}p_2d = \phi_{3+} \exp i\hbar^{-1}p_3d \tag{8-23}$$

$$p_2(\phi_{2+} \exp i\hbar^{-1}p_2d - \phi_{2-} \exp -i\hbar^{-1}p_2d) = p_3\phi_{3+} \exp i\hbar^{-1}p_3d \tag{8-24}$$

In contrast to the applications considered previously, we have here four equations with four unknowns. Moveover, these four equations are homogeneous, and hence have nonvanishing solutions only if the determinant of their coefficients vanishes. Since these coefficients are functions of p_1, p_2 and p_3, this implies that p_1, p_2 and p_3 must be related in such a way that the determinant does vanish. This condition imposes a constraint upon the allowed values of the energy.

Before solving Eqs. (8-21) to (8-24) in general, we first consider an illustrative though somewhat artificial example, namely, the special case when V_1 and V_3 become infinite. While the wave function must be continuous for proper behavior, the infinite discontinuity in the potential-energy function may well cause a discontinuity in the derivative of the wave function. Therefore Eqs. (8-22) and (8-24), which deal with the continuity of this derivative, do not apply in this case. Furthermore, the real exponential wave functions in the regions $q < 0$ and $q > d$ now vanish, since (ip_1) and (ip_3) become infinite. Therefore the wave function vanishes everywhere outside the well; the continuity requirement then implies that the wave function inside the well equal zero at the boundaries of the inaccessible regions, so that

$$\phi_{2+} + \phi_{2-} = 0 \tag{8-25}$$

$$\phi_{2+} \exp i\hbar^{-1}p_2d + \phi_{2-} \exp -i\hbar^{-1}p_2d = 0 \tag{8-26}$$

These two homogeneous equations have nonvanishing solutions only if the determinant of their coefficients vanishes:

$$\exp -i\hbar^{-1}p_2 d = \exp i\hbar^{-1}p_2 d \tag{8-27}$$

Equation (8-27) is valid only if $\hbar^{-1}p_2 d = n\pi$, where n is an integer, i.e., if

$$p_2 = \frac{n\pi\hbar}{d} = \frac{nh}{2d} \tag{8-28}$$

$$E - V_2 = \frac{p_2{}^2}{2m} = \frac{n^2h^2}{8md^2} \tag{8-29}$$

Equation (8-28) can be used for finding the de Broglie wavelength of electrons trapped in the potential well. It is observed that this wavelength equals twice the width of the well, or an integral fraction thereof; in other words, nodes occur at the walls of the well, and standing waves are set up in between. Equation (8-29) gives just the quantized energy values that were given in Prob. 5-9*a*; we have here presented the derivation of those values. Note further that the separation between the allowed values of both the momentum and the energy increases with decreasing width of the well and that these allowed values approach each other when the well is expanded.

The wave functions given in Prob. 5-9*a* can also be found. By substitution of Eq. (8-25) into Eq. (8-3), with the addition of the subscript 2 to denote the region of the well,

$$\begin{aligned}\psi &= \phi_{2+} \exp i\hbar^{-1}p_2 q + \phi_{2-} \exp -i\hbar^{-1}p_2 q \\ &= \phi_{2+}(\exp i\hbar^{-1}p_2 q - \exp -i\hbar^{-1}p_2 q) \\ &= 2i\phi_{2+} \sin \hbar^{-1}p_2 q\end{aligned}$$

Since p_2 is given by Eq. (8-28),

$$\psi = 2i\phi_{2+} \sin \frac{n\pi q}{d}$$

When ϕ_{2+} is chosen such that ψ is normalized, then this last expression agrees with the stationary wave function of Prob. 5-9*a*. Presently we shall see that the same conclusions apply qualitatively for the case of a potential well of finite depth.

Let us now consider such a potential well of finite depth. In this case the determinant of the coefficients of Eqs. (8-21) to (8-24) must vanish:

$$\begin{vmatrix} 1 & -1 & -1 & 0 \\ -p_1 & -p_2 & +p_2 & 0 \\ 0 & D & D^{-1} & -1 \\ 0 & p_2D & -p_2D^{-1} & -p_3 \end{vmatrix} = 0 \tag{8-30}$$

where $D \equiv \exp i\hbar^{-1}p_2d$ and the factor $\exp i\hbar^{-1}p_3d$ has been canceled out. The left-hand side of Eq. (8-30) has already been evaluated in solving Eqs. (8-5a) to (8-8a). Equation (8-30) can therefore be rewritten

$$p_2(p_1 + p_3)(D^{-1} + D) + (p_1p_3 + p_2^2)(D^{-1} - D) = 0$$

therefore

$$\frac{p_2(p_1 + p_3)}{p_1p_3 + p_2^2} = -\frac{D^{-1} - D}{D^{-1} + D}$$

In this case p_2 is real, p_1 and p_3 are purely imaginary, and D is complex. From the definition of D,

$$-\frac{D^{-1} - D}{D^{-1} + D} = -i \tan \hbar^{-1}p_2d$$

so that

$$\tan \hbar^{-1}p_2d = \frac{i(p_1 + p_3)p_2}{p_1p_3 + p_2^2} \tag{8-31}$$

Equation (8-31) represents a constraint on p_1, p_2, and p_3 for each value of d, and since each of these functions depends on E, it represents a constraint on E for each set of values of d, V_1, V_2, and V_3. In Fig. 8-4 we show a graphical solution of Eq. (8-31); first both sides of this equation are plotted as functions of p_2 for various values of d, p_1, and p_3, and then these curves are superimposed such that the abscissae of the points of intersection represent the values allowed by Eq. (8-31) for each set of values chosen for p_1, p_3, and d.

---

problem 8-4. (a) Show that a plot of the right-hand side of Eq. (8-31) vs. p_2 starts at the origin with slope equal to $i(p_1^{-1} + p_3^{-1})$, reaches a maximum of height $\frac{1}{2}i(p_1p_3)^{-\frac{1}{2}}(p_1 + p_3)$, at $p_2 = (p_1p_3)$,$^{\frac{1}{2}}$ and approaches zero asymptotically as p_2 increases indefinitely.

(b) Show that the plot of the left-hand side of Eq. (8-31) vs. p_2 has vertical asymptotes when $p_2 = (2n + 1)h/4d$, where n is an integer.

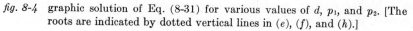

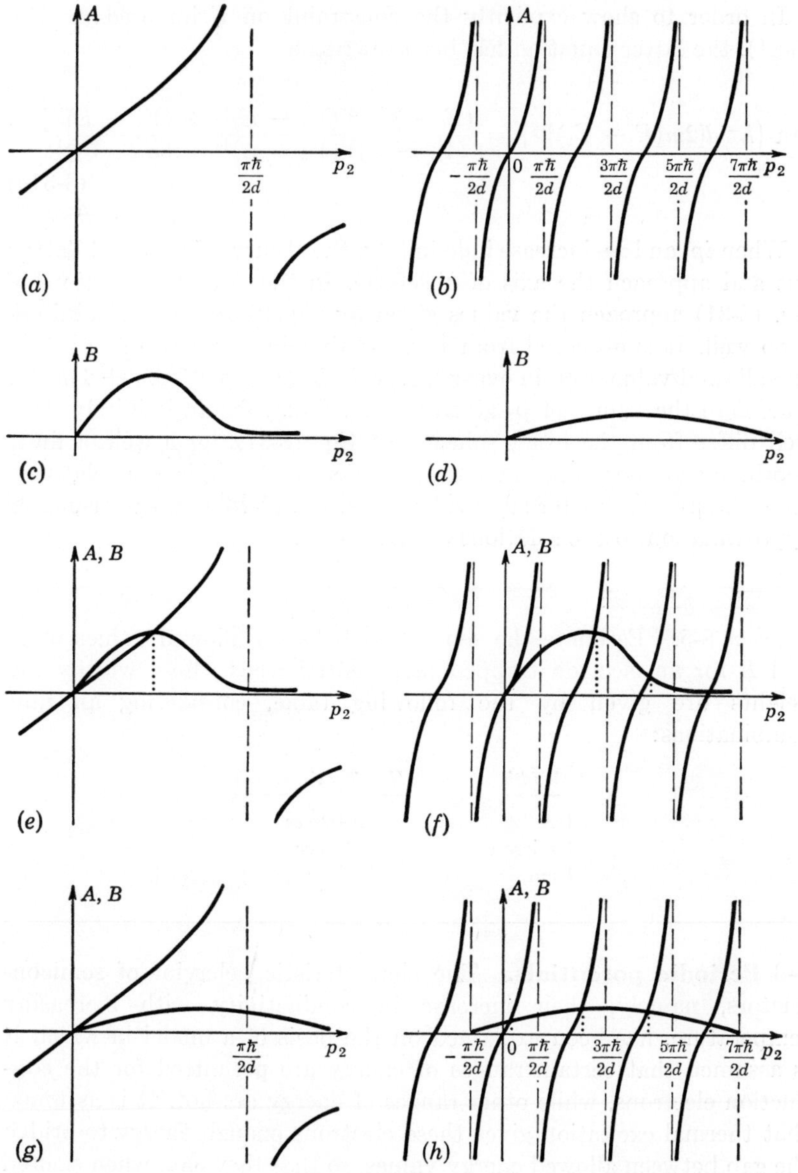

fig. 8-4 graphic solution of Eq. (8-31) for various values of d, p_1, and p_2. [The roots are indicated by dotted vertical lines in (e), (f), and (h).]

$$A = \tan(\hbar^{-1}p_2 d); \qquad B = \frac{i(p_1 + p_3)}{p_1 p_3 + p_2{}^2}\, p_2$$

(a) Small d; (b) large d; (c) small p_1 and p_3; (d) large p_1 and p_3; (e) small d, p_1 and p_3; (f) large d, small p_1 and p_3; (g) small d, large p_1, and p_3; (h) large d, p_1, and p_3.

In order to show explicitly the constraint on E imposed by Eq. (8-31), the latter equation has been rewritten

$$\tan \{\hbar^{-1}d[2m(E - V_2)]^{1/2}\} = \frac{(E - V_2)^{1/2}[(V_1 - E)^{1/2} + (V_3 - E)^{1/2}]}{(V_1 - E)^{1/2}(V_3 - E)^{1/2} + (E - V_2)^{1/2}} \tag{8-31a}$$

When ip_1 and ip_3 increase indefinitely, the B curves in Fig. 8-4 flatten out and approach the axis of abscissae. In that case the solutions of Eq. (8-31) approach the values given by Eq. (8-28) for an infinitely deep well. It is observed from Fig. 8-4 that in any case there is but one allowed value of p_2 in every interval $nh/2d \leq p_2 \leq (2n + 1)h/4d$. Therefore the values of p_2 given by Eq. (8-28) for an infinitely deep well differ from the exact solution of Eq. (8-31), for a well of finite depth, by at most the amount $h/4d$. For small n this is a relatively large difference, but for large values of n, Eq. (8-28) gives a reasonable approximation to the solutions of Eq. (8-31).

---

problem 8-5. Estimate the separation between allowed values of p_2 and E for an electron trapped in potential wells whose widths and heights are given by the following table, considering all nine combinations:

Width	*Height* ($V_1 = V_3$)
1 A	0.025 *ev*
1 micron	0.25 *ev*
1 cm	2.5 *ev*

8-8 Periodic potentials. The characteristic behavior of semiconductors, namely, their increase in conductivity with increasing temperature, has been explained on the basis of a model in which it is assumed that certain ranges of energy are permitted for the conduction electrons, while other ranges of energy are not. It is assumed that thermal excitation gives these electrons enough energy to bridge the gap between allowed energy values, so that they can, when excited to a higher energy, contribute more effectively to the conduction process. We shall now investigate how ranges of allowed and forbidden energies arise.

As a simple model consider the behavior of the electrons in a one-dimensional array of atoms at equal distances, as would be the case in a one-dimensional crystal. We assume a piecewise constant potential. This model may be considered as a case intermediate between a potential-energy barrier, which can be penetrated without restriction on momentum and energy, and that of a potential-energy well, in which only discrete values of momentum and energy are possible.

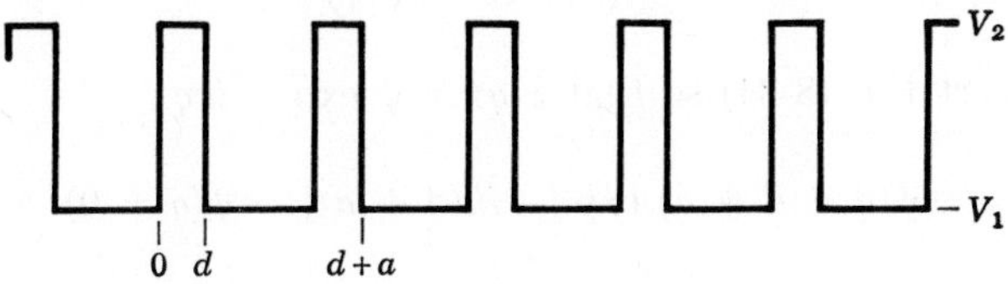

fig. 8-5 periodic potential

To determine the wave function and energy for the electrons in a periodic potential field, solve Schroedinger's equation for the following potential function (see Fig. 8-5):

$$\left.\begin{array}{llc} V = V_1 < E & \text{for} & l(d+a) < q < ld + (l+1)a \\ V = V_2 > E & \text{for} & ld + (l+1)a < q < l(d+a) \end{array}\right\} \quad \begin{array}{l}\text{where } l \text{ is} \\ \text{an integer}\end{array} \tag{8-32}$$

The solution presented here is due to Kronig and Penney.† Let us assume that the electron distribution has the same periodicity as does the potential function. The square of the absolute magnitude of the wave function therefore obeys the condition

$$|\psi|^2_{q+d+a} = |\psi|^2_q \tag{8-33}$$

This condition does not necessarily mean that the wave function itself is periodic. Indeed, for any real parameter k, if

$$\psi = \pi(q) \exp ikq \tag{8-34}$$

then

$$|\psi| = |\pi(q)|$$

Accordingly, Eq. (8-33) imposes only the condition that $\pi(q)$ be periodic, with a period $(d + a)$. The quantity $(d + a)$ is called the "lattice constant" of the structure. A function of the type given by

† *Proc. Roy. Soc.* (*London*), **130**, 499 (1931).

Eq. (8-34) is called a Bloch function. If the function $\pi(q)$ is to be periodic, then its derivative should also be periodic.

Thus

$$\pi(d + a) = \pi(0)$$

and

$$\left(\frac{d\pi}{dq}\right)_{d+a} = \left(\frac{d\pi}{dq}\right)_0$$

If we invert Eq. (8-34) so that $\pi(q) = \psi \exp -ikq$,

$$\psi(q = d + a) \exp [-ik(d + a)] = \psi(q = 0) \tag{8-35}$$

Differentiation of π gives, in terms of ψ and k,

$$\left(\frac{d\psi}{dq} - ik\psi\right)_{q=d+a} \exp [-ik(d + a)] = \left(\frac{d\psi}{dq} - ik\psi\right)_{q=0} \tag{8-36}$$

When Eq. (8-35) is substituted into Eq. (8-36),

$$\left(\frac{d\psi}{dq}\right)_{q=d+a} \exp [-ik(d + a)] = \left(\frac{d\psi}{dq}\right)_{q=0} \tag{8-37}$$

For the regions where $V = V_1$, the general solution can be written in the form

$$\psi = \phi_{1+} \exp i\hbar^{-1}p_1q + \phi_{1-} \exp -i\hbar^{-1}p_1q$$

and for the regions where $V = V_2$

$$\psi = \phi_{2+} \exp i\hbar^{-1}p_2q + \phi_{2-} \exp -i\hbar^{-1}p_2q$$

When these expressions are substituted into Eqs. (8-35) and (8-37),

$$\{\phi_{1+} \exp [i\hbar^{-1}p_1(d + a)] + \phi_{1-} \exp [-i\hbar^{-1}p_1(d + a)]\} \exp [-ik(d + a)] = \phi_{2+} + \phi_{2-} \tag{8-38}$$

$$p_1\{\phi_{1+} \exp [i\hbar^{-1}p_1(d + a)] - \phi_{1-} \exp [-i\hbar^{-1}p_1(d + a)] \exp [-ik(d + a)]\} = p_2(\phi_{2+} - \phi_{2-}) \tag{8-39}$$

In addition to these two equations there are the usual requirements of smooth splicing at $q = d$:

$$\phi_{1+} \exp i\hbar^{-1}p_1d + \phi_{1-} \exp -i\hbar^{-1}p_1d = \phi_{2+} \exp i\hbar^{-1}p_2d + \phi_{2-} \exp -i\hbar^{-1}p_2d \tag{8-40}$$

$$p_1(\phi_{1+} \exp i\hbar^{-1}p_1 d - \phi_{1-} \exp -i\hbar^{-1}p_1 d) \\ = p_2[\phi_{2+} \exp (i\hbar^{-1}p_2 d) - \phi_{2-} \exp (-i\hbar^{-1}p_2 d)] \quad (8\text{-}41)$$

Before solving Eqs. (8-38) to (8-41), we shall discuss a few properties of the Bloch wave function.

8-9 The Bloch function. We have seen that the Bloch function is made up of a periodic factor having the same periodicity as that of the crystal structure in which the electrons move, and a factor that is just the wave function of a free-electron beam. We can say that the free-electron wave function is "modulated" by the crystal structure. For the free electron beam having a wave function $\psi = \exp ikq$ the the momentum was found to be $k\hbar$. The expectation value of the momentum for the modulated beam is

$$\bar{p} = \frac{\oint \pi^* \exp(-ikq)\left(-i\hbar \frac{\partial}{\partial q}\right)(\pi \exp ikq)\, dq}{\oint \pi^* \pi\, dq}$$

$$= \frac{\oint \pi^*(-i\hbar)\left[\left(\frac{\partial \pi}{\partial q}\right) + ik\pi\right] dq}{\oint \pi^*\pi\, dq} = k\hbar + \frac{\oint \pi^* \left(-i\hbar \frac{\partial}{\partial q}\right) \pi\, dq}{\oint \pi^* \pi\, dq}$$

Thus the expectation value of the momentum of the modulated beam equals the momentum of the unmodulated beam plus the expectation value of momentum for a hypothetical system with wave function $\pi(q)$.

The function $\pi(q)$ is the same in each potential well of Fig. (8-5); the factor exp ikq in the wave function might be thought of as "carrying" a wave function $\pi(q)$ from well to well. If the classically inaccessible regions were very narrow and steep, one would expect $\pi(q)$ to equal approximately the sine function of the particle in the infinitely deep well. The difference between the case of a particle in a single well and that of a particle in a periodic potential is that in the former case the wave function had to go to zero in the adjacent inacessible region, while in the latter it merely has to splice on to the wave function in the next well, and eventually electrodes provide sources and sinks for electrons that are carried around and back by an external route. We shall see, however, that Eqs. (8-38) to (8-41) *cannot* be solved for *all* values of the energy; the periodic potential therefore acts as a filter, allowing only electrons with appropriate values of the energy to be transmitted.

---

problem 8-6. Find an expression for the current associated with the Bloch function.

8-10 Energy bands. We now proceed to solve Eqs. (8-38) to (8-41):

$$\phi_{1+} \exp\,[i(\hbar^{-1}p_1 - k)(d + a)] + \phi_{1-} \exp\,[-i(\hbar^{-1}p_1 + k)(d + a)] + \\ - \phi_{2+} - \phi_{2-} = 0$$

$$\phi_{1+}p_1 \exp\,[i(\hbar^{-1}p_1 - k)(d + a)] - p_1\phi_{1-} \exp\,[-i(\hbar^{-1}p_1 + k)(d + a)] + \\ - p_2\phi_{2+} + p_2\phi_{2-} = 0$$

$$\phi_{1+} \exp\,(i\hbar^{-1}p_1 d) + \phi_{1-} \exp\,(-i\hbar^{-1}p_1 d) - \phi_{2+} \exp\,(i\hbar^{-1}p_2 d) + \\ - \phi_{2-} \exp\,(-i\hbar^{-1}p_2 d) = 0$$

$$\phi_{1+}p_1 \exp\,(i\hbar^{-1}p_1 d) - p_1\phi_{1-} \exp\,(-i\hbar^{-1}p_1 d) - p_2\phi_{2+} \exp\,(i\hbar^{-1}p_2 d) + \\ + p_2\phi_{2-} \exp\,(-i\hbar^{-1}p_2 d) = 0$$

These equations have nonvanishing solutions only if

$$\begin{vmatrix} \exp[i(\hbar^{-1}p_1 - k)(d + a)] & \exp[-i(\hbar^{-1}p_1 + k)(d + a)] & -1 & -1 \\ p_1 \exp[i(\hbar^{-1}p_1 - k)(d + a)] & - p_1 \exp[-i(\hbar^{-1}p_1 + k)(d + a)] & -p_2 & -p_2 \\ \exp i\hbar^{-1}p_1 d & + \exp -i\hbar^{-1}p_1 d & - \exp i\hbar^{-1}p_2 d & - \exp i\hbar^{-1}p_2 d \\ p_1 \exp i\hbar^{-1}p_1 d & -p_1 \exp -i\hbar^{-1}p_1 d & -p_2 \exp i\hbar^{-1}p_2 d & + p_2 \exp -i\hbar^{-1}p_1 d \end{vmatrix} = 0 \quad (8\text{-}42)$$

If we set $G = \exp -ik(a + d)$,

$$G^2 + \frac{p_1^2 + p_2^2}{ip_1p_2} \sin \hbar^{-1}p_1 a \sinh\,(i\hbar^{-1}p_2 d)G + \\ -2 \cos \hbar^{-1}p_1 a \cosh\,(i\hbar^{-1}p_2 d)G = -1 \quad (8\text{-}43)$$

Take the complex conjugate of both sides of this equation (remembering that ip_2 is real):

$$G^{*2} + \frac{p_1^2 + p_2^2}{ip_1p_2} \sin \hbar^{-1}p_1 a \sinh\,(i\hbar^{-1}p_2 d)G^* + \\ -2 \cos \hbar^{-1}p_1 a \cosh\,(i\hbar^{-1}p_2 d)G^* = -1 \quad (8\text{-}44)$$

When Eq. (8-44) is subtracted from Eq. (8-43) and the definition $G \equiv \exp -ik(a + d)$ is substituted,

$$\sin 2k(a + d) + \frac{p_1^2 + p_2^2}{ip_1p_2} \sin \hbar^{-1}p_1 a \sinh i\hbar^{-1}p_2 d \sin k(\mathbf{a} + d) + \\ -2 \cos \hbar^{-1}p_1 a \cosh i\hbar^{-1}p_2 d \sin k(a + d) = 0 \quad (8\text{-}45)$$

Since $\sin 2k(a + d) = 2 \sin k(a + d) \cos k(a + d)$, Eq. (8-45) is satisfied if $\sin k(a + d) = 0$, or

$$\cos k(a + d) = -\frac{p_1^2 + p_2^2}{2ip_1p_2} \sin \hbar^{-1}p_1a \sinh i\hbar^{-1}p_2d + \\ + \cos \hbar^{-1}p_1a \cosh i\hbar^{-1}p_2d \quad (8\text{-}46)$$

Since the left-hand side of Eq. (8-46) never exceeds the range $-1 \leq \cos k(a + d) \leq +1$, the right-hand side of this equation should remain within that same range. When the right-hand side of Eq. (8-46) is rewritten explicitly as a function of E, V_1 and V_2,

$$\cos k(a + d) = \\ = \frac{(V_1 + V_2) - 2E}{\sqrt{(E - V_1)(V_2 - E)}} \sin [\hbar^{-1}a \sqrt{2m(E - V_1)}] \sinh [\hbar^{-1}d \sqrt{2m(V_2 - E)}] + \\ -2 \cos [\hbar^{-1}a \sqrt{2m(E - V_1)}] \cosh [\hbar^{-1}d \sqrt{2m(V_2 - E)}] \quad (8\text{-}47)$$

In Fig. (8-6), E is plotted against the right-hand side of Eq. (8-47), for a fixed set of V, a, d values, and is represented by the undulating line. The crosshatched portions indicate the values of E which are in accord with Eq. (8-47).†

8-11 Summary. We have examined a number of idealized systems that approximate the behavior of various atomic and molecular systems. This study has revealed a number of phenomena that agree with experimental observations, but could not have been predicted from classical mechanics.

We have found that electrons and other lightweight particles can penetrate regions in which the potential energy exceeds the total energy; this penetration of classically inaccessible regions accounts for such phenomena as thermionic and field emission, radioactive disintegration, the umbrella-like inversion in certain molecular species, and permits the rotation of nonspherical molecules in liquids and solids. These phenomena may be interpreted in terms of the uncertainty principle, according to which there is a finite probability of finding a particle at a position different from its classically expected value. When the deviation from this expected position is of the same order of magnitude as the physical size of the barrier, then there is a

† Further details are given in R. B. Leighton, "Principles of Modern Physics," McGraw-Hill Book Company, Inc., New York, 1959.

finite probability that a particle will penetrate the barrier. It has also been demonstrated that when a beam of electrons impinges on a sharp discontinuity in the electric potential, some electrons from the beam are reflected even when the entire region under consideration is classically accessible. If we were to attempt to follow the course of a

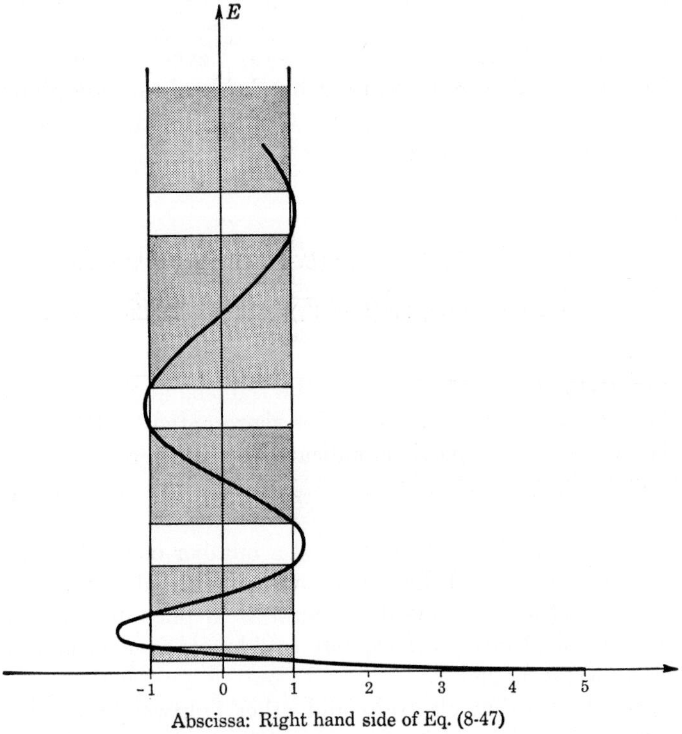

fig. 8-6 graphical solution of Eq. (8-47). (*From "Principles of Modern Physics," by R. B. Leighton. Copyright, 1959. McGraw-Hill Book Company. Used by permission.*)

particular electron in the beam, we could only make a probability statement about its future beyond the discontinuity. Of course, we have already demonstrated in Chap. 4 the futility of tracking a single electron.

Furthermore, we have observed that the energy of electrons, trapped in a classically accessible region that is surrounded by infinitely wide inaccessible regions, can only have certain discrete values. If we accept this model as a qualitative description of the behavior of electrons in an isolated atom, then this quantization can be related to the sharp lines of the absorption and emission spectra of isolated atoms.

Finally, we found that electrons in an infinitely long row of potential wells are limited to finite *ranges* of energy values. These allowed ranges of energy become narrower as the width or height of the barriers separating the wells is increased. In the limit of infinitely high or infinitely wide barriers, the allowed energy ranges or "bands" approach the sharp values characteristic of isolated wells.

One might conclude that the interaction of several wells tends to broaden the discrete energy levels. Whereas the methods used in the present chapter are not convenient for use with a finite number of wells, we shall find in an example discussed in Chap. 14, that each energy level for a single well gives rise to two distinct levels when two such wells are brought near each other. This splitting will be shown to account for molecular binding. When three wells are brought together, each single-well energy level splits into three discrete levels; for an infinite number of wells there are "infinitely" many levels within a finite energy range, as was found in Sec. 8-10.

Having dealt exclusively with potential functions that have zero gradient everywhere except possibly at a finite number of points, we shall next consider a few systems whose potential-energy function is more complex.

electrons in small fields

chapter

9

9-1 Introduction. The purpose of the present chapter is twofold. In the first place we shall find a connecting link between classical and wave mechanics, and we shall use this link for a quantitative estimate of the limitations of classical mechanics. Second, we use these results for an approximate treatment of the behavior of a stream of electrons in a moderate external field.

The potential functions discussed in Chaps. 4 and 8 have zero gradient everywhere, except possibly at a finite number of points. The approximation method developed in the present chapter is useful for cases where the gradient is relatively small, though not necessarily zero, everywhere.

9-2 Relaxation method for solving the wave equation. Consider Schroedinger's stationary wave equation for linear motion of a particle with mass m,

$$-\frac{\hbar^2}{2m}\frac{d^2\psi_n}{dq^2} + V\psi_n = E_n\psi_n$$

and make the following transformations:

$$x \equiv \hbar^{-1}q$$
$$p^2 \equiv 2m(E_n - V)$$

The wave equation then assumes a form closely resembling the stationary wave equation, Eq. (2-15):

$$\frac{d^2\psi_n}{dx^2} = -p^2(x)\psi_n \tag{9-1}$$

The approximate method discussed here is not limited to wave mechanics, but is quite general. It is convenient where dp^2/dx is sufficiently small; we shall find that this condition is not usually satisfied by the fields acting on electrons within an atom, but is frequently satisfied when electrons move in externally imposed ("man-made") fields; the condition is not satisfied within the nucleus, but can be used for particles escaping from the nucleus.

If p^2 were independent of x, then Eq. (9-1) would be the stationary harmonic wave equation, with general solution

$$\psi_n = \phi_{n+} \exp ipx + \phi_{n-} \exp -ipx \tag{9-2}$$

To solve Eq. (9-1) for the cases when p^2 does vary with x, we define a new variable $S(x)$ by means of Eq. (9-3):

$$\psi_n \equiv \exp iS \tag{9-3}$$

When this definition is substituted in Eq. (9-1), the following differential equation results:

$$\left(\frac{dS}{dx}\right)^2 = p^2(x) + i\,\frac{d^2S}{dx^2} \tag{9-4}$$

When Eq. (9-3) is compared with Eq. (9-2), the equation for the cases when p^2 is independent of x, it follows that for those special cases S depends linearly on x.

---

problem 9-1. Solve Eq. (9-4) for the special case that $d^2S/dx^2 = 0$ and find ψ_n for this case.

Does $d^2S/dx^2 = 0$ imply that p^2 is independent of x?

Since in general p^2 varies with x, S is not generally a linear function of x, and d^2S/dx^2 does not generally equal zero. Nevertheless, in solving Eq. (9-4), we shall start by setting d^2S/dx^2 equal to zero as a first approximation and by solving for dS/dx with the use of that approximation. Since d^2S/dx^2 is not zero unless p is independent of x, we shall certainly not expect to find the correct dS/dx; we can expect to find an S whose second derivative does not vanish at all! In that case, however, we shall substitute the second derivative of S just found in Eq. (9-4)and solve the resulting equation once more for dS/dx. We shall repeat the process several times, each cycle consisting of the following steps:

→ *A* Find an approximate expression for $\dfrac{d^2S}{dx^2}$

B Substitute this expression into Eq. (9-4)

C Solve the resulting equation for $\dfrac{dS}{dx}$

D Differentiate the last expression in order to → (return to *A*)

This procedure is a special case of a general method called the "relaxation method." This method consists of replacing at least one term involving the independent variable in the equation by an approximation; this invalidates the equal sign in the equation, because there is now a difference between both sides of the resulting "equation," this difference being small when the approximation made is a valid one. If, by successive steps such as outlined above, the difference between the two sides is gradually made to approach zero, then the method converges, and the independent variable can be found to any desired degree of accuracy by repeating the approximation cycle a sufficient number of times.

Let us apply the relaxation method to the solution of Eq. (9-4):

$$\begin{aligned}
&A \quad \frac{d^2S}{dx^2} = 0\\
&B \quad \left(\frac{dS}{dx}\right)^2 = p^2(x)\\
&C \quad \frac{dS}{dx} = \pm p(x)\\
&A \quad \frac{d^2S}{dx^2} = \pm \frac{dp}{dx}\\
&B \quad \left(\frac{dS}{dx}\right)^2 = p^2 \pm i\,\frac{dp}{dx}\\
&C \quad \frac{dS}{dx} = \pm \left(p^2 \pm i\,\frac{dp}{dx}\right)^{1/2}
\end{aligned}$$

$$A \quad \frac{d^2S}{dx^2} = \pm \frac{d}{dx}\left(p^2 \pm i\frac{dp}{dx}\right)^{1/2}$$

$$\vdots$$

etc.

When the procedure is carried on indefinitely, the result is

$$\frac{dS}{dx} = \pm\left(p^2 \pm i\frac{d}{dx}\left\{p^2 \pm i\frac{d}{dx}\left[p^2 \pm i\frac{d}{dx}\left(p^2 \pm i\frac{d}{dx}\cdots\right)^{1/2}\right]^{1/2}\right\}^{1/2}\right)^{1/2} \tag{9-5}$$

Equation (9-5) would be exact if an infinite number of steps were used. The procedure converges sufficiently fast to allow relatively few terms if

$$\left|\frac{dp}{dx}\right| \ll |p^2|$$

or in terms of variables V and q

$$\left|\frac{dV}{dq}\right| \ll \hbar^{-1}m^{1/2}[2|E - V|]^{3/2} \qquad \text{[inequality (9-1)]}$$

When inequality (9-1) is valid, the following binomial expansion may be used:

$$\left(p^2 \pm i\frac{dp}{dx}\right)^{1/2} = p\left(1 \pm ip^{-2}\frac{dp}{dx}\right)^{1/2} = p\left(1 \pm \tfrac{1}{2}ip^{-2}\frac{dp}{dx}\right) =$$
$$= p \pm \tfrac{1}{2}i\frac{d\ln p}{dx}$$

Accordingly, Eq. (9-5) becomes approximately

$$\frac{dS}{dx} = \pm p + \tfrac{1}{2}i\frac{d\ln p}{dx}$$

Hence $S = \pm\int p\,dx + \tfrac{1}{2}i\ln p + C_\pm$, where $C_\pm$ is independent of x.

When this last expression for S is substituted in Eq. (9-3) and the variables q and V are reintroduced, we find for ψ_n the following approximate expression:

$$\psi_n = \phi_{n\pm} \frac{\exp\{\pm i\hbar^{-1}\int[2m(E - V)]^{1/2}\,dq\}}{[2m(E - V)]^{1/4}} \tag{9-6}$$

where $\phi_{n\pm} = \exp iC_{\pm}$.

---

problem 9-2. Find the lowest value of the quantum number n of the hydrogen atom, for which the left-hand side of inequality (9-1) is less than 1 per cent of the right-hand side. (*Hint:* Recall from Sec. 1-4 that the potential energy equals $-e^2/r$ and the kinetic energy equals minus one-half the potential energy; $r = n^2\hbar^2/e^2m_e$.)

The implication of Prob. 9-2 is that Eq. (9-6) does not represent a good approximation for the so-called inner orbits of the hydrogen atom, where the potential gradient is steep, but that it is valid for the outer orbits (those with large n).

It should be noted that near a classical turning point, that is, where $V \simeq E$, the right-hand side of inequality (9-1) becomes very small, so that the relaxation method does not converge near such a turning point. Therefore another approximate expression must be found for regions near classical turning points. In such regions the function $p^2(x)$ is very small, so that the expression $d^2\psi_n/dx^2$ in Eq. (9-1) is approximately equal to zero. Thus in a region near a classical turning point the wave function ψ_n is a linear function of the coordinates; this fact was used by Kramers† and others to splice together the approximate equations given by Eq. (9-6) which may be valid everywhere except in a small region at and near turning points. Equation (9-6) was originally derived in a manner different from the one used in this chapter by Wentzel,‡ Brillouin§ and Kramers; it is called the WBK equation. In the next section we shall discuss some of the intuitive background that led to the derivation of the WBK equation. For the splicing procedure near classical turning points and the resulting connection with the Sommerfeld quantum condition [Eq. (1-10)], the reader is referred to the articles by the three authors referred to above and to Sommerfeld.‖

---

† *Z. Physik*, **39**, 828 (1926).
‡ *Z. Physik*, **38**, 518 (1926).
§ *Compt. rend.*, **183**, 24 (1926).
‖ A. Sommerfeld, "Atombau und Spektrallinien, Wellenmechanischer Ergänzungsband," pp. 158–165, Friedr. Vieweg & Sohn, Brunswick, Germany, 1929.

problem 9-3. Show that the WBK function does not behave properly at a classical turning point.

9-3 Physical interpretation of the WBK expression. In interpreting Eq. (9-6) we should first examine the meaning of inequality (9-1), which states the limitation of the WBK expression. It is interesting to note the explicit appearance of the quantity $\hbar$ on the right-hand side of that inequality, for its numerical value appears to affect the validity of the inequality. If we did not know the numerical value of Planck's constant, but suspected its existence on the basis of Planck's work on blackbody radiation, then we would state that the smaller the magnitude of $\hbar$, the larger would be the range of values of the field within which the present approximation method would be valid; in the limit of vanishingly small $\hbar$, the inequality would hold for any magnitude of the field. Since $\hbar$ is one of the fundamental constants of physics, and is not zero, there is a definite upper limit to the fields for which our relaxation method converges sufficiently. Wentzel, Brillouin, and Kramers made use of the smallness of $\hbar$ in their derivation of the WBK expression. The results obtained in this chapter by the relaxation method agree with those found by W, K, and B.

Also of interest in inequality (9-1) is the appearance of the mass in the right-hand member. This presence of m indicates that the relaxation method would be valid for a wider range of field strengths for heavy particles than it would for light particles. Since the neglect of quantization ($\hbar \simeq 0$) and the use of large masses are characterstic of classical mechanics, we can expect that the neglect of all but the leading term in Eq. (9-5) would yield results that have some features in common with classical mechanics. That this is so can be seen when we write the expression for the probability density derived from Eq. (9-6):

$$|\psi_n|^2 = \frac{|\phi_{n\pm} \exp \{\pm i\hbar^{-1}\int[2m(E - V)]^{1/2}\,dq\}|^2}{[2m(E - V)]^{1/2}}$$

For classically accessible regions V is less than E, so that p is real. Then

$$|\psi_n|^2 = \frac{|\phi_{n\pm}|^2}{[2m(E - V)]^{1/2}} = \frac{|\phi_{n\pm}|^2}{p}$$

Thus the probability of finding a particle anywhere within a classically accessible region is inversely proportional to the local momentum of that particle, that is, the faster the particle moves through a given region, the less likelihood there is of finding it in that region. This is in complete agreement with classical mechanics, but is not generally true in atomic systems.

---

problem 9-4. Sketch and compare the functions $|\psi_n|^2$ and $1/p$ for the state of the linear harmonic oscillator discussed in Chap. 5.

We conclude that the WBK approximation is valid for sufficiently small fields, relatively large masses, and large quantum numbers (see Prob. 9-2) and that the finite magnitude of $\hbar$ imposes an upper limit on the field or a lower limit on the mass to which the WBK result can be successfully applied.

9-4 Electrons in a uniform field. As an application of the WBK expression, let us find the wave function of an electron beam moving in a uniform electric field. The potential energy of electrons in such a field is given by

$$V = -Feq \tag{9-7}$$

where F is the field strength, e the magnitude of the electronic charge, and q the position of an electron. This potential corresponds to a force propelling electrons in the positive q direction.

When Eq. (9-7) is substituted into the definition of p^2, we obtain

$$p^2 = 2m(E + Feq)$$

Consequently, Eq. (9-6) becomes, for a current in the positive q direction,

$$\begin{aligned} \psi_n &= \phi_{n\pm} \frac{\exp\{+i\hbar^{-1}\int[2m(E + Feq)]^{1/2}\,dq\}}{[2m(E + Feq)]^{1/4}} \\ &= \phi_{n\pm} \frac{\exp\{+i(3\hbar Fe)^{-1}[2^{3/2}m^{1/2}(E + Feq)^{3/2}]\}}{[2m(E + Feq)]^{1/4}} \end{aligned} \tag{9-8}$$

If we limit ourselves to values of E exceeding $(-Feq)$, we find that the probability distribution of the beam of electrons is

$$|\psi|_n^2 \propto [2m(E + Feq)]^{-1/2}$$

The attenuation of this distribution with increasing distance is due to the acceleration of the electrons so that the probability of finding an electron in a given volume element decreases as the volume element travels in the positive q direction.

The current associated with this electron beam is also of interest. From Eq. (9-6) it follows, if we discard the minus sign, that

$$\psi = \phi p^{-1/2} \exp(i\hbar^{-1}\textstyle\int p\, dq)$$

$$\mathcal{P}\psi = \psi\left(p + \tfrac{1}{2}i\hbar^{-1}\frac{d \ln p}{dq}\right)$$

$$\psi^*\mathcal{P}\psi = \psi^*\psi\left(p + \tfrac{1}{2}i\hbar\frac{d \ln p}{dq}\right)$$

$$\psi\mathcal{P}^*\psi^* = \psi^*\psi\left(p^* - \tfrac{1}{2}i\hbar\frac{d \ln p^*}{dq}\right)$$

therefore

$$\text{Current} = \frac{\psi^*\psi}{2m}\left\{p + p^* + \tfrac{1}{2}i\hbar\frac{d}{dq}\left[\ln\left(\frac{p}{p^*}\right)\right]\right\}$$

In classically accessible regions p is real, so that

$$\text{Current} = \frac{\psi^*\psi}{m}\,p$$

In our example of a uniform field the current becomes

$$\text{Current} \propto m^{-1}[2m(E + Feq)]^{-1/2}[2m(E + Feq)]^{1/2} = m^{-1}$$

The current is therefore independent of position, as it should be for unidirectional, divergenceless flow. The fact that the charge density attenuates with increasing q but that the current remains uniform is explained by the fact that the decrease in charge density is just offset by the increase in velocity with increasing q and that the current is determined by the product of charge density and velocity.

---

problem 9-5. In some solid-state diodes, use is made of the fact that electrons penetrate classically inaccessible regions under the influence of an external field. Find an expression for the charge-density distribution inside such an inaccessible region as a function of the magnitude of the external field. [*Hint:* Adapt Eq. (9-8) to this purpose.]

9-5 Summary. We have developed an approximate method of solving Schroedinger's equation that is especially valid for potential fields whose gradients are relatively small or for particles whose mass is not very small. We have also developed a quantitative criterion for the validity of classical mechanics and for the validity of the WBK approximation. It was shown by example that in the Bohr model for the hydrogen atom, classical behavior may be approached by electrons having large quantum numbers, in agreement with Bohr's correspondence principle. It was further demonstrated that the WBK may be applied to electrons in a moderate "man-made" external field, but that inside atoms the fields on the electrons are too large to allow use of the WBK results. In the following four chapters we shall deal with the analytical solution of the Schroedinger equation for such atomic and molecular systems. Only a few particular systems lend themselves to such analytical solution. In Chap. 17 we shall consider an approximation method that can be used in systems having fields whose magnitude lies beyond the range allowed by the WBK method.

development of operator algebra for the harmonic oscillator

chapter

10

10-1 Introduction. The linear harmonic oscillator (referred to below as LHO) is a useful model in atomic and molecular physics. Here we shall apply some of the ideas developed in Chap. 5 to the LHO; we shall relate the commutation properties of quantum mechanical operators of the LHO to quantization of its energy.

The harmonic oscillator is defined as a system whose displacement from equilibrium is opposed by a restoring force which is proportional to the displacement from equilibrium. Examples are: a pendulum oscillating with a small amplitude; two particles connected to each other through a spring. When the displacement can be expressed in terms of a single coordinate, the oscillator is called linear. The two examples above represent linear oscillators if the pendulum is constrained to move in a single plane and the particles are constrained to move along a straight line joining them. If the displacement of the LHO is denoted by q, the restoring force is given by $(-kq)$, where k is a constant characteristic of the oscillator, and the energy of the oscillator is

$$E = \frac{1}{2}\left(\frac{p^2}{\mu} + kq^2\right) \tag{10-1}$$

where p is the linear momentum of an oscillator with reduced mass μ.

10-2 Rules of operator algebra for the linear harmonic oscillator. In Chap. 5 it was shown that any state of a system is expressible in terms of the stationary states of that system. We shall now find all stationary state wave functions Ψ_n for the LHO. For stationary states $\Psi_n = \psi_n \exp -i\hbar^{-1}E_n t$, and $\mathcal{H}\Psi_n = E_n\Psi_n$. For the LHO,

$$\mathcal{H} = \tfrac{1}{2}(\mu^{-1}\mathcal{P}^2 + kQ^2)$$

The Hamiltonian can be written in a more symmetrical form by defining $\mathcal{A} \equiv \mu^{-\frac{1}{2}}\mathcal{P}$, $\mathcal{B} \equiv k^{\frac{1}{2}}Q$:

$$(\mathcal{A}^2 + \mathcal{B}^2)\psi_n = 2E_n\psi_n \tag{10-2}$$

The operators $\mathcal{A}$ and $\mathcal{B}$ do not commute, for

$$\mathcal{A}\mathcal{B} - \mathcal{B}\mathcal{A} = -i\hbar k^{\frac{1}{2}}\mu^{-\frac{1}{2}}$$

---

problem 10-1. Prove that $\mathcal{A}\mathcal{B} - \mathcal{B}\mathcal{A} = -i\hbar k^{\frac{1}{2}}\mu^{-\frac{1}{2}}$

The expression $\mathcal{A}^2 + \mathcal{B}^2$ can be rewritten in two ways:

$$\mathcal{A}^2 + \mathcal{B}^2 = (\mathcal{A} + i\mathcal{B})(\mathcal{A} - i\mathcal{B}) + \hbar\omega_0 \tag{10-3a}$$
$$\mathcal{A}^2 + \mathcal{B}^2 = (\mathcal{A} - i\mathcal{B})(\mathcal{A} + i\mathcal{B}) - \hbar\omega_0 \tag{10-3b}$$

where $\omega_0 = k^{\frac{1}{2}}\mu^{-\frac{1}{2}}$, the natural angular frequency of the oscillator.

---

problem 10-2. Prove Eqs. (10-3*a*) and (10-3*b*).

10-3 Solution of the wave equation for the linear harmonic oscillator. Equation (10-2) will now be solved in two stages; in the first stage a method will be derived for generating *all* solutions of Eq. (10-2), if *any one* solution is known; in the second stage, *one particular* solution will be found. This procedure has wide applicability and will be used again in Chaps. 11 and 13.

Stage one consists of proving and applying the following theorem:

***theorem* 10-1.** If ψ_n is an eigenfunction of $(\mathcal{A}^2 + \mathcal{B}^2)$ with eigenvalue $2E_n$, then $(\mathcal{A} \pm i\mathcal{B})^v\psi_n$ are also eigenfunctions of $(\mathcal{A}^2 + \mathcal{B}^2)$ but with eigenvalues $2(E_n \pm v\hbar\omega_0)$ where v is a positive integer.

***proof of theorem* 10-1.** We first prove that $(\mathcal{A} + i\mathcal{B})\psi_n$ is an eigenfunction of $(\mathcal{A}^2 + \mathcal{B}^2)$, if ψ_n is. To do so, operate on both sides of Eq. (10-2) with $(\mathcal{A} + i\mathcal{B})$:

$$(\mathcal{A} + i\mathcal{B})(\mathcal{A}^2 + \mathcal{B}^2)\psi_n = 2E_n(\mathcal{A} + i\mathcal{B})\psi_n$$

Substitute here the expression for $(\mathcal{A}^2 + \mathcal{B}^2)$ given by Eq. (10-3*b*):

$$(\mathcal{A} + i\mathcal{B})(\mathcal{A} - i\mathcal{B})(\mathcal{A} + i\mathcal{B})\psi_n = 2E_n(\mathcal{A} + i\mathcal{B})\psi_n + \hbar\omega_0(\mathcal{A} + i\mathcal{B})\psi_n$$

Substitute for $(\mathcal{A} + i\mathcal{B})(\mathcal{A} - i\mathcal{B})$ the expression given by Eq. (10-3*a*):

$$(\mathcal{A}^2 + \mathcal{B}^2)[(\mathcal{A} + i\mathcal{B})\psi_n] = 2E_n(\mathcal{A} + i\mathcal{B})\psi_n + 2\hbar\omega_0[(\mathcal{A} + i\mathcal{B})\psi_n]$$

Therefore

$$(\mathcal{A}^2 + \mathcal{B}^2)[(\mathcal{A} + i\mathcal{B})\psi_n] = 2(E_n + \hbar\omega_0)[(\mathcal{A} + i\mathcal{B})\psi_n]$$

Thus $(\mathcal{A} + i\mathcal{B})\psi_n$ has been shown to be an eigenfunction of $(\mathcal{A}^2 + \mathcal{B}^2)$ with eigenvalue $2(E_n + \hbar\omega_0)$. When the same procedure is applied to $(\mathcal{A} + i\mathcal{B})\psi_n$ as has been done for ψ_n, it can be shown that $(\mathcal{A} + i\mathcal{B})^2\psi_n$ is an eigenfunction of $(\mathcal{A}^2 + \mathcal{B}^2)$ with eigenvalue $2(E_n + 2\hbar\omega_0)$. Extending this procedure completes the general proof of the theorem for the $(\mathcal{A} + i\mathcal{B})$ operators. A similar argument may be used for the $(\mathcal{A} - i\mathcal{B})$ operator. This completes the first stage of the solution of Eq. (10-2).

10-4 Normalization for the linear harmonic oscillator. Before going to the second stage of the derivation of the eigenfunctions, we shall consider the normalization of the functions just derived. When the operators $(\mathcal{A} \pm i\mathcal{B})$ are applied to a normalized function, the resulting function is not normalized. To normalize the resulting function, one must find the integral

$$\oint(\mathcal{A} \pm i\mathcal{B})^*\psi_n^*(\mathcal{A} \pm i\mathcal{B})\psi_n\,dq$$

assuming that $\oint\psi_n^*\psi_n\,dq$ equals unity. Since $\mathcal{A}^* = -\mathcal{A}$ and $\mathcal{B}^* = \mathcal{B}$,

$$\begin{aligned}\oint(\mathcal{A} \pm i\mathcal{B})^*\psi_n^*(\mathcal{A} \pm i\mathcal{B})\psi_n\,dq &= -\oint(\mathcal{A} \pm i\mathcal{B})\psi_n^*(\mathcal{A} \pm i\mathcal{B})\psi_n\,dq = \\ &= -\oint\mathcal{A}\psi_n^*\mathcal{A}\psi_n\,dq \mp i\oint\mathcal{A}\psi_n^*\mathcal{B}\psi_n\,dq \mp i\oint\mathcal{B}\psi_n^*\mathcal{A}\psi_n\,dq + \oint\mathcal{B}\psi_n^*\mathcal{B}\psi_n\,dq\end{aligned}$$

Since $\mathcal{A}$ and $\mathcal{B}$ are Hermitian,

$$\oint(\mathcal{A} \pm i\mathcal{B})^*\psi_n^*(\mathcal{A} \pm i\mathcal{B})\psi_n\,dq = \oint\psi_n(\mathcal{A}^2 + \mathcal{B}^2 \mp i\mathcal{B}\mathcal{A} \pm i\mathcal{A}\mathcal{B})\psi_u^*\,dq = $$
$$= \oint\psi_n[\mathcal{A}^2 + \mathcal{B}^2 \pm i(-i\hbar\omega_0)]\psi_n^*\,dq$$

Since $(\mathcal{A}^2 + \mathcal{B}^2)\psi_n = 2E_n\psi_n$, $(\mathcal{A}^2 + \mathcal{B}^2)\psi_n^* = 2E_n\psi_n^*$.
Therefore, remembering that ψ_n is normalized,

$$\oint(\mathcal{A} \pm \mathcal{B})^*\psi_n^*(\mathcal{A} \pm i\mathcal{B})\psi_n\,dq = (2E_n \pm \hbar\omega_0)$$

We conclude that if the function ψ_n is normalized, then the functions $(\mathcal{A} \pm i\mathcal{B})\psi_n/(2E_n \pm \hbar\omega_0)^{1/2}$ are also normalized.

---

problem 10-3. Determine whether the operators $(\mathcal{A} \pm i\mathcal{B})$ are Hermitian.

The operators $\mathfrak{M} \equiv (\mathcal{A} + i\mathcal{B})/(2E_n + \hbar\omega_0)^{1/2}$,
and $\mathfrak{N} \equiv (\mathcal{A} - i\mathcal{B})/(2E_n - \hbar\omega_0)^{1/2}$

transform the normalized function ψ_n into two new functions $\psi_{n\pm1}$, both of which are also normalized. Since the operators $\mathfrak{M}$ and $\mathfrak{N}$ transform one normalized wave function into another one, they are called "normalized" operators; it should be noted that the normalizing constants in the denominators of $\mathfrak{M}$ and $\mathfrak{N}$ depend on the quantum number of the function upon which they operate; therefore, in performing the operations $\mathfrak{M}$ and $\mathfrak{N}$ several times in succession, a different normalizing constant must be used each time that $\mathfrak{M}$ or $\mathfrak{N}$ is applied.

---

problem 10-4. (*a*) Show that $\mathfrak{M}\mathfrak{N}\psi = \psi_n$.
(*b*) Show that if $\mathfrak{M}^v\psi_n = \psi_{n+v}$, then $\psi_n = \mathfrak{N}^v\psi_{n+v}$
and that if $\mathfrak{N}^v\psi_n = \psi_{n-v}$, then $\psi_n = \mathfrak{M}^v\psi_{n-v}$.

(*c*) Show that $\mathcal{A}\mathcal{B}\psi_n \neq \psi_n$.

10-5 Termination of the generating procedures. The second stage in solving Eq. (10-2) consists of finding a particular solution. The $\mathcal{A}$ operator differentiates, the $\mathcal{B}$ operator multiplies; hence if we should obtain zero as a result of applying the $\mathfrak{M}$ or $\mathfrak{N}$ operator, then further application of these operators would again give zero. The last functions found by these generating procedures that would be different from zero would satisfy the conditions

$$\mathfrak{M}\psi_n = 0 \tag{10-4a}$$

$$\mathfrak{N}\psi_n = 0 \tag{10-4b}$$

Using the definitions of $\mathfrak{A}$ and $\mathfrak{B}$

$$\frac{i\hbar}{\sqrt{\mu}} \frac{\partial \psi_n}{\partial q} = \pm i \sqrt{k}\, q\psi_n$$

These equations have as solutions

$$\psi_n = C \exp \pm \tfrac{1}{2}\mu\omega_0\hbar^{-1}q^2$$

where the positive exponential function corresponds to Eq. (10-4*a*) and the negative one to Eq. (10-4*b*), and C is a normalization constant. Of these two functions, only the one with the *negative* exponent is an acceptable wave function; the function with the positive exponent goes to infinity as q becomes infinite, and is therefore unacceptable. Therefore, no wave function exists that could terminate the generating procedure using the $\mathfrak{M}$ operator. The generating procedure using the $\mathfrak{N}$ operator, on the other hand, eventually and inevitably terminates with the function $C \exp -\tfrac{1}{2}\mu\omega_0\hbar^{-1}q^2$. We assign the quantum number $n = 0$ to this terminating wave function so that

$$\psi_0 = C \exp -\tfrac{1}{2}\mu\omega_0\hbar^{-1}q^2$$

for the lowest quantized state of the LHO.

---

problem 10-5. Using the definitions of $\mathfrak{A}$ and $\mathfrak{B}$ and the expression found for ψ_0, show explicitly that $\mathfrak{N}\psi_0 = 0$.

10-6 Uniqueness of the set of eigenfunctions. In Sec. 10-5 we found a wave function ψ_0 representing the space dependence of a LHO that has the peculiar property, that $\mathfrak{N}\psi_0 = 0$. According to Theorem 10-1, if ψ_0 is a wave function, then the set $\psi_n = \mathfrak{M}^n\psi_0$ represents other wave functions of the harmonic oscillator. In the present section we shall prove that the set $\psi_n = \mathfrak{M}^n\psi_0$ represents *all* stationary wave functions of the LHO, in other words, that any function ψ_m that cannot be expressed as $\mathfrak{M}^m\psi_0$, where m is a positive integer, is not a satisfactory LHO wave function. To do so, we use the following theorem:

***theorem* 10-2.** The square of any variable whose corresponding operator is Hermitian cannot have a negative expectation value.

***proof of theorem* 10-2.** If Ψ is a normalized wave function, and $\mathfrak{F}$ is Hermitian,

$$\overline{f^2} = \oint \Psi^* \mathfrak{F}^2 \Psi \, dq = \oint \mathfrak{F}\Psi \mathfrak{F}^* \Psi^* \, dq = \oint |\mathfrak{F}\Psi|^2 \, dq$$

Since $|\mathfrak{F}\Psi|^2$ is nonnegative, $\overline{f^2}$ must be nonnegative.

Now let us consider an eigenfunction ψ_m of the operator $(\mathfrak{A}^2 + \mathfrak{B}^2)$, with eigenvalue $2E_m$. Then, according to Theorem 10-1, there must be a function $\mathfrak{N}^v\psi_m$ that is also an eigenfunction of operator $(\mathfrak{A}^2 + \mathfrak{B}^2)$, with eigenvalue $2(E_m - v\hbar\omega_0)$, where v is an arbitrary positive integer. This appears to imply that v can be chosen sufficiently large to cause the expression $2(E_m - v\hbar\omega_0)$ to be negative. This clearly violates Theorem 10-2, for $\mathfrak{A}$ and $\mathfrak{B}$ are Hermitian operators, so that neither $\mathfrak{A}^2$ nor $\mathfrak{B}^2$ can have negative expectation values, and consequently $(\mathfrak{A}^2 + \mathfrak{B}^2)$ could not possibly have negative eigenvalues. The only way to avoid negative eigenvalues is to terminate the generating procedure before v is sufficiently large to cause a negative eigenvalue. However, we have already shown that there is only one function that can terminate the generating procedure, and that is ψ_0. Therefore, the only wave functions that do not violate Theorem 10-2 are those for which $\mathfrak{N}^m\psi_m = \psi_0$; according to Prob. 10-4*b* this implies that $\psi_m = \mathfrak{M}^m\psi_0$. Thus we have shown that only functions of the form $\mathfrak{M}^m\psi_0$ are properly behaved wave functions for the LHO.

---

problem 10-6. Prove that the functions $\psi_n = \mathfrak{M}^n\psi_0$ form an orthonormal set. (*Hint:* Prove that these functions are nondegenerate eigenfunctions of a Hermitian operator.)

The eigenfunctions $\psi_m = \mathfrak{M}^m\psi_0$ of the Hamiltonian operator of the LHO, and their respective eigenvalues $(E_0 + m\hbar\omega_0)$ can be thought of as a "ladder" of states, in which each stationary state is represented by a "rung" consisting of a stationary wave function and the corresponding energy value (see Table 10-1). It is noted that each rung has an energy value that differs from the energy values of adjacent rungs by one unit of $\hbar\omega_0$; it should be recalled that the magnitude of the "quantum" of energy $\hbar\omega_0$ was determined by the value of the operator-commutator $(\mathcal{A}\mathcal{B} - \mathcal{B}\mathcal{A})$.

---

problem 10-7. Find a lower limit of the product of the standard deviations in momentum and position for each stationary state of the LHO.

10-7 The ground state of the linear harmonic oscillator. In Sec. 10-6 the lowest rung of the ladder of eigenfunctions of the Hamiltonian operator of the LHO was found; when normalized, the eigenfunction for this rung is

$$\psi_0 = (k\mu)^{1/8}(\pi\hbar)^{-1/4} \exp\left[-\tfrac{1}{2}\hbar^{-1}(k\mu)^{1/2}q^2\right] \tag{10-5}$$

This is just the wave function that was considered in detail in Chap. 5

table 10-1

the quantum states of the linear harmonic oscillator

quantum number n	eigenfunction ψ_n	energy E_n
∞	$\mathfrak{M}^\infty\psi_0$	∞
.	.	.
.	.	.
.	.	.
n	$\mathfrak{M}^n\psi_0$	$E_0 + n\hbar\omega_0$
.	.	.
.	.	.
.	.	.
2	$\mathfrak{M}^2\psi_0$	$E_0 + 2\hbar\omega_0$
1	$\mathfrak{M}\psi_0$	$E_0 + \hbar\omega_0$
0	ψ_0	E_0

as an example for extracting information from wave functions [see Eq. (5-5)]. It was found there that the energy for this lowest rung is $\frac{1}{2}\hbar\omega_0$; this energy results from the fact that even in its lowest-energy state, the displacement of the oscillator fluctuates around its equilibrium position. Any deviation from this position results in positive values of the potential and kinetic energies for the LHO.

---

problem 10-8. Use Eq. (10-3*a*) to confirm that the lowest eigenvalue of the Hamiltonian operator for the LHO is $\frac{1}{2}\hbar\omega_0$.

Figure 10-1 shows the relative probability, $|\psi_0|^2$, of finding a LHO at different displacements from its equilibrium position, when this oscil-

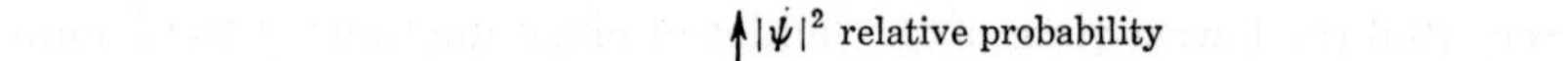

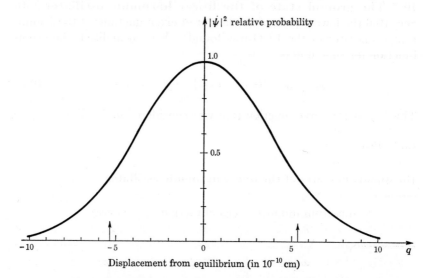

fig. 10-1 relative probability of finding a linear harmonic oscillator with $k = 14 \times 10^5$ dynes cm^{-1} and $\mu = 10 \times 10^{-24}$ g, at different displacements from its equilibrium position. (The short vertical arrows indicate the maximum displacements, $\pm q_{\max}$, for a classical oscillator with this energy.)

lator is in its ground state. This figure contrasts markedly with the "classical" behavior of such an oscillator. In its lowest-energy state we would classically expect an oscillator to be at rest in its equilibrium position, with zero probability for any finite displacement from equilibrium. Figure 10-1 on the other hand shows a gaussian distribution around equilibrium; we have pointed out before that in accordance with the uncertainty principle an oscillator cannot be completely at rest. If we admit the presence of fluctuations around the equilibrium positions, then there is still a difference between classical behavior and that found for the ground state of the LHO. Classically, we would expect the most probable position to be found where the momentum has the smallest magnitude, that is, near the classical turning points, with zero probability of penetration into regions where $V > E$. In Fig. 10-1, the most probable position is at equilibrium, where the classical probability would be a minimum; there is in addition a finite probability of finding the oscillator in the classically inaccessible region. It should be recalled that the WBK results derived in Chap. 9 predicted a "classical" probability distribution, that is, one inversely proportional to local momentum; it is clear that the WBK approximation is not valid for the ground state of the LHO. According to the correspondence principle, we would expect that states with higher quantum numbers would more nearly approach classical behavior; that this is indeed the case is shown in Fig. 10-3.

---

problem 10-9. Prove that every stationary wave function has a point of inflection at every classical turning point. (*Hint:* Set $E = V$ in Schroedinger's equation.)

---

problem 10-10. (*a*) Express the location of the classical turning points of a LHO in its ground state, in terms of its energy.

(*b*) Find the probability that a LHO, with $k = 14 \times 10^5$ dynes cm^{-1} and $\mu = 10^{-23}$ g, has, in its ground state, a displacement greater than the classical maximum amplitude.

(*c*) Repeat part (*b*) using $k = 14 \times 10^5$ dynes cm^{-1} and $\mu = 10^{-21}$ g.

(*d*) Compare the results of parts (*b*) and (*c*) and give your conclusions.

In the classically inaccessible region, the kinetic energy of the LHO would be negative, and the momentum imaginary. It was shown in Chap. 5, however, that for the ground state of the LHO the kinetic energy is not determinate, its expectation value being $\frac{1}{4}\hbar\omega_0$. Thus the value of the observed kinetic energy would represent the average over a large ensemble of LHO's, some of which may at a given moment have penetrated beyond the classical turning points. As shown in Prob. 10-10, the fraction that has penetrated does not exceed $\frac{1}{2}$; while some oscillators might make a negative contribution to the average, the expectation value of kinetic energy is certainly not negative. This is in agreement with Theorem 10-2.

10-8 Higher-energy states of the linear harmonic oscillator. It has been shown above that the LHO can exist in a semi-infinite number of discrete states whose quantum numbers run from zero through all positive integers. The normalized eigenfunctions of the Hamiltonian operator are of the form

$$\psi_n = \mathfrak{M}^n(\mu\omega_0\pi^{-1}\hbar^{-1})^{1/4} \exp -\tfrac{1}{2}\mu\omega_0\hbar^{-1}q^2 \tag{10-6}$$

with corresponding energies,

$$E_n = (n + \tfrac{1}{2})\hbar\omega_0 \tag{10-7}$$

Equations (10-6) and (10-7) give all stationary wave functions and quantized energies for the LHO. It is seen that successive energy levels are separated by the quantities $\hbar\omega_0$; ω_0, and therefore the separation increases with increasing restoring force and decreasing mass so that for systems with strong restoring force and lightweight particles, the energy levels are comparatively widely separated. When the LHO is relatively free to oscillate (small k) and the particles heavy, the energy levels lie comparatively close together. As the restoring force approaches zero, the motion approaches that of a free particle, and the array of energy levels approaches a continuum.

Let us consider the state with $n = 1$; this state has $E = \tfrac{3}{2}\hbar\omega_0$, and its wave function is

$$\psi_1 = \mathfrak{M}\psi_0 \tag{10-8}$$

where $\mathfrak{N}\psi_0 = 0$.

From the definitions of $\mathfrak{M}$ and $\mathfrak{N}$,

$$\psi_1 = \frac{(\mathcal{A} + i\mathcal{B})\psi_0}{(2E_0 + \hbar\omega_0)^{1/2}}$$

$$(\mathcal{A} - i\mathcal{B})\psi_0 = 0$$

From the last equation it follows that $i\mathcal{B}\psi_0 = \mathcal{A}\psi_0$. When this result is substituted in Eq. (10-8),

$$\psi_1 = \frac{2i\mathcal{B}\psi_0}{(2E_0 + \hbar\omega_0)^{1/2}} = \frac{2ik^{1/2}q(\mu\omega_0\pi^{-1}\hbar^{-1})^{1/4} \exp -\tfrac{1}{2}\mu\omega_0\hbar^{-1}q^2}{(2\hbar\omega_0)^{1/2}}$$

$$= i\,\frac{2^{1/2}k^{3/8}\mu^{3/8}}{\pi^{1/4}\hbar^{3/4}}\, q \exp -\tfrac{1}{2}\mu\omega_0\hbar^{-1}q^2 \tag{10-9}$$

---

problem 10-11. According to the definition of $\mathfrak{M}$ as a normalized operator, Eq. (10-9) should represent a normalized function. Confirm this by direct integration.

The i in front of the right-hand side of Eq. (10-9) has no physical significance; since in expectation values, probability densities, and currents, the wave function always occurs in combination with its complex conjugate, the factor i always cancels out. Since division by i does not affect normalization and also does not affect the validity of the function as a wave function, the factor i can therefore be omitted from Eq. (10-9).

(A useful recursion formula for finding higher-energy wave functions is derived in Sec. 10-9.)

---

problem 10-12. It was shown in Chap. 6 that only complex wave functions have a probability current associated with them. Show that multiplication of a real wave function by the factor i does not introduce a probability current.

Figure 10-2 shows the wave functions for a LHO for different values of n.

In order to facilitate the graphical representation of wave functions for any value of n, two helpful concepts are (1) the parity of the function and (2) the number of times that the function crosses the q axis. The function $\psi_0 = C \exp -\frac{1}{2}h^{-1}\mu\omega_0 q^2$ is, for example, an even function. The application of the operator ($\mathfrak{A}$) involves differentiation, and hence changes the parity of the function to which it is applied. The application of the operator ($\mathfrak{B}$) involves multiplication by q, and hence changes the parity of the function to which it is applied. The application of ($\mathfrak{M}$) therefore changes the parity of a function. Since ψ_0 is even, ψ_1 is odd, ψ_2 is even, etc. In general, the parity of ψ_n equals the parity of n, that is, ψ_n is even if n is even; ψ_n is odd if n is odd.

It is further observed that ψ_0 does not cross the q axis, that ψ_1 crosses once; ψ_2, twice, etc. In general ψ_n crosses the q axis n times.

---

problem 10-13. A LHO ($\omega_0 = 3.60 \times 10^{14}$ sec^{-1}) with a reduced mass of 12.3×10^{-24} g is in a state where its energy is 2.47×10^{-12} erg.

(*a*) Find the classical turning points for the oscillator in this state.
(*b*) Make a sketch of $|\psi|^2$ vs. q for the oscillator in this state, and let the range of q extend from -1.2 times the classical amplitude to $+1.2$ times the classical amplitude.

---

problem 10-14. Prove that no stationary state of the LHO has a probability current associated with it.

Figure 10-3 shows the square of the absolute magnitude of a wave function of the LHO having a very large value of n. The contour

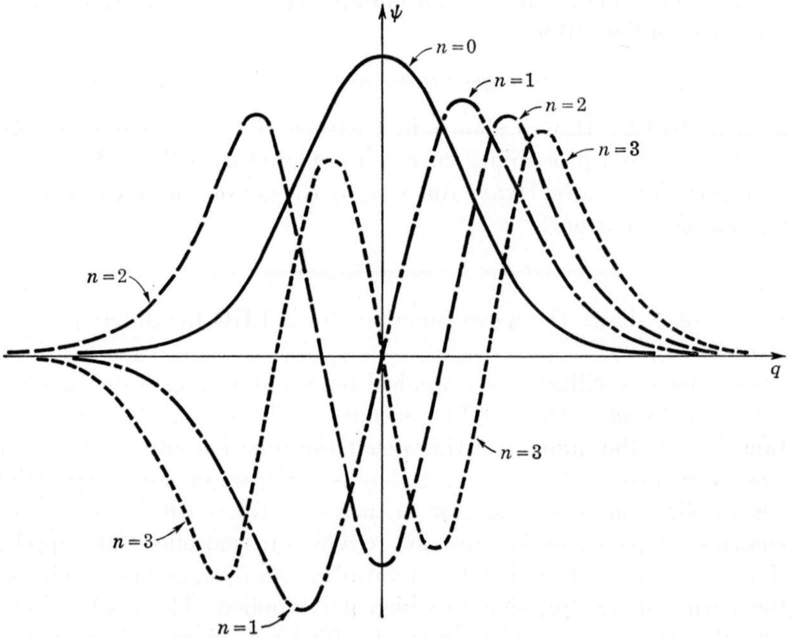

fig. 10-2 eigenfunctions of four different states of a linear harmonic oscillator

indicated by the dotted line represents the classical probability distribution for a LHO with the same value of energy. The vertical arrows indicate the classical maximum displacements from equilibrium for this oscillator.

For much larger n, the detail of the solid undulating line is lost so that it is no longer possible to distinguish the results of wave mechanics from those of classical mechanics. For high values of n the classical probability distribution is approached. This is another example of the "correspondence principle," according to which the results of

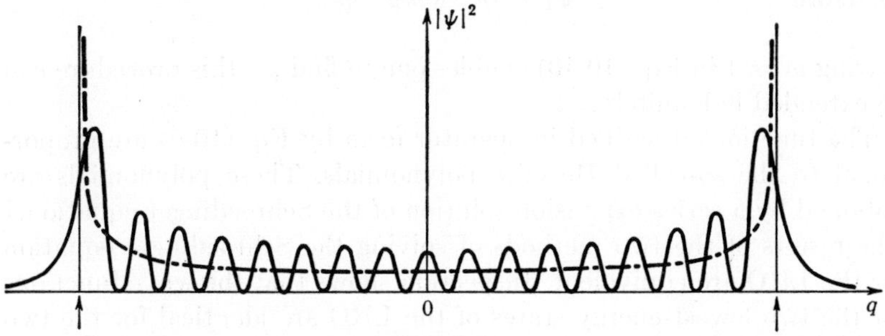

fig. 10-3 probability density of a high-energy state of a linear harmonic oscillator. (*After L. Pauling and E. B. Wilson, Jr., "Introduction to Quantum Mechanics," McGraw-Hill Book Company, Inc., New York, 1935. Used by permission.*)

wave mechanics approach those of classical mechanics for high values of the quantum number.

10-9 Recursion formula relating the eigenfunctions of the linear harmonic oscillator. An interesting relation exists between the wave functions of adjacent rungs of a ladder. Remember that

$$\mathfrak{M}\psi_m = \psi_{m+1} \qquad \text{and} \qquad \mathfrak{N}\psi_m = \psi_{n-1}$$

where
$$\mathfrak{M} \equiv \frac{\mathcal{A} + i\mathcal{B}}{(2E_m + \hbar\omega_0)^{1/2}} \equiv \frac{\mathcal{A} + i\mathcal{B}}{(2\hbar\omega_0)^{1/2}(m+1)^{1/2}}$$

and
$$\mathfrak{N} \equiv \frac{\mathcal{A} - i\mathcal{B}}{(2E_m - \hbar\omega_0)^{1/2}} \equiv \frac{\mathcal{A} - i\mathcal{B}}{(2\hbar\omega_0)^{1/2}m^{1/2}}$$

Then
$$(\mathcal{A} + i\mathcal{B})\psi_m = (2\hbar\omega_0)^{1/2}(m+1)^{1/2}\psi_{m+1}$$

and
$$(\mathcal{A} - i\mathcal{B})\psi_m = (2\hbar\omega_0)^{1/2}m^{1/2}\psi_{m-1}$$

Subtraction of the second from the first of these equations produces

$$2ik^{1/2}q\psi_m = (2\hbar\omega_0)^{1/2}[(m+1)^{1/2}\psi_{m+1} - m^{1/2}\psi_{m-1}]$$

therefore
$$q\psi_m = \frac{-i\hbar^{1/2}}{(4k\mu)^{1/4}}[(m+1)^{1/2}\psi_{m+1} - m^{1/2}\psi_{m-1}] \qquad (10\text{-}10)$$

Equation (10-10) gives a recursion relation for all normalized stationary wave functions of the LHO; if we set $m = 0$, we can find ψ_1 by straight substitution

$$q\psi_0 = \frac{-i\hbar^{1/2}}{(4k\mu)^{1/4}}\psi_1$$

therefore $$\psi_1 = i\hbar^{-1/2}(4k\mu)^{1/4}q\psi_0$$

Setting $m = 1$ in Eq. (10-10) enables one to find ψ_2; this procedure can be extended indefinitely.

The functions described in operator form by Eq. (10-6) are proportional to the so-called Hermite polynomials. These polynomials are obtained by a series-expansion solution of the Schroedinger equation.† The results of the two methods of solving the Schroedinger equation for the LHO are equivalent. Inspection shows that the wave functions for the two lowest-energy states of the LHO are identical for the two methods.

---

problem 10-15. Find normalized wave functions for the LHO having $n = 1$, $n = 2$, and $n = 3$;. compare the results with the Hermite polynomials.

10-10 Selection rule for the linear harmonic oscillator. In Chap. 5 it was shown that radiation may be absorbed whose frequency equals the "beat" frequency between two stationary states. It was also shown, however, that such absorption can only occur if the absolute magnitude of the integral $\oint \psi_m^* q \psi_n \, dq$ does not vanish. If we substitute Eq. (10-10) into this integral, we find the following condition for a spectral line:

$$(m+1)^{1/2}\int_{-\infty}^{\infty} \psi_{m+1}^*\psi_n \, dq - m^{1/2}\int_{-\infty}^{\infty} \psi_{m-1}^*\psi_n \, dq \neq 0 \qquad \text{(inequality 10-1)}$$

Since ψ_{m+1}, ψ_{m-1}, and ψ_n are nondegenerate eigenfunctions of the Hermitian operator $(\mathcal{A}^2 + \mathcal{B}^2)$, these three functions are orthogonal as long as $n \neq m \pm 1$. Inequality (10-1) can therefore be satisfied only if $n = m \pm 1$. Thus interaction with radiation for the LHO can involve only adjacent rungs on the eigenfunction ladder. The selection rules

† L. Pauling and E. B. Wilson, Jr., "Introduction to Quantum Mechanics," chap. III, McGraw-Hill Book Company, Inc., New York, 1935. H. Eyring, J. Walter, G. E. Kimbal, "Quantum Chemistry," chaps. IV and V, John Wiley & Sons, Inc., New York, 1944.

just derived for the LHO are consistent with the one derived in Chap. 5, namely, that transitions can only occur between stationary states whose wave functions have different parities. However, the selection rules for the LHO are more restrictive than those derived in Chap. 5, for the latter did not explicitly forbid transitions with $\Delta n = 3, 5, 7$, etc. We have now shown that in the LHO transitions with $\Delta n = 3, 5, 7$, etc. are forbidden, as are transitions with Δn even.

---

problem 10-16. A LHO having a permanent dipole moment has $\mu = 2 \times 10^{-24}$ g and $k = 5 \times 10^5$ dynes/cm. Determine at what wavelength(s), in units of centimeters, this oscillator would absorb radiant energy due to changes in its vibrational energy.

10-11 The three-dimensional harmonic oscillator. The potential energy of a three-dimensional harmonic oscillator is given by Eq. (10-11).

$$V = \tfrac{1}{2}(k_x x^2 + k_y y^2 + k_z z^2) \qquad (10\text{-}11)$$

where x, y, and z are cartesian coordinates. When $k_x = k_y = k_z = k$, the oscillator is called "isotropic." We shall discuss here the general case when the restoring-force constant is not necessarily the same in all directions. We can write Schroedinger's stationary equation for the three-dimensional harmonic oscillator in the following form:

$$(\mathcal{A}^2 + \mathcal{B}^2)_x\psi_n + (\mathcal{A}^2 + \mathcal{B}^2)_y\psi_n + (\mathcal{A}^2 + \mathcal{B}^2)_z\psi_n = 2E_n\psi_n \qquad (10\text{-}12)$$

where

$$(\mathcal{A}^2 + \mathcal{B}^2)_x = \mathcal{A}_x^2 + \mathcal{B}_x^2, \text{ etc.}$$
$$\mathcal{A}_x = -i\mu^{-1/2}\hbar\frac{\partial}{\partial x}, \text{ etc.}$$
$$\mathcal{B}_x = k^{1/2}x, \text{ etc.}$$

From Eq. (10-12) it follows that ψ_n can be simultaneously an eigenfunction of the three operators $(\mathcal{A}^2 + \mathcal{B}^2)_x$, $(\mathcal{A}^{2''} + \mathcal{B}^2)_y$, and $(\mathcal{A}^2 + \mathcal{B}^2)_z$; if we label their respective eigenvalues $2E_{n_x}$, $2E_{n_y}$, and $2E_{n_z}$, then

$$(\mathcal{A}^2 + \mathcal{B}^2)_x\psi_n = 2E_{n_x}\psi_n \qquad (10\text{-}13x)$$
$$(\mathcal{A}^2 + \mathcal{B}^2)_y\psi_n = 2E_{n_y}\psi_n \qquad (10\text{-}13y)$$
$$(\mathcal{A}^2 + \mathcal{B}^2)_z\psi_n = 2E_{n_z}\psi_n \qquad (10\text{-}13z)$$

Equations (10-13x), (10-13y), and (10-13z) are consistent with Eq. (10-12) if

$$E_n = E_{n_x} + E_{n_y} + E_{n_z} \qquad (10\text{-}14)$$

If we set $q = x$, we see that Eq. (10-13x) is completely analogous with Eq. (10-2); similarly, equating q to y and to z shows that Eqs. (10-13y) and (10-13z) are also analogous to Eq. (10-2). Their solutions, ψ_{0x}, ψ_{0y}, and ψ_{0z} etc., will also be analogous with those of Eq. (10-2). It should be observed, however, that the three equations (10-13) are *partial* differential equations, so that the solution of each should contain an arbitrary function of the other two coordinates. Solving Eq. (10-13x),

$$\psi_n = F(y,z)(\mathcal{A} + i\mathcal{B})_x{}^{n_x}\psi_{0x} \qquad (10\text{-}15x)$$

Similarly, the dependence of ψ_n on y is found by solving Eq. (10-13y):

$$\psi_n = F(x,z)(\mathcal{A} + i\mathcal{B})_y{}^{n_y}\psi_{0y} \qquad (10\text{-}15y)$$

and again,

$$\psi_n = F(x,y)(\mathcal{A} + i\mathcal{B})_z{}^{n_z}\psi_{0z} \qquad (10\text{-}15z)$$

Since Eqs. (10-15x), (10-15y), and (10-15z) all give expressions for the same function ψ_n, they imply that

$$\psi_n = C(\mathcal{A} + i\mathcal{B})_x{}^{n_x}\psi_{0x} \cdot (\mathcal{A} + i\mathcal{B})_y{}^{n_y}\psi_{0y} \cdot (\mathcal{A} + i\mathcal{B})_z{}^{n_z}\psi_{0z} \qquad (10\text{-}16)$$

where C is a normalizing constant, independent of x, y, and z. From the solution of Eq. (10-2) it follows, furthermore, that

$$E_{n_x} = (n_x + \tfrac{1}{2})\hbar\omega_{0x} \qquad E_{n_y} = (n_y + \tfrac{1}{2})\hbar\omega_{0y} \qquad E_{n_z} = (n_z + \tfrac{1}{2})\hbar\omega_{0z}$$

where $\qquad \omega_{0x} = \left(\dfrac{k_x}{\mu}\right)^{1/2} \qquad \omega_{0y} = \left(\dfrac{k_y}{\mu}\right)^{1/2} \qquad \omega_{0z} = \left(\dfrac{k_y}{\mu}\right)^{1/2}$

so that $E_n = [(n_x + \tfrac{1}{2})\omega_{0x} + (n_y + \tfrac{1}{2})\omega_{0y} + (n_z + \tfrac{1}{2})\omega_{0z}]\hbar$

Further, the unnormalized functions ψ_{0x}, ψ_{0y}, and ψ_{0z} are

$$\psi_{0x} = \exp -\tfrac{1}{2}\hbar^{-1}\mu\omega_{0x}x^2 \qquad (10\text{-}17x)$$
$$\psi_{0y} = \exp -\tfrac{1}{2}\hbar^{-1}\mu\omega_{0y}y^2 \qquad (10\text{-}17y)$$
$$\psi_{0z} = \exp -\tfrac{1}{2}\hbar^{-1}\mu\omega_{0z}z^2 \qquad (10\text{-}17z)$$

Thus the wave function of the three-dimensional harmonic oscillator is just the product of the wave functions of three linear harmonic oscillators. The energy of the three-dimensional harmonic oscillator equals the sum of the energies of the three linear harmonic oscillators. It can be shown by the same type of argument that whenever the Hamiltonian of a system can be written as the sum of several terms, each of which depends on only one coordinate, then the wave function can be factored into functions, each of only one coordinate, and the energy is the sum of corresponding energy terms. In other words, if

$$\mathcal{H}(q_1,q_2, \ldots ,q_k \ldots) = \sum_k \mathcal{H}_k(q_k)$$

then $$\psi_n = \Pi_k \psi_{nk}(q_k)$$

and $$E_n = \sum_k E_{nk}$$

where $$\mathcal{H}_k \psi_{nk} = E_{nk} \psi_{nk}$$

The subscript n then denotes the nth stationary state, the subscript k the kth coordinate.

---

problem 10-17. An isotropic two-dimensional harmonic oscillator has a determinate energy, which equals $3h$ times its natural frequency.

(*a*) Find the degeneracy of this energy level.

(*b*) Find the wave function for each state having this energy.

(*c*) Find the locus of the classical turning points of this oscillator.

(*d*) What is the probability of finding this oscillator in the classically inaccessible region?

---

problem 10-18. A three-dimensional harmonic oscillator has the following potential function:

$$V = 10^4 \text{ g sec}^{-2}(x^2 + 4y^2 + 9z^2)$$

(*a*) Make a diagram showing the lowest six energy levels, and their degeneracies.

(*b*) Join the pairs of levels that can be involved in the absorption of radiation by arrows in this diagram.

---

problem 10-19. Repeat Prob. 10-18 for the following potential function:

$$V = 10^4 \text{ g sec}^{-2}(x^2 + 2y^2 + 3z^2)$$

10-12 The isotropic three-dimensional harmonic oscillator. When the three restoring forces k_x, k_y, and k_z equal each other, the potential energy can be written

$$V = \tfrac{1}{2}k(x^2 + y^2 + z^2)$$

where $k = k_x = k_y = k_z$.

The potential energy in this case depends only on the magnitude of the displacement from equilibrium, not on its direction. In general a problem in which the potential depends only on the magnitude of the displacement from a given point is called a "central-field" problem; such problems are generally most easily solved in spherical polar coordinates:

$$r^2 = x^2 + y^2 + z^2 \tag{10-18}$$
$$x = r \sin\theta \cos\phi \tag{10-19}$$
$$y = r \sin\theta \sin\phi \tag{10-20}$$
$$z = r \cos\theta \tag{10-21}$$

Although we are to consider the central field in Chap. 11, let us consider here the isotropic three-dimensional harmonic oscillator as a special case of the central-field problem. The potential energy of such an oscillator is, in terms of spherical polar coordinates,

$$V = \tfrac{1}{2}kr^2 \tag{10-22}$$

From Eqs. (10-17) it follows that the ground-state wave function is, for this case,

$$\psi_0 = C \exp -\tfrac{1}{2}\hbar^{-1}\mu\omega_0 r^2 \tag{10-23}$$

where C is independent of r, θ, and ϕ. It is observed that this wave function is spherically symmetrical, that is, independent of θ and ϕ.

The first excited level of the isotropic three-dimensional oscillator is threefold degenerate, for

$$E = (n_x + n_y + n_z + \tfrac{3}{2})\hbar\omega_0 \tag{10-24}$$

so that the three excited states are denoted by three different sets of quantum numbers:

$$(a)\ n_x = 0,\ n_y = 0,\ n_z = 1$$
$$(b)\ n_x = 0,\ n_y = 1,\ n_z = 0$$
$$(c)\ n_x = 1,\ n_y = 0,\ n_z = 0$$

Each of these three states has an energy $E = \frac{5}{2}\hbar\omega_0$. We find the wave functions of each state from Secs. 10-9 and 10-10:

$$\begin{aligned}\psi_{0x} &= C_x \exp -\tfrac{1}{2}\hbar^{-1}\mu\omega_0 x^2\\ \psi_{0y} &= C_y \exp -\tfrac{1}{2}\hbar^{-1}\mu\omega_0 y^2\\ \psi_{1z} &= C_z z \exp -\tfrac{1}{2}\hbar^{-1}\mu\omega_0 z^2\end{aligned}$$

Therefore in terms of polar spherical coordinates,

$$\psi(n_x = 0, n_y = 0, n_z = 1) = Cr \exp(-\tfrac{1}{2}\hbar^{-1}\mu\omega_0 r^2)\cos\theta \tag{10-25}$$
$$\psi(n_x = 0, n_y = 1, n_z = 0) = Cr \exp(-\tfrac{1}{2}\hbar^{-1}\mu\omega_0 r^2)\sin\theta\sin\phi \tag{10-26}$$
$$\psi(n_x = 1, n_y = 0, n_z = 0) = Cr \exp(-\tfrac{1}{2}\hbar^{-1}\mu\omega_0 r^2)\sin\theta\cos\phi \tag{10-27}$$

---

problem 10-20. Find the degeneracy of the energy level $E = \frac{7}{2}\hbar\omega_0$, and the (unnormalized) wave functions for each state in this level.

It should be noted that none of the wave functions having $E = \frac{5}{2}\hbar\omega_0$ is spherically symmetrical. The wave function having $n_z = 1$ is cylindrically symmetrical around the Z axis, and has its maximum values along that axis. The other two functions have their maxima along the Y and X axes, respectively. We shall encounter the angular dependences of these functions again when we consider the central-field problem in Chap. 11; it will be seen that in general the radial dependence of the wave functions depends on the form of the central-field potential, but that their angular dependence is the same for all central-field wave functions.

10-13 Summary. A generating procedure has been developed for finding the complete orthogonal set of eigenfunctions of the harmonic oscillator. It was found that even in its lowest energy state, the LHO has a finite kinetic energy due to fluctuations around the equilibrium position. The isotropic three-dimensional harmonic oscillator has been considered as a particular central-field system.

the central field

chapter

11

11-1 Introduction. In Chap. 10 a particular example of three-dimensional motion was discussed, namely, the harmonic oscillator. It was pointed out that when the three-dimensional oscillator is isotropic, the potential energy depends on the magnitude of the displacement from equilibrium, but not on its direction. Therefore no resultant torque acts on the isotropic harmonic oscillator. In general, when the potential energy function is spherically symmetrical, we refer to the force as a "central-field" force. In the present chapter we propose to extend the discussion of the isotropic harmonic oscillator to a general central-field system. This discussion is applicable to both the motion of electrons in an atom and to the motions of the atoms in a diatomic molecule.† Since in a central field there are no resultant torques, angular momentum is conserved. We therefore start with a discussion of the angular momentum, its components, and its wave-mechanical operators. The angular momentum, as contrasted with the total energy of a system, may be found even when the exact nature of the central field is not known. It will be shown here that in all central fields the *angular* dependence of the wave functions is independent of the nature of the central field; their *radial* dependence, on the other hand, is determined by the particular form of the central field.

† In classical mechanics the rotation of two particles, of masses m_1 and m_2, around their common center of mass is transformed into the motion of a single particle of reduced mass $\mu = \dfrac{m_1 m_2}{m_1 + m_2}$ about the common center.

11-2 The angular-momentum operator. In classical mechanics the angular momentum **L** of a moving particle is defined as the vector product of the position vector **r** and the linear momentum **p** of that particle:

$$\mathbf{L} = \mathbf{r} \times \mathbf{p} \tag{11-1}$$

According to the second postulate, the angular-momentum operator $\mathfrak{L}$ is then

$$\mathfrak{L} = \mathbf{r} \times \mathcal{P} = -i\hbar\mathbf{r} \times \nabla \tag{11-2}$$

The cartesian components of $\mathfrak{L}$ may be found by applying the rules of vector multiplication. In the determinantal notation for vector products, $\mathfrak{L}$ is written as follows:

$$\mathfrak{L} = -i\hbar \begin{vmatrix} \hat{\mathbf{i}} & \hat{\mathbf{j}} & \hat{\mathbf{k}} \\ x & y & z \\ \dfrac{\partial}{\partial x} & \dfrac{\partial}{\partial y} & \dfrac{\partial}{dz} \end{vmatrix}$$

and therefore

$$\mathfrak{L}_x = -i\hbar\left(y\frac{\partial}{\partial z} - z\frac{\partial}{\partial y}\right) \tag{11-3}$$

$$\mathfrak{L}_y = -i\hbar\left(z\frac{\partial}{\partial x} - x\frac{\partial}{\partial z}\right) \tag{11-4}$$

$$\mathfrak{L}_z = -i\hbar\left(x\frac{\partial}{\partial y} - y\frac{\partial}{\partial x}\right) \tag{11-5}$$

---

problem 11-1. Prove that $\mathfrak{L}_x$, $\mathfrak{L}_y$, and $\mathfrak{L}_z$ are Hermitian.

An interesting relation results when we investigate whether or not the cartesian components of $\mathfrak{L}$ commute:

$$\mathfrak{L}_x\mathfrak{L}_y = -\hbar^2\left(y\frac{\partial}{\partial x} + yz\frac{\partial^2}{\partial z\,\partial x} - yx\frac{\partial^2}{\partial z^2} - z^2\frac{\partial^2}{\partial x\,\partial y} + xz\frac{\partial^2}{\partial y\,\partial z}\right)$$

$$\mathfrak{L}_y\mathfrak{L}_x = -\hbar^2\left(yz\frac{\partial^2}{\partial x\,\partial z} - z^2\frac{\partial^2}{\partial x\,\partial y} - xy\frac{\partial^2}{\partial z^2} + x\frac{\partial}{\partial y} + xz\frac{\partial^2}{\partial y\,\partial z}\right)$$

Therefore

$$\mathfrak{L}_x\mathfrak{L}_y - \mathfrak{L}_y\mathfrak{L}_x = -\hbar^2\left(y\frac{\partial}{\partial x} - x\frac{\partial}{\partial y}\right) = i\hbar\mathfrak{L}_z$$

This last equation is interesting from two points of view. In the first place, it demonstrates that $\mathfrak{L}_x$ and $\mathfrak{L}_y$ do not commute. In the second place it shows a relation between the three components of $\boldsymbol{\mathfrak{L}}$. By cyclic permutation this relation can be extended:

$$\mathfrak{L}_y\mathfrak{L}_z - \mathfrak{L}_z\mathfrak{L}_y = i\hbar\mathfrak{L}_x \tag{11-6x}$$
$$\mathfrak{L}_z\mathfrak{L}_x - \mathfrak{L}_x\mathfrak{L}_z = i\hbar\mathfrak{L}_y \tag{11-6y}$$
$$\mathfrak{L}_x\mathfrak{L}_y - \mathfrak{L}_y\mathfrak{L}_x = i\hbar\mathfrak{L}_z \tag{11-6z}$$

The left-hand sides of these three equations are the cartesian components of the vector $\boldsymbol{\mathfrak{L}} \times \boldsymbol{\mathfrak{L}}$, while the right-hand sides are the components of $i\hbar\boldsymbol{\mathfrak{L}}$. Therefore we can combine these three scalar equations into one vector equation:

$$\boldsymbol{\mathfrak{L}} \times \boldsymbol{\mathfrak{L}} = i\hbar\boldsymbol{\mathfrak{L}} \tag{11-6}$$

This equation differs strikingly from the corresponding equation in vector algebra, where the vector product of a vector with itself vanishes. In function algebra all functions commute; we have seen, however, that in wave mechanics operators generally do *not* commute with each other. It is this fact which has led to Eq. (11-6).

Central-field problems are conveniently solved in terms of spherical polar coordinates r, θ, and ϕ, for the potential energy is independent of θ and ϕ. The relations between cartesian and spherical coordinates have already been given by Eqs. (10-19) to (10-21).

To write the components of angular momentum in terms of these spherical coordinates, we remember that

$$\left(\frac{\partial}{\partial x}\right)_{y,z} = \left(\frac{\partial r}{\partial x}\right)_{y,z}\left(\frac{\partial}{\partial r}\right)_{\theta,\phi} + \left(\frac{\partial \theta}{\partial x}\right)_{y,z}\left(\frac{\partial}{\partial \theta}\right)_{r,\phi} + \left(\frac{\partial \phi}{\partial x}\right)_{y,z}\left(\frac{\partial}{\partial \phi}\right)_{r,\theta}, \text{ etc.} \tag{11-7}$$

$$r^2 = x^2 + y^2 + z^2 \tag{11-8}$$

$$\tan\phi = \frac{y}{x} \tag{11-9ϕ}$$

$$\tan\theta = \frac{(x^2 + y^2)^{1/2}}{z} \tag{11-9θ}$$

Therefore

$$\mathfrak{L}_x = i\hbar\left(\sin\phi\,\frac{\partial}{\partial\theta} + \cot\theta\cos\phi\,\frac{\partial}{\partial\phi}\right) \tag{11-10}$$

$$\mathfrak{L}_y = i\hbar\left(-\cos\phi\,\frac{\partial}{\partial\theta} + \cot\theta\sin\phi\,\frac{\partial}{\partial\phi}\right) \tag{11-11}$$

$$\mathfrak{L}_z = -i\hbar\,\frac{\partial}{\partial\phi} \tag{11-12}$$

problem 11-2. Derive Eqs. (11-10) to (11-12).

The first two of these equations can be combined with the third to give an expression useful for later applications:

$$\mathfrak{L}_x \pm i\mathfrak{L}_y = \pm \exp \pm i\phi \left(\hbar \frac{\partial}{\partial \theta} \mp \cot \theta \mathfrak{L}_z \right) \tag{11-13}$$

Since the three cartesian components of angular momentum do not commute with each other, they cannot all three be simultaneously determinate. Let us choose the Z-axis parallel to the direction in which one component of angular momentum is determinate. In that case, the wave function must be an eigenfunction of the operator $\mathfrak{L}_z$:

$$\mathfrak{L}_z \Psi = L_z \Psi \tag{11-14}$$

where L_z is independent of coordinates and time.

From Eq. (11-12) it follows that Ψ, in addition to being a solution of Schroedinger's equation, must in this case also satisfy the partial differential equation

$$-i\hbar \frac{\partial \Psi}{\partial \phi} = L_z \Psi \tag{11-15}$$

This equation is easily integrated; its general solution is

$$\Psi = F(r,\theta,t) \exp (i\hbar^{-1} L_z \phi) \tag{11-16}$$

where $F(r,\theta,t)$ is independent of ϕ. As in the case of the three-dimensional oscillator, we "separate" the independent variables by solving partial differential equations; any form of the function $F(r,\theta,t)$ satisfies Eq. (11-15), but only the particular dependence on ϕ given by Eq. (11-16) makes L_z determinate.

Now we should recall a requirement of proper behavior to which we have not yet needed to pay attention. This requirement is the single valuedness of wave functions. In this case increasing the angle ϕ by 2π should not change the wave function, so that

$$F(r,\theta,t) \exp [i\hbar^{-1} L_z(\phi + 2\pi)] = F(r,\theta,t) \exp (i\hbar^{-1} L_z \phi)$$

When both sides of the last equation are divided by the right-hand side,

$$\exp i\hbar^{-1}2\pi L_z = 1$$

or

$$\hbar^{-1}2\pi L_z = 2m\pi$$

where m is an integer.

Therefore, if the Z component of angular momentum is to be determinate, it is limited to the values

$$L_z = m\hbar \tag{11-17}$$

When Eq. (11-17) is substituted into Eq. (11-16),

$$\Psi = F(r,\theta,t) \exp im\phi \tag{11-18}$$

From Eq. (11-18) we find that the probability density of particles, whose component of angular momentum is determinate, is independent of the angle ϕ:

$$|\Psi|^2 = |F(r,\theta,t)|^2$$

Therefore the angular position around the Z axis is indeterminate when the Z component of angular momentum is determinate. This conclusion is consistent with the uncertainty principle, because knowledge about the angular momentum is gained at the expense of knowledge about the angular position.

Since the eigenfunction given by Eq. (11-18) is a complex function of the angle ϕ, a circulating current is associated with it. If we consider an electron of mass m_e and charge e,

$$\text{Electric current} = e \times \text{probability current} = \frac{-i\hbar}{2m_e} e(\Psi^*\nabla\Psi - \Psi\nabla\Psi^*)$$

In this example $\Psi = \exp im\phi$; therefore the current equals $mem_e^{-1}\hbar$. It is observed that the current is quantized in integral units of $em_e^{-1}\hbar$. (As we shall see below, the dependences of Ψ on θ and r are real, hence do not contribute to the magnetic moment due to the orbital motion of the electron.)

---

problem 11-3. (*a*) By means of classical physics, find the magnetic dipole moment associated with the circulating current found above.

(*b*) Relate the direction of the dipole moment to that of the angular momentum.

(*c*) Relate the classical magnetic dipole moment to the Bohr magneton.

(*d*) Will there be a magnetic dipole moment for all values of m?

---

problem 11-4. Find the expectation value and standard deviation of the Z component of angular momentum for a system whose wave function has the angular dependence $\cos m\phi$.

The determinacy of one component of angular momentum has given us the dependence of the wave function on one of the angular coordinates, ϕ. To find the dependence of the wave function on the other angular coordinate, θ, we must have some knowledge of the absolute magnitude of angular momentum.

11-3 The total angular momentum. The square of the magnitude of angular momentum is

$$L^2 = L_x^2 + L_y^2 + L_z^2$$

Its corresponding operator is

$$\mathcal{L}^2 = \mathcal{L}_x^2 + \mathcal{L}_y^2 + \mathcal{L}_z^2 = (\mathcal{L}_x + i\mathcal{L}_y)(\mathcal{L}_x - i\mathcal{L}_y) - \hbar\mathcal{L}_z + \mathcal{L}_z^2 \qquad \text{(11-19}a\text{)}$$

or

$$\mathcal{L}^2 = \qquad = (\mathcal{L}_x - i\mathcal{L}_y)(\mathcal{L}_x + i\mathcal{L}_y) + \hbar\mathcal{L}_z + \mathcal{L}_z^2 \qquad \text{(11-19}b\text{)}$$

Equations (11-19*a*) and (11-19*b*) follow from the commutation relations, Eqs. (11-6); they are similar to Eqs. (10-3*a*) and (10-3*b*). $\mathcal{L}^2$ and $\mathcal{L}_z$ commute; this is shown as follows:

$$\mathcal{L}_z\mathcal{L}^2 = \mathcal{L}_z(\mathcal{L}_x^2 + \mathcal{L}_y^2 + \mathcal{L}_z^2) = (\mathcal{L}_z\mathcal{L}_x)\mathcal{L}_x + (\mathcal{L}_z\mathcal{L}_y)\mathcal{L}_y + \mathcal{L}_z^3$$

From Eqs. (11-6*x*) and (11-6*y*),

$$\begin{aligned}\mathcal{L}_z\mathcal{L}^2 &= (i\hbar\mathcal{L}_y + \mathcal{L}_x\mathcal{L}_z)\mathcal{L}_x + (\mathcal{L}_y\mathcal{L}_z - i\hbar\mathcal{L}_x)\mathcal{L}_y + \mathcal{L}_z^3 = \\ &= i\hbar(\mathcal{L}_y\mathcal{L}_x - \mathcal{L}_x\mathcal{L}_y) + \mathcal{L}_x\mathcal{L}_z\mathcal{L}_x + \mathcal{L}_y\mathcal{L}_z\mathcal{L}_y + \mathcal{L}_z^3\end{aligned}$$

Substitution of Eq. (11-6*z*) gives

$$\mathcal{L}_z\mathcal{L}^2 = \hbar^2\mathcal{L}_z + \mathcal{L}_x\mathcal{L}_z\mathcal{L}_x + \mathcal{L}_y\mathcal{L}_z\mathcal{L}_y + \mathcal{L}_z^3$$

and similarly

$$\mathcal{L}^2\mathcal{L}_z = \mathcal{L}_x(\mathcal{L}_z\mathcal{L}_x - i\hbar\mathcal{L}_y) + \mathcal{L}_y(\mathcal{L}_z\mathcal{L}_y + i\hbar\mathcal{L}_x) + \mathcal{L}_z^3 =$$
$$= \mathcal{L}_x\mathcal{L}_z\mathcal{L}_x + \hbar^2\mathcal{L}_z + \mathcal{L}_y\mathcal{L}_z\mathcal{L}_y + \mathcal{L}_z^3$$

Therefore, $\mathcal{L}_z\mathcal{L}^2 = \mathcal{L}^2\mathcal{L}_z$.

Since $\mathcal{L}^2$ and $\mathcal{L}_z$ commute, L^2 and L_z can be simultaneously determinate, so that all nondegenerate eigenfunctions of $\mathcal{L}_z$ are also eigenfunctions of $\mathcal{L}^2$.

11-4 The generation of eigenfunctions of $\mathcal{L}_z$ and $\mathcal{L}^2$. The procedure for finding the dependence of the wave function on the angle θ follows the same logical argument as that used in Chap. 10 for finding the eigenfunctions of the operator $(\mathcal{A}^2 + \mathcal{B}^2)$.

***theorem* 11-1.** If ψ_m is an eigenfunction of $\mathcal{L}_z$ with eigenvalue equal to $m\hbar$, then the function $(\mathcal{L}_x \pm i\mathcal{L}_y)^v\psi_m$ is also an eigenfunction of $\mathcal{L}_z$, with eigenvalue $(m \pm v)\hbar$, where v is a nonnegative integer.

***proof of theorem* 11-1**

$$\mathcal{L}_z(\mathcal{L}_x \pm i\mathcal{L}_y) = \mathcal{L}_z\mathcal{L}_x \pm i\mathcal{L}_z\mathcal{L}_y$$

From Eqs. (11-6y) and (11-6x),

$$\mathcal{L}_z(\mathcal{L}_x \pm i\mathcal{L}_y) = i\hbar\mathcal{L}_y + \mathcal{L}_x\mathcal{L}_z \pm i(\mathcal{L}_y\mathcal{L}_z - i\hbar\mathcal{L}_x) =$$
$$= i\hbar\mathcal{L}_y + \mathcal{L}_x\mathcal{L}_z \pm i\mathcal{L}_y\mathcal{L}_z \pm \hbar\mathcal{L}_x =$$
$$= \pm\hbar(\mathcal{L}_x \pm i\mathcal{L}_y) + (\mathcal{L}_x \pm i\mathcal{L}_y)\mathcal{L}_z = (\mathcal{L}_x \pm i\mathcal{L}_y)(\mathcal{L}_z \pm \hbar)$$

Therefore

$$\mathcal{L}_z(\mathcal{L}_x \pm i\mathcal{L}_y)\psi_m = (\mathcal{L}_x \pm i\mathcal{L}_y)(\mathcal{L}_x \pm \hbar)\psi_m$$

Since $\mathcal{L}_z\psi_m = m\hbar\psi_m$,

$$\mathcal{L}_z[(\mathcal{L}_x \pm i\mathcal{L}_y)\psi_m] = (m \pm 1)\hbar(\mathcal{L}_x \pm i\mathcal{L}_y)\psi_m$$

Therefore, if ψ_m is an eigenfunction of $\mathcal{L}_z$ with eigenvalue $m\hbar$, then $(\mathcal{L}_x \pm i\mathcal{L}_y)\psi_m$ are eigenfunctions of $\mathcal{L}_z$ with eigenvalues $(m \pm 1)\hbar$. Repetition of this argument proves Theorem 11-1.

We have now found an operator that generates a ladder of eigenfunctions; the next two steps consist of looking for a termination of the ladder and proving the uniqueness of the ladder.

11-5 Termination of the generating procedure. The generating procedure terminates if one or two values of m exist so that

$$(\mathfrak{L}_x + i\mathfrak{L}_y)\psi_l = 0 \tag{11-20}$$
$$(\mathfrak{L}_x - i\mathfrak{L}_y)\psi_{l'} = 0 \tag{11-21}$$

Here l would be the maximum; l', the minimum value of m.

Equation (11-20) can be rewritten, using Eq. (11-13),

$$\exp(i\phi)\left(\hbar\frac{\partial\psi_l}{\partial\theta} - \cot\theta\mathfrak{L}_z\psi_l\right) = 0$$

Since $\mathfrak{L}_z\psi_l = l\hbar\psi_l$,

$$\frac{\partial\psi_l}{\partial\theta} = l\cot\theta\psi_l$$

therefore

$$\frac{d\psi_l}{\psi_l} = l\frac{\cos\theta\,d\theta}{\sin\theta}$$

and $\psi_l = G(r,\phi)(\sin\theta)^l$, where $G(r,\phi)$ is independent of θ. Since the dependence of ψ_l on ϕ is found from Eq. (11-18),

$$\psi_l = R(r)(\sin\theta)^l \exp il\phi \tag{11-22}$$

where $R(r)$ is independent of ϕ and θ and is determined by the form of the central-field potential function.

The wave function given by Eq. (11-22) is properly behaved only if $l \geq 0$, for if l were less than zero, ψ would become infinite as θ approaches zero. This wave function therefore represents the top rung of the ladder. Similarly, the ladder has a lower terminal rung if

$$\psi_{l'} = R_{l'}(r)\left(\frac{1}{\sin\theta}\right)^{l'} \exp il'\phi \tag{11-23}$$

This function is properly behaved only if $l' \leq 0$.

---

problem 11-5. Compare the angular dependences of the wave functions having $l = 1$ with the wave functions found in Chap 10 for the three-dimensional harmonic oscillator having $E = \frac{5}{2}\hbar\omega_0$.

---

problem 11-6. Find the angular dependences of all the eigenfunctions of $\mathfrak{L}_z$ belonging to a ladder having as maximum value of $m = l = 2$, and a minimum value of $m = l' = -2$. Plot the dependence on θ on polar graph paper. Also plot the dependence on ϕ of the real and imaginary part of these eigenfunctions on polar graph paper.

11-6 Eigenvalues of the total angular momentum. In Sec. 11-3 it was shown that $\mathfrak{L}^2$ and $\mathfrak{L}_z$ commute, so that all nondegenerate eigenfunctions of $\mathfrak{L}_z$ are also eigenfunctions of $\mathfrak{L}^2$. In this section we find the eigenvalues for $\mathfrak{L}^2$ of the eigenfunctions derived in Sec. 11-5. Let us first examine the function for the top rung of the ladder ψ_l, which is defined by the expression

$$(\mathfrak{L}_x + i\mathfrak{L}_y)\psi_l = 0 \tag{11-20}$$

In applying the operator $\mathfrak{L}^2$, we use the form given by Eq. (11-19*b*):

$$\begin{aligned}\mathfrak{L}^2\psi_l &= (\mathfrak{L}_x - i\mathfrak{L}_y)(\mathfrak{L}_x + i\mathfrak{L}_y)\psi_l + \hbar\mathfrak{L}_z\psi_l + \mathfrak{L}_z{}^2\psi_l \\ &= (\mathfrak{L}_x - i\mathfrak{L}_y)\cdot 0 + l\hbar^2\psi_l + l^2\hbar^2\psi_l = l(l+1)\hbar^2\psi_l\end{aligned}$$

Thus the function for the top rung of the ladder has an angular momentum whose magnitude is $\sqrt{l(l+1)}\,\hbar$ and whose Z component is $l\hbar$; accordingly the angle between the angular momentum and the Z axis is quantized, as shown in Fig. 11-1.

Since $\mathfrak{L}_z$ does not commute with $\mathfrak{L}_x$ and $\mathfrak{L}_y$, the values of the individual X and Y components of angular momentum are not known when its Z component is determinate. Therefore the angular-momentum vector lies anywhere along the surface of a cone whose height is $l\hbar$ and whose lateral height is $\sqrt{l(l+1)}\,\hbar$, as shown in Fig. 11-1.

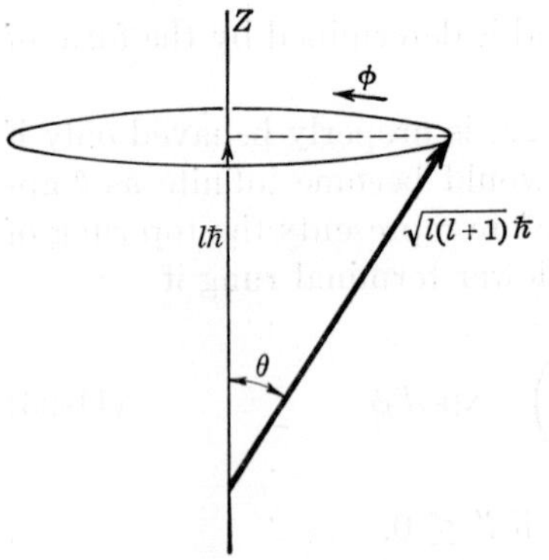

fig. 11-1 orientations and magnitude of the orbital angular momentum

It can similarly be shown that for the bottom rung of the ladder the eigenvalue of $\mathfrak{L}^2$ is $-l'(-l'+1)\hbar^2$, where l' is a negative integer.

To find the eigenvalues of $\mathfrak{L}^2$ for the other eigenfunctions, we use the following theorem.

***theorem* 11-2.** If ψ_m is an eigenfunction of $\mathfrak{L}^2$ with eigenvalue L^2 then $(\mathfrak{L}_x \pm i\mathfrak{L}_y)\psi_m$ is also an eigenfunction of $\mathfrak{L}^2$, with the same eigenvalue L^2.

***proof of theorem* 11-2.** The proof, given in Sec. 11-3, that $\mathfrak{L}$ commutes with $\mathfrak{L}_z$ can be extended to $\mathfrak{L}_x$ and to $\mathfrak{L}_y$. Since $\mathfrak{L}^2$ commutes with $\mathfrak{L}_x$ and with $\mathfrak{L}_y$,

$$\mathfrak{L}^2(\mathfrak{L}_x \pm i\mathfrak{L}_y)\psi_m = (\mathfrak{L}_x \pm i\mathfrak{L}_y)\mathfrak{L}^2\psi_m$$

Therefore, if $\mathfrak{L}^2\psi_m = L^2\psi_m$, then

$$\mathfrak{L}^2(\mathfrak{L}_x \pm i\mathfrak{L}_y)\psi_m = L^2(\mathfrak{L}_x \pm i\mathfrak{L}_y)\psi_m$$

Theorem 11-2 leads to the conclusion that the eigenvalues of $\mathfrak{L}^2$ are $l(l+1)\hbar^2$ for every rung of a ladder, not only for the top rung of the ladder. In particular, the eigenvalue of $\mathfrak{L}^2$ for the bottom rung of the ladder should be $l(l+1)\hbar^2$. Since it has already been shown that for the bottom of the ladder the eigenvalue of $\mathfrak{L}^2$ is $-l'(-l'+1)\hbar^2$,

$$l(l+1) = -l'(-l+1)$$

hence

$$(l-l')(l+l') = -(l+l')$$

Therefore either $l + l' = 0$, or $(l - l') = -1$. Since $l \geq 0$, and $l' \leq 0$, $(l - l') \geq 0$; hence $(l - l') \neq -1$. Therefore $l = -l'$.

Thus we see that for every value of l there is a ladder of $(2l + 1)$ eigenfunctions; the eigenvalues of $\mathfrak{L}^2$ are $l(l+1)\hbar^2$ for each of these functions, the eigenvalues of $\mathfrak{L}_z$ vary in units of $\hbar$ from $l\hbar$ to $-l\hbar$, as summarized in Table 11-1. If we define ψ_l for the top of the ladder by Eq. (11-20), then the eigenfunctions of $\mathfrak{L}^2$ and $\mathfrak{L}_z$ for the remaining rungs of the ladder are denoted by $(\mathfrak{L}_x - i\mathfrak{L}_y)^{l-m}\psi_l$, with $-l \leq m \leq l$. We therefore deal with two quantum numbers, l for the magnitude of the angular momentum and m for its Z component. It should be noted that with two degrees of freedom, θ and ϕ, we have introduced *two* quantum numbers. In Chap. 10 we similarly observed that the *three*-dimensional harmonic oscillator required *three* quantum numbers, n_x, n_y, and n_z. It is generally true that the number of quantum numbers describing the stationary states of a system equals the number of degrees of freedom of a system. A third quantum number, for the radial motion, will be found in Chap. 13.

In Fig. 11-2 are shown the loci of the angular momentum vector for a given value of l and all possible corresponding values of m; it appears that the angular momentum has quantized magnitude according to the relation $L = \sqrt{l(l+1)}\hbar$, and quantized orientation according to the relation $\cos\theta = \dfrac{m}{\sqrt{l(l+1)}}$, where $-l \leq m \leq +l$. A wave function determined by the two quantum numbers l and m is denoted by the symbol $\psi_l{}^m$.

When $l = 0$, m can only have the value zero. In this case the wave function is independent of the angles ϕ and θ, and hence is spherically

table 11-1

eigenfunctions and eigenvalues of $\mathcal{L}^2$ and $\mathcal{L}_z$ for a given l

eigenfunction	eigenvalue of $\mathcal{L}_z$	eigenvalue of $\mathcal{L}^2$
$\psi_l = (\sin\theta)^l \exp il\phi$	$l\hbar$	
$(\mathcal{L}_x - i\mathcal{L}_y)\psi_l$	$(l-1)\hbar$	
$(\mathcal{L}_x - i\mathcal{L}_y)^2\psi_l$	$(l-2)\hbar$	
.		
.		
$(\mathcal{L}_x - i\mathcal{L}_y)^{l-m}\psi_l$	$m\hbar$	
.		
.		
$(\mathcal{L}_x - i\mathcal{L}_y)^l\psi_l$	0	$l(l+1)\hbar^2$
.		
.		
$(\mathcal{L}_x + i\mathcal{L}_y)^{l-m}\psi_{-l}$	$-m\hbar$	
.		
.		
$(\mathcal{L}_x + i\mathcal{L}_y)^2\psi_{-l}$	$-(l-2)\hbar$	
$(\mathcal{L}_x + i\mathcal{L}_y)\psi_{-l}$	$-(l-1)\hbar$	
$\psi_{-l} = -(\sin\theta)^l \exp -il\phi$	$-l\hbar$	

l is called the orbital quantum number.
m is called the magnetic quantum number.
$l(l+1)\hbar^2$ is the orbital angular momentum squared.

symmetrical. When $l = 1$ and $m = 1$, $\psi = \sin\theta \exp i\phi$; when $l = 1$ and $m = 0$,

$$\psi = (\mathfrak{L}_x - i\mathfrak{L}_y)\sin\theta \exp i\phi =$$
$$= -\exp(-i\phi)\left(\hbar\frac{\partial}{\partial\theta} + \cos\theta\,\mathfrak{L}_z\right)\sin\theta\exp i\phi =$$
$$= -\exp(-i\phi)\hbar(\cos\theta + \cot\theta\sin\theta)\exp i\phi = -2\hbar\cos\theta$$

Thus the angular dependences of the three wave functions having $l = 1$ are: $\sin\theta \exp i\phi$; $\cos\theta$; $\sin\theta \exp -i\phi$.

It is observed that it is impossible to align the angular momentum with the Z axis because of the fluctuations of L_x and L_y, which are such that

$$L_x^2 + L_y^2 = L^2 - L_z^2$$
$$= [l(l+1) - m^2]\hbar^2$$

It is further observed that the number of allowed orientations increases with the quantum number l, and that, in fact, there are $(2l + 1)$ different values of m for each l. When l is very large, then the number of different orientations becomes so large, that a continuous distribution is approached; this is another example of Bohr's correspondence principle. Furthermore, the expression $l/\sqrt{l(l+1)}$ then approaches unity, so that orientation of the angular momentum parallel to the Z axis becomes possible in the limit of very large l.

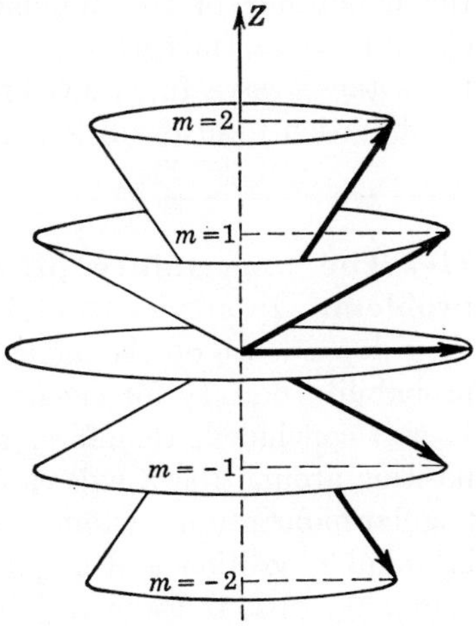

fig. 11-2 orientations of the angular-momentum vectors for $l = 2$

---

problem 11-7. Show that ψ_l^m is an eigenfunction of operator $\mathfrak{L}_x^2 + \mathfrak{L}_y^2$ with eigenvalue $[l(l+1) - m^2]\hbar^2$.

---

problem 11-8. Find the expectation values of the following quantities for a hydrogen-like atom, when $l = 5$, $m = 3$, and when L_z is accurately known:

(*a*) L_x
(*b*) $L_x^2 + L_y^2$

(*c*) L^2
(*d*) The angle, in degrees, that **L** makes with the Z axis

---

problem 11-9. An isotropic three-dimensional harmonic oscillator has the following determinate properties:
(*a*) Energy equals $\frac{5}{2}h$ times its natural frequency.
(*b*) Z component of angular momentum equals $\hbar$.
Find the radial and angular dependences of its wave function. Find the magnitude of the angular momentum. [*Hint:* Find all possible eigenfunctions (in cartesian coordinates) satisfying condition *a*. Express these wave functions in spherical coordinates, and take linear combination to fit condition *b*.]

11-7 The uncertainty principle applied to the central-field problem. In previous sections the eigenfunctions of $\mathfrak{L}_z$ were found; their dependence on the angle ϕ was of the form exp $im\phi$, so that the probability density for eigenstates of $\mathfrak{L}_z$ is cylindrically symmetrical. It was concluded, therefore, that no information about the angular position around the Z axis can be obtained when the Z component of angular momentum is assumed determinate. To relate the uncertainties in angular position and angular momentum for *any* state, we apply inequality (6-4) to these variables for any normalized wave function Ψ

$$|\Delta L_z| \cdot |\Delta\phi| \geq \oint \Psi^* |\tfrac{1}{2}i(\mathfrak{L}_z\phi - \phi\mathfrak{L}_z)| \Psi \, d\phi = \tfrac{1}{2}\hbar \qquad (11\text{-}24)$$

Equation (11-24) demonstrates that angular momentum and angular position are related in a manner analogous to the relation between linear momentum and position.

An interesting relation exists between the standard deviations in the three components of angular momentum:

$$|\Delta L_x| \, |\Delta L_y| \geq \oint \Psi^* |\tfrac{1}{2}i(\mathfrak{L}_x\mathfrak{L}_y - \mathfrak{L}_y\mathfrak{L}_x)| \Psi \, dq$$

From Eq. (11-6*z*) it follows that

$$|\Delta L_x| \, |\Delta L_y| \geq |-\tfrac{1}{2}\hbar \oint \Psi^* \mathfrak{L}_z \Psi \, dq|$$

For an eigenstate of $\mathfrak{L}_z$, $\mathfrak{L}_z\Psi = m\hbar\Psi$; therefore

$$|\Delta L_x| \, |\Delta L_y| \geq \tfrac{1}{2}m\hbar^2$$

In this case the lower limit of the product of the standard deviations in L_x and L_y depends on the value of L_z.

Since in an eigenstate of $\mathfrak{L}_z$ both L^2 and L_z are determinate, and since

$$L_x^2 + L_y^2 = L^2 - L_z^2$$

it is observed that $L_x^2 + L_y^2$, the square of the component of the angular momentum in a plane normal to the Z axis, is also determinate. Thus $(L_x^2 + L_y^2)$ is determinate in an eigenstate of $\mathfrak{L}_z$, in spite of the fact that L_x and L_y are themselves not determinate. This is consistent with our model of an angular momentum that has a determinate magnitude and whose angle with respect to the Z axis is determinate, but whose angular position can be anywhere on the surface of a cone having an axis coincident with the Z axis.

All eigenfunctions of $\mathfrak{L}_z$ having the same value of l but different values of m, form a nondegenerate set. Therefore all such functions are eigenfunctions of $\mathfrak{L}^2$, which commutes with $\mathfrak{L}_z$. Since they have the same value of l, they are *degenerate* eigenfunctions $\mathfrak{L}^2$; although $\mathfrak{L}^2$ commutes with $\mathfrak{L}_x$ and $\mathfrak{L}_y$, they are not necessarily eigenfunctions of $\mathfrak{L}_x$ and of $\mathfrak{L}_y$. Since $\mathfrak{L}_z$ does not commute with either $\mathfrak{L}_x$ or $\mathfrak{L}_y$, the eigenfunctions of $\mathfrak{L}_z$ are generally not eigenfunctions of $\mathfrak{L}_x$ and of $\mathfrak{L}_y$. Yet, since $\mathfrak{L}^2$ commutes with $\mathfrak{L}_x$ and with $\mathfrak{L}_y$, all nondegenerate eigenfunctions of $\mathfrak{L}_x$ are eigenfunctions of $\mathfrak{L}^2$, as are all nondegenerate eigenfunctions of $\mathfrak{L}_y$. In the language of set theory (see Chap. 6), we say that for a given value of l the set of eigenfunctions of $\mathfrak{L}_z$ forms a subset of the eigenfunctions of $\mathfrak{L}^2$, as do the eigenfunctions of $\mathfrak{L}_x$ and of $\mathfrak{L}_y$. Since $\mathfrak{L}_x$, $\mathfrak{L}_y$, and $\mathfrak{L}_z$ do not commute, they have no common eigenfunctions except the trivial function zero, which is an eigenfunction of every linear operator, but which is not properly behaved. This is schematically indicated in Fig. 11-3. All functions within the circle are eigenfunctions of $\mathfrak{L}^2$, but only those within the indicated sectors are eigenfunctions, respectively, of $\mathfrak{L}_x$, $\mathfrak{L}_y$, and $\mathfrak{L}_z$.

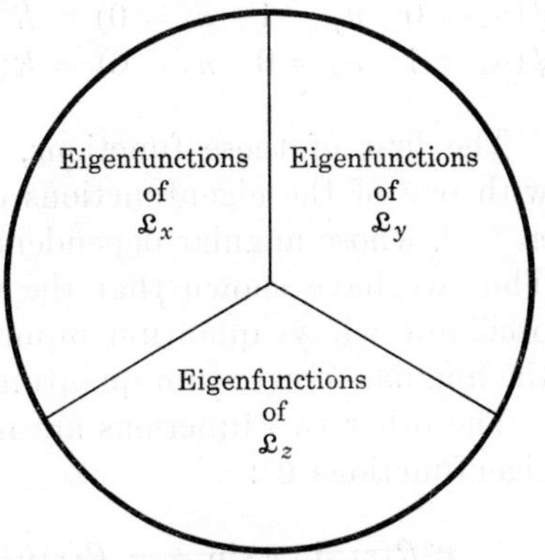

fig. 11-3 set-theoretical description of the eigenfunctions of the $\mathfrak{L}^2$, $\mathfrak{L}_x$, $\mathfrak{L}_y$, and $\mathfrak{L}_z$ operators

Any eigenfunction of $\mathfrak{L}^2$ is expressible as a linear combination of eigenfunctions of one of the components of the angular-momentum operator. If, for instance, ψ_l^m an $\psi_l^{m'}$ are two eigenfunctions of $\mathfrak{L}_z$ with a different Z component but the same magnitude of total angular momentum,

$$\mathfrak{L}^2\psi_l^m = l(l+1)\hbar^2\psi_l^m$$
$$\mathfrak{L}^2\psi_l^{m'} = l(l+1)\hbar^2\psi_l^{m'}$$

Then any linear combination of ψ_l^m and $\psi_l^{m'}$ is also an eigenfunction of $\mathfrak{L}^2$, with the same eigenvalue:

$$\mathfrak{L}^2(a_m\psi_l^m + a_{m'}\psi_l^{m'}) = a_m\mathfrak{L}^2\psi_l^m + a_{m'}\mathfrak{L}^2\psi_l^m =$$
$$= a_m l(l+1)\hbar^2\psi_l^m + a_{m'}l(l+1)\hbar^2\psi_l^{m'} = l(l+1)\hbar^2(a_m\psi_l^m + a_{m'}\psi_l^{m'})$$

Therefore any function in one sector of the circle of Fig. 11-3 can be expressed as a linear combination of the functions in another sector of that circle. Such linear combinations are demonstrated by considering the wave functions of the isotropic harmonic oscillator found in Chap. 10; since such an oscillator moves in a central field, the results of the present chapter are applicable to this oscillator. For the energy level $E = \frac{5}{2}\hbar\omega_0$, we found the following angular dependences of the wave functions of this threefold degenerate level:

$$\left.\begin{aligned} \psi(n_x = 0 \quad n_y = 0 \quad n_z = 1) &= R(r)\cos\theta \\ \psi(n_x = 0 \quad n_y = 1 \quad n_z = 0) &= R(r)\sin\theta\sin\phi \\ \psi(n_x = 1 \quad n_y = 0 \quad n_z = 0) &= R(r)\sin\theta\cos\phi \end{aligned}\right\} \quad \begin{array}{l}\text{where } R(r) \text{ is the ap-}\\ \text{propriate function of}\\ \text{the radial coordinate}\end{array}$$

The first of these functions, $R(r)\cos\theta$, is immediately identified with one of the eigenfunctions of $\mathfrak{L}_z$, namely, the one having $l = 1$, $m = 0$, whose angular dependence was found in Sec. 11-6 to be $\cos\theta$. Thus we have shown that the three-dimensional isotropic harmonic oscillator whose quantum numbers are $n_x = 0$, $n_y = 0$, $n_z = 1$, has the angular-momentum quantum numbers, $l = 1$, $m = 0$.

The other two functions are not eigenfunctions of $\mathfrak{L}_z$, but they are eigenfunctions $\mathfrak{L}^2$:

$$\mathfrak{L}^2R(r)\sin\theta\sin\phi = R(r)\mathfrak{L}^2\sin\theta\{\tfrac{1}{2}i[\exp(-i\phi) - \exp i\phi]\}$$

Since we have already found that $\sin\theta\exp i\phi$ and $\sin\theta\exp -i\phi$ are eigenfunctions of $\mathfrak{L}^2$ corresponding to $l = 1$,

$$\mathfrak{L}^2\sin\theta\exp i\phi = 2\hbar^2\sin\theta\exp i\phi$$
$$\mathfrak{L}^2\sin\theta\exp -i\phi = 2\hbar^2\sin\theta\exp -i\phi$$

and hence

$$\mathfrak{L}^2\sin\theta\sin\phi = 2\hbar^2\sin\theta\sin\phi \tag{11-25}$$

We shall use the following notation:

$$\begin{aligned}\psi(n_x = 0, n_y = 0, n_z = 1) &\equiv \psi_{p_z}\\ \psi(n_x = 0, n_y = 1, n_z = 0) &\equiv \psi_{p_y}\\ \psi(n_x = 1, n_y = 0, n_z = 0) &\equiv \psi_{p_x}\end{aligned}$$

---

problem 11-10. Show that ψ_{p_z} is an eigenfunction of $\mathcal{L}^2$, and find its eigenvalue.

We have thus found that ψ_{p_z}, ψ_{p_y} and ψ_{p_x} are all degenerate eigenfunctions of $\mathcal{L}^2$, with eigenvalue $2\hbar^2$, but that only ψ_{p_z} is an eigenfunction of $\mathcal{L}_z$, with eigenvalue zero. The other two eigenfunctions of $\mathcal{L}_z$ having $l = 1$ are linear combinations of ψ_{p_x} and ψ_{p_y}:

$$\psi_{p_x} \pm i\psi_{p_y} = R(r) \sin\theta (\cos\phi \pm i \sin\phi) = R(r) \sin\theta \exp \pm i\phi$$
$$\mathcal{L}_z(\psi_{p_x} \pm i\psi_{p_y}) = \pm\hbar(\psi_{p_x} \pm \psi_{p_y}) \tag{11-26}$$

11-8 Uniqueness of the ladder. We shall now show that the functions $(\mathcal{L}_x - i\mathcal{L}_y)^{l-m}\psi_l$ are the *only* eigenfunctions of $\mathcal{L}^2$ and $\mathcal{L}_z$. As before, we suppose that there might be an eigenfunction $\psi_{m+\delta}$ of $\mathcal{L}_z$, whose eigenvalue would be $(m + \delta)\hbar$, where $0 < \delta < 1$. Repeated application of the operators $(\mathcal{L}_x \pm i\mathcal{L}_y)$ would produce other eigenfunctions of $\mathcal{L}_z$ whose eigenvalues would differ from $(m + \delta)\hbar$ by an integral multiple of $\hbar$. All these eigenfunctions of $\mathcal{L}_z$ would be degenerate eigenfunctions of $\mathcal{L}^2$. Eventually, the eigenvalue of $\mathcal{L}_z{}^2$ would exceed the eigenvalue of $\mathcal{L}^2$, so that the eigenvalue of $(\mathcal{L}_x{}^2 + \mathcal{L}_y{}^2)$ would become negative. Since $\mathcal{L}_x$ and $\mathcal{L}_y$ are Hermitian, $(\mathcal{L}_x{}^2 + \mathcal{L}_y{}^2)$ cannot have negative eigenvalues, so that $\mathcal{L}_z{}^2$ cannot have eigenvalues exceeding those of $\mathcal{L}^2$ for any given common eigenfunction. The generating procedure using the operators $(\mathcal{L}_x \pm i\mathcal{L}_y)$ can, therefore, not be continued indefinitely, but must terminate. The only way for terminating the generating procedure is for ψ_m to belong to the set of functions $(\mathcal{L}_x - i\mathcal{L}_y)^{l-m}\psi_l$; this condition excludes functions such as $\psi_{m+\delta}$ as eigenfunctions $\mathcal{L}_z$. Thus we have proven the uniqueness of the ladder of eigenfunctions generated by repeated application of $(\mathcal{L}_x - i\mathcal{L}_y)$ to ψ_l.

11-9 Angular distribution of the electron charge in atoms. In Chap. 7 it was shown that the square of the absolute magnitude of the wave function gives the relative probability of finding an electron in a given differential volume element. We shall apply this interpretation to the eigenfunctions of $\mathcal{L}^2$ derived in the present chapter. It should be noted that in a spherically symmetrical potential the wave function is not generally spherically symmetrical; only wave functions having $l = 0$ are spherically symmetrical.

First we examine the wave function having $l = 1$, $m = 0$; $\psi = \cos\theta$. This wave function is independent of ϕ; the probability density is

$$|\psi_1{}^0|^2 = \cos^2\theta$$

This density is plotted as a function of the angle θ in Fig. 11-4; it has its maximum values at $\theta = 0$ and $\theta = \pi$, in other words along the Z axis. This density distribution has the shape similar to a dumbell with axis parallel to the Z axis.

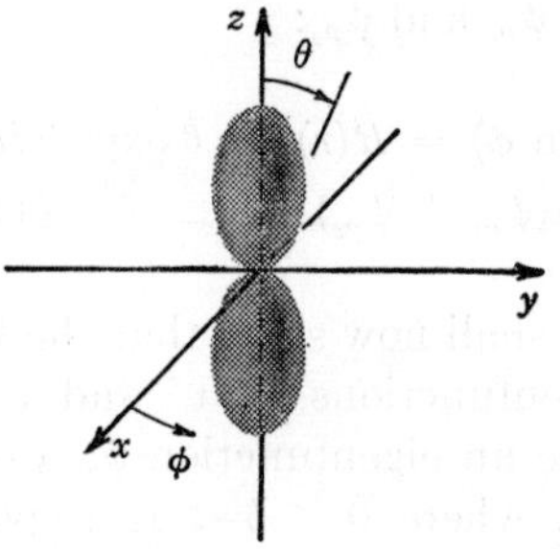

fig. 11-4 probability density as a function of θ and ϕ for a state having $l = 1$, $m = 0$

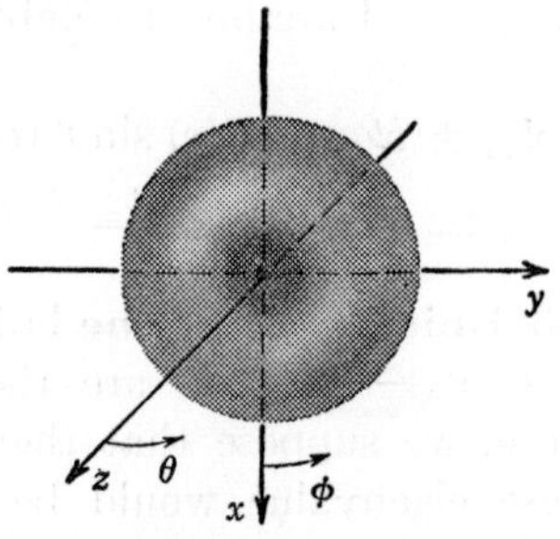

fig. 11-5 probability density as a function of θ and ϕ for states having $l = 1$, $m = \pm 1$

The wave function having $l = 1$, $m = 1$ is $\psi = \sin\theta \exp i\phi$. The probability density for this state as well as for the one having $l = 1$, $m = -1$ is

$$|\psi_1{}^{\pm 1}|^2 = \sin^2\theta$$

This density is independent of the angle ϕ, and has its maximum values when $\theta = \pi/2$ and $\theta = 3\pi/2$, that is in the equatorial plane. Accordingly, the angular distribution of the probability density for the states having $l = 1$ and $m = \pm 1$ is as shown in Fig. 11-5.

Since in the states having $m = \pm 1$ the electrons are, on the average, farther away from the Z axis than they are in the state having $m = 0$, the angular-momentum component along the Z axis has greater absolute value for the former states ($\hbar$) than for the latter (0).

In Chap. 7 it was pointed out that, while wave functions are linearly superimposable, the probability densities are not. It is therefore interesting to find the angular distribution of the probability densities for the three stationary wave functions of the isotropic harmonic oscillator having $E = \frac{5}{2}\hbar\omega_0$. In Sec. 11-7 these functions were shown to be eigenfunctions of $\mathcal{L}^2$, and linearly related to the eigenfunctions of $\mathcal{L}_z$ whose probability densities have just been discussed (radial dependence omitted here):

$$\begin{aligned}\psi_{p_x} &= \sin\theta\cos\phi \propto (\psi_1{}^1 + \psi_1{}^{-1})\\ \psi_{p_y} &= \sin\theta\sin\phi \propto (\psi_1{}^1 - \psi_1{}^{-1})\\ \psi_{p_z} &= \cos\theta = \psi_1{}^0\end{aligned}$$

The probability density distribution for ψ_{p_z} is identical with that drawn in Fig. 11-4. Those for ψ_{p_x} and ψ_{p_y} have their maxima, respectively, along the X and Y axes, as shown in Fig. 11-6x and 11-6y.

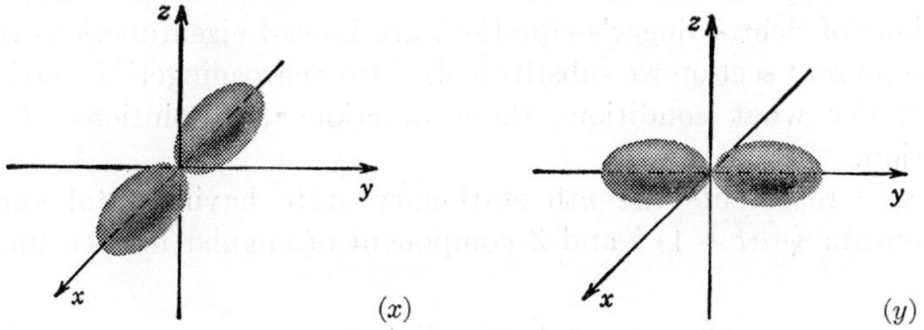

fig. 11-6 probability density as function of θ and ϕ for ψ_{100} and ψ_{010}

It is observed that Fig. 11-5 differs fundamentally from Fig. 11-6x and 11-6y in that in the latter there is definite knowledge about the angular position of the electron. This knowledge is gained at the expense of knowledge about angular momentum, for, as was shown in Sec. 11-7, L_z is indeterminate for the states whose wave functions are ψ_{p_x} and ψ_{p_y}.

---

problem 11-11. Plot, as functions of θ, the probability distributions of the states associated with the following quantum numbers in a central-field system:

(*a*) $l = 0, m = 0$
(*b*) $l = 1, m = -1$
(*c*) $l = 2, m = \pm 2$
(*d*) $l = 2, m = \pm 1$
(*e*) $l = 2, m = 0$

---

problem 11-12. Find the expectation values of the magnitude and the Z component of angular momentum, as well as their standard deviation, for states whose wave functions have the following angular dependence:

(*a*) $\sin\phi \sin\theta$ (*b*) $\cos 2\phi \sin^2\theta$

11-10 Schroedinger's equation in polar coordinates. In discussing the eigenfunctions of the angular-momentum operator we have so far assumed tacitly that these functions are acceptable wave functions, that is, that they satisfy Schroedinger's equation. This assumption was made plausible by demonstrating that some wave functions for the isotropic harmonic oscillator, which were found in Chap. 10 as solutions of Schroedinger's equation, are indeed eigenfunctions of $\mathcal{L}^2$. In the present section we substitute ψ_l^m into Schroedinger's equation to find under what conditions these functions are solutions of that equation.

If ψ_{nl}^m represents the nth stationary state having total angular momentum $\sqrt{l(l+1)}\,\hbar$ and Z component of angular momentum $m\hbar$,

$$\mathcal{H}\psi_{nl}^m = E_n\psi_{nl}^m$$

Since $\mathcal{P}^2 = \mathcal{P}_x^2 + \mathcal{P}_y^2 + \mathcal{P}_z^2 = -\hbar^2\nabla^2$, we find in spherical polar coordinates

$$-\frac{\hbar^2}{2\mu r^2}\left[\frac{\partial}{\partial r}\left(r^2\frac{\partial\psi_{nl}^m}{\partial r}\right) + \frac{1}{\sin\theta}\frac{\partial}{\partial\theta}\left(\sin\theta\frac{\partial\psi_{nl}^m}{\partial\theta}\right) + \frac{1}{\sin^2\theta}\frac{\partial^2\psi_{nl}^m}{\partial\phi^2}\right] = \\ = [E_n - V(r)]\psi_{nl}^m \quad (11\text{-}27)$$

Since $$\frac{1}{\sin\theta}\frac{\partial}{\partial\theta}\left(\sin\theta\frac{\partial\psi_{nl}^m}{\partial\theta}\right) = \frac{\partial^2\psi_{nl}^m}{\partial\theta^2} + \cot\theta\frac{\partial\psi_{nl}^m}{\partial\theta},$$

$$\mathcal{L}^2\psi_{nl}^m = (\mathcal{L}_x + i\mathcal{L}_y)(\mathcal{L}_x - i\mathcal{L}_y)\psi_{nl}^m - \hbar\mathcal{L}_z\psi_{nl}^m + \mathcal{L}_z^2\psi_{nl}^m = \\ = -\hbar^2\left(\frac{\partial^2\psi_{nl}^m}{\partial\theta^2} + \cot\theta\frac{\partial\psi_{nl}^m}{\partial\theta} - m^2\csc^2\theta\,\psi_{nl}^m\right)$$

Eq. (11-27) can be written in the following operator form:

$$\frac{1}{2\mu r^2}\left[-\hbar^2\frac{\partial}{\partial r}\left(r^2\frac{\partial\psi_{nl}^m}{\partial r}\right) + \mathcal{L}^2\psi_{nl}^m\right] = [E_n - V(r)]\psi_{nl}^m \quad (11\text{-}28)$$

The term $\frac{1}{2}\mu^{-1}r^{-2}\mathfrak{L}^2\psi_{nl}{}^m$ corresponds to the kinetic energy of a rotating body whose angular momentum is **L**, and whose moment of inertia is μr^2. This kinetic energy depends on both the rotational (angular) and the radial motion.

---

problem 11-13. (*a*) Derive

$$\mathfrak{L}^2\psi_{nl}{}^m = -\hbar^2\left(\frac{\partial^2\psi_{nl}{}^m}{\partial\theta^2} + \cot\theta\,\frac{\partial\psi_{nl}{}^m}{\partial\theta} + \frac{1}{\sin^2\theta}\,\frac{\partial^2\psi_{nl}{}^m}{\partial\phi^2}\right)$$

[*Hint:* Start with Eq. (11-19*a*).]

(*b*) Show that, when L_z is determinate,

$$\mathfrak{L}^2\psi_{nl}{}^m = -\hbar^2\left(\frac{\partial^2\psi_{nl}{}^m}{\partial\theta^2} + \cot\theta\,\frac{\partial\psi_{nl}{}^m}{\partial\theta} - m^2\csc^2\theta\,\psi_{nl}{}^m\right)$$

Since $\mathfrak{L}^2\psi_{nl}{}^m = l(l+1)\hbar^2\psi_{nl}{}^m$, Schroedinger's equation becomes

$$-\frac{\hbar^2}{2\mu r^2}\left[\frac{\partial}{\partial r}\left(r^2\,\frac{\partial\psi_{nl}{}^m}{\partial r}\right) - l(l+1)\psi_{nl}{}^m\right] = [E_n - V(r)]\psi_{nl}{}^m \qquad (11\text{-}29)$$

Equation (11-29) does not explicitly depend on the angles θ and ϕ, nor on the quantum number m. Therefore all the eigenfunctions of $\mathfrak{L}^2$ found in this chapter are solutions of Schroedinger's equation as long as their *radial* dependence satisfies Eq. (11-29). For proper radial dependence, we refer to the functions found in Chap. 10 for the isotropic harmonic oscillator, and to Chap. 13 for the coulombic central field.

---

problem 11-14. Show that if $V(r) = \frac{1}{2}kr^2$, the function ψ_{p_z} does indeed satisfy Eq. (11-29).

11-11 Orbitals and hybridization. The model presented in this chapter for an electron in an atom differs from that postulated by Bohr in that Bohr's distinct orbits are replaced by electron clouds whose density varies with location. Such clouds generally have a net angular momentum; some of the components of angular momentum, but not more than one component at any time, may be determinate in an atom. It has been shown that eigenfunctions of $\mathfrak{L}^2$ can represent stationary wave functions, and that the degeneracy of a state having angular momentum $\sqrt{l(l+1)}\,\hbar$ equals $(2l+1)$. Since any linear combination of degenerate eigenfunctions is also an eigenfunction (see Chap. 5), any linear combination of $(2l+1)$ degenerate eigenfunctions can represent a stationary state:

$$\psi = \sum_{m=-l}^{l} \phi_l^m \psi_l^m \tag{11-30}$$

where ϕ_l^m is independent of the angles ϕ and θ.

The wave function given by Eq. (11-30), while an eigenfunction of $\mathfrak{L}^2$, is not generally an eigenfunction of $\mathfrak{L}_z$.

The state of an electron in an atom is denoted by its quantum numbers. A state of an electron described by a given set of quantum numbers is called an orbital. Thus the functions ψ_{p_x}, $\psi_2{}^0$, $\sin\theta \exp i\phi$, $\cos\theta$ all describe orbitals of an electron in an atomic system; each is determined by values of n_x, n_y, n_z, or of l and m. The wave functions of Prob. 11-12 cannot be assigned definite values of the quantum number m, for they are linear combinations of the functions $\psi_1{}^{-1}$ and $\psi_1{}^1$. A state whose wave function is not itself an eigenfunction of $\mathfrak{L}_z$, but a linear combination of eigenfunctions of $\mathfrak{L}_z$ is said to be represented by a hybrid orbital. The functions ψ_{p_x} and ψ_{p_y} are both examples of hybrid orbitals.

The coefficients ϕ_l^m in Eq. (11-30) are generally determined by the boundary constraints on an atomic system. In isolated atoms, the only constraint is the proper behavior of wave functions; in such systems spectroscopic measurements generally do not give sufficient information for determining the coefficients ϕ_l^m. While spectroscopic measurements (without the use of an externally applied field) suffice to give the energy changes, additional measurements, for instance, those made in the presence of an external magnetic field are necessary to determine the value of m.

11-12 Spectroscopic notation. A notation first used by spectroscopists to describe the spectral-line series has been adopted to identify the orbital angular-momentum quantum numbers. In this notation letters are used to denote different values of l.

States with $l = 0$ are called s states; such states are the upper states involved in the sharp series spectra of the alkali elements. s states have only one value of m, namely, $m = 0$; from Sec. 11-6 it follows that such states give rise to a spherically symmetrical probability density of the electron cloud around the nuclear charge.

States with $l = 1$ are called p states; they are the upper states involved in the principal series spectra of the alkali elements. p states may have three values of m: $+1, 0, -1$, or three possible orientations of the orbital angular momentum.

States with $l = 2$, are called d states after the diffuse series in which they occur; states with $l = 3$, are called f states after the fundamental series in which they occur.

The adjectives, principal, sharp, diffuse, fundamental, have only historical interest for us here.

Hybrid orbitals are denoted by their component orbitals; for example, the orbital whose wave function is a linear combination of s, p_x, p_y, and p_z orbitals is denoted by sp^3; other hybrid orbitals are d^3s, sp^2.

11-13 The rotational energy of diatomic molecules. In the previous sections we discussed principally the behavior of electrons in a central field. Here we shall examine the rotation of diatomic molecules. Since no resultant torque acts in a central field, the rotational energy of these molecules is entirely kinetic. Therefore

$$E_{\text{rot}} = \text{KE}_{\text{rot}} = \frac{L^2}{2I}$$

where **L** is the angular momentum and I is the moment of inertia. The value of I depends on the expectation value of the interatomic distance, where

$$\overline{\frac{1}{r^2}} = \oint \psi_{nl}^{*m} r^{-2} \psi_{nl}^{m} \, dq = 4\pi \int_0^\infty \psi_{nl}^{*m} \psi_{nl}^{m} \, dr$$

Since $L^2 = l(l + 1)\hbar^2$, we have, using the spectroscopic rotational quantum number J instead of l,

$$E_{\text{rot}} = J(J + 1)\hbar^2 \overline{\frac{1}{2\mu r^2}} \tag{11-31}$$

where J may have the values $0, 1, 2, 3, \ldots$. In Chap. 12 we shall show how one may obtain $\overline{1/r^2}$ from spectroscopic data with the use of Eq. (11-31).

11-14 Summary. The operator method for generating "ladders" of eigenfunctions has been extended to any central-field potential function. It was found that the magnitude of the angular momentum is quantized according to the relation $\sqrt{l(l+1)}\,\hbar$, where l is a positive integer, and that the orientation of the angular momentum is quantized with respect to any direction in which its component is assumed determinate. The angle θ between the angular momentum and the latter direction is limited to the values

$$\cos\theta = \frac{m}{\sqrt{l(l+1)}}$$

where m is also an integer.

It was found that not more than one cartesian component of the angular-momentum vector can be determinate at any given time. The angular-momentum vector can never be aligned with the direction in which one of its components is assumed determinate, because the other components are never zero determinate, but, instead, fluctuate in such a way that the angular-momentum vector lies somewhere on the surface of a cone.

It was found, furthermore, that for each value of the angular-momentum quantum number l there are $(2l + 1)$ degenerate wave functions. This degeneracy can be removed by external constraints, so that those linear combinations of the degenerate functions occur that conform to these constraints. This process is called "hybridization."

Finally, it was shown how the general development could be used to find the rotational energy of a diatomic molecule.

The eigenfunctions of the operator $\mathcal{L}^2$ have been expressed in a general operator form. In the next chapter we shall show that these functions are equivalent to the so-called spherical harmonics, and we shall use some of their properties to derive the selection rules for the central field.

spherical harmonics and selection rules

chapter

12

12-1 Introduction. In Chap. 11 the eigenfunctions of the $\mathcal{L}^2$ operator were expressed in operator form; it was found that for any value of the quantum number l there are $(2l + 1)$ wave functions, which are generated by the expression

$$\psi_l{}^m = (\mathcal{L}_x - i\mathcal{L}_y)^{l-m}[(\sin\theta)^l \exp il\phi] \qquad (12\text{-}1)$$

In the present chapter we shall show that the functions generated according to Eq. (12-1) are equivalent to the so-called spherical harmonics and that certain important properties of these spherical harmonics follow directly from Eq. (12-1).

We shall, furthermore, apply the properties of the functions found in Chap. 11 to the derivation of the selection rules in rotational spectra.

12-2 Normalization. To normalize the operators $\mathcal{L}_x \pm i\mathcal{L}_y$, we proceed in a manner analogous to the normalization of the operators $(\mathcal{A} \pm i\mathcal{B})$ in Chap. 10; it is necessary to evaluate the integral

$$\oint[(\mathcal{L}_x \pm i\mathcal{L}_y)\psi_m]^*[(\mathcal{L}_x \pm i\mathcal{L}_y)\psi_m]\, dq$$

subject to the assumption that ψ_m is normalized.

From Eq. (11-13),

$$(\mathcal{L}_x \pm i\mathcal{L}_y)^* = \pm \exp(\mp i\phi)\left(\hbar\frac{\partial}{\partial\theta} \mp \cot\theta\, \mathcal{L}_z^*\right)$$

From Eq. (11-12), $\mathfrak{L}_z^* = -\mathfrak{L}_z$. Therefore

$$(\mathfrak{L}_x \pm i\mathfrak{L}_y)^* = \pm \exp(\mp i\phi)\left(\hbar \frac{\partial}{\partial\theta} \pm \cot\theta\, \mathfrak{L}_z\right) = -(\mathfrak{L}_x \mp i\mathfrak{L}_y)$$

so that

$$\begin{aligned}\oint[(\mathfrak{L}_x \pm i\mathfrak{L}_y)\psi_m]^*[(\mathfrak{L}_x \pm i\mathfrak{L}_y)\psi_m]\,dq &= \\ = -\oint(\mathfrak{L}_x \mp i\mathfrak{L}_y)\psi_m^*(\mathfrak{L}_x \pm i\mathfrak{L}_y)\psi_m\,dq &= -\oint\mathfrak{L}_x\psi_m^*\mathfrak{L}_x\psi_m\,dq + \\ \mp i\oint\mathfrak{L}_x\psi_m^*\mathfrak{L}_y\psi_m\,dq \pm i\oint\mathfrak{L}_y\psi_m^*\mathfrak{L}_x\psi_m^*\,dq &- \oint\mathfrak{L}_y\psi_m^*\mathfrak{L}_y\psi_m\,dq\end{aligned}$$

---

problem 12-1. Prove that the operators $(\mathfrak{L}_x \pm i\mathfrak{L}_y)$ are *not* Hermitian.

Using the fact that $\mathfrak{L}_x$ and $\mathfrak{L}_y$ are each Hermitian, we find

$$\begin{aligned}\oint[(\mathfrak{L}_x \pm i\mathfrak{L}_y)\psi_m]^*[(\mathfrak{L}_x \pm i\mathfrak{L}_y)\psi_m]\,dq &= \\ = -\oint\psi_m(\mathfrak{L}_x^* \pm i\mathfrak{L}_y^*)(\mathfrak{L}_x \mp i\mathfrak{L}_y)\psi_m^*\,dq &= \\ = -\oint\psi_m(\mathfrak{L}_x \mp i\mathfrak{L}_y)^*(\mathfrak{L}_x \mp i\mathfrak{L}_y)\psi_m^*\,dq\end{aligned}$$

From Eqs. (11-19*a*) and (11-19*b*) it follows that

$$(\mathfrak{L}_x \pm i\mathfrak{L}_y)(\mathfrak{L}_x \mp i\mathfrak{L}_y) = \mathfrak{L}^2 \pm \hbar\mathfrak{L}_z - \mathfrak{L}_z{}^2$$

Furthermore, $(\mathfrak{L}_x \mp i\mathfrak{L}_y)^* = -(\mathfrak{L}_x \pm i\mathfrak{L}_y)$; therefore

$$\oint[(\mathfrak{L}_x \pm i\mathfrak{L}_y)\psi_m]^*[(\mathfrak{L}_x \pm i\mathfrak{L}_y)\psi_m]\,dq = \oint\psi_m(\mathfrak{L}^2 \pm \hbar\mathfrak{L}_z - \mathfrak{L}_z{}^2)\psi_m^*\,dq$$

Since $\mathfrak{L}^2\psi_m = l(l+1)\hbar^2\psi_m$, $\mathfrak{L}^2\psi_m^* = l(l+1)\hbar^2\psi_m^*$. Since $\mathfrak{L}_z\psi_m = m\hbar\psi_m$, $\mathfrak{L}_z\psi_m^* = -(\mathfrak{L}_z\psi_m)^* = -m\hbar\psi_m^*$. Therefore

$$\begin{aligned}\oint[(\mathfrak{L}_x \pm i\mathfrak{L}_y)\psi_m]^*[(\mathfrak{L}_x \pm i\mathfrak{L}_y)\psi_m]\,dq &= [l(l+1) \mp m - m^2]\hbar^2\oint\psi_m\psi_m^*\,dq = \\ &= (l \mp m)(l \pm m + 1)\hbar^2\oint\psi_m\psi_m^*\,dq\end{aligned}$$

Hence the normalizing constant is $[(l \mp m)(l \pm m + 1)]^{1/2}\hbar$ and the normalized operators are

$$\frac{\mathfrak{L}_x + i\mathfrak{L}_y}{\hbar[(l-m)(l+m+1)]^{1/2}} \tag{12-2a}$$

and

$$\frac{\mathfrak{L}_x - i\mathfrak{L}_y}{\hbar[(l+m)(l-m+1)]^{1/2}} \tag{12-2b}$$

12-3 Legendre's differential equations. Since $\psi_l{}^m$ is an eigenfunction of $\mathfrak{L}^2$, $\mathfrak{L}^2\psi_l{}^m = l(l+1)\hbar^2\psi_l{}^m$. According to the result of Prob. 11-13,

$$\mathfrak{L}^2\psi_l{}^m = -\hbar^2\left(\frac{\partial^2\psi_l{}^m}{\partial\theta^2} + \cot\theta\,\frac{\partial\psi_l{}^m}{\partial\theta} - m^2\csc^2\theta\,\psi_l{}^m\right)$$

Therefore

$$\frac{\partial^2\psi_l{}^m}{\partial\theta^2} + \cot\theta\,\frac{\partial\psi_l{}^m}{\partial\theta} - m^2\csc^2\theta\psi_l{}^m + l(l+1)\psi_l{}^m = 0 \qquad (12\text{-}3)$$

When m is set equal to zero in Eq. (12-3),

$$\frac{\partial^2\psi_l{}^0}{\partial\theta^2} + \cot\theta\,\frac{\partial\psi_l{}^0}{\partial\theta} + l(l+1)\psi_l{}^0 = 0 \qquad (12\text{-}4)$$

Equation (12-4) is called Legendre's equation, whereas Eq. (12-3) is called the associated Legendre equation. The solutions of Eq. (12-3) are called spherical harmonics; each solution can be expressed as the product of the function exp $im\phi$ and a function of θ. The latter function is called a Legendre polynomial if $m = 0$, and an associated Legendre polynomial if $m \neq 0$.

12-4 Rodrigues's formula. An important relation involving spherical harmonics is Rodrigues's formula; we shall prove that this formula is equivalent to the ladder generation expression of Chap. 11. To do so, apply the operator $(\mathfrak{L}_x + i\mathfrak{L}_y)$ to the function $\psi_l{}^{-l}$:

$$(\mathfrak{L}_x + i\mathfrak{L}_y)\psi_l{}^{-l} = \exp i\phi\left(\hbar\,\frac{\partial}{\partial\theta} - \cot\theta\mathfrak{L}_z\right)\psi_l{}^{-l} =$$
$$= \exp i\phi\hbar\left(\frac{\partial}{\partial\theta} + l\cot\theta\right)\psi_l{}^{-l} = \hbar\exp i\phi\,\sin^{-l}\theta\,\frac{\partial}{\partial\theta}\,(\sin^{l}\theta\psi_l{}^{-l})$$

Since $\psi_l{}^{-l} = \exp(-il\phi)\sin^l\theta$,

$$\psi_l{}^{-l+1} = \hbar\exp[-i(l-1)\phi]\sin^{-l}\theta\,\frac{\partial}{\partial\theta}\,(\sin^{2l}\theta)$$

where $\psi_l{}^{-l+1}$ is not yet normalized. When the operator $(\mathfrak{L}_x + i\mathfrak{L}_y)$ is applied k times and each function normalized,

$$\psi_l{}^{-l+k} = \frac{\exp i(k-l)\phi}{2^{l+1}l!}\sqrt{\frac{(2l+1)!}{[2l(2l-1)\cdots(2l-k+1)][1\cdot 2\cdots k]\pi}}\,\times$$
$$\times\,\sin^{k-l}\theta\left(\frac{1}{\sin\theta}\frac{\partial}{\partial\theta}\right)^k\sin^{2l}\theta \qquad (12\text{-}5)$$

In particular, when $k = l$,

$$\psi_l^0 = \frac{1}{2^l l!}\left(\frac{2l+1}{4\pi}\right)^{1/2}\left(\frac{1}{\sin\theta}\frac{\partial}{\partial\theta}\right)^l \sin^{2l}\theta$$

If we define $\xi \equiv \cos\theta$,

$$\psi_l^0 = \frac{1}{2^l l!}\left(\frac{2l+1}{4\pi}\right)^{1/2}\frac{d^l}{d\xi^l}(\xi^2-1)^l \tag{12-6}$$

Rodrigues's formula† defines Legendre's polynomials as follows:

$$P_l(\xi) = \frac{1}{2^l l!}\frac{d^l}{d\xi^l}(\xi^2-1)^l \tag{12-7}$$

(See also Prob. 2-22.)

Equations (12-6) and (12-7) give the equivalence relation between ψ_l^0 and Legendre's polynomials:

$$\psi_l^0 = \left(\frac{2l+1}{4\pi}\right)^{1/2} P_l \tag{12-8}$$

It is evident that P_l is not normalized, while ψ_l^0 is. Setting $k = l + m$ in Eq. (12-5) gives

$$\psi_l^m = \exp(im\phi)\sqrt{\frac{(l-m)!}{(l+m)!}}(1-\xi^2)^{m/2}\frac{d^m}{d\xi^m}\psi_l^0 \tag{12-9}$$

Since the associated Legendre polynomials are defined

$$P_l^m = (1-\xi^2)^{m/2}\frac{d^m}{d\xi^m}P_l$$

$$\psi_l^m = \sqrt{\frac{(l-m)!}{(l+m)!}\frac{(2l+1)}{4\pi}}\,P_l^m \exp im\phi \tag{12-10}$$

The derivation of Eq. (12-10) has completed our proof of the equiva-

---

† See, for instance, L. A. Pipes "Applied Mathematics for Engineers and Physicists," 2d ed., chap. 14, McGraw-Hill Book Company, Inc., New York, 1958.

lence of ψ_l^m and spherical harmonics; ψ_l^m is normalized, while the spherical harmonics are not.

12-5 Recursion relations between spherical harmonics. Some useful recursion relations between the functions ψ_l^m can be found by rewriting Eqs. (12-4) and (12-3) in terms of the coordinate ξ:

$$(1-\xi^2)\frac{\partial^2\psi_l^0}{\partial\xi^2} - 2\xi\frac{\partial\psi_l^0}{\partial\xi} + l(l+1)\psi_l^0 = 0 \qquad (12\text{-}11)$$

$$(1-\xi^2)\frac{\partial^2\psi_l^m}{\partial\xi^2} - 2\xi\frac{\partial\psi_l^m}{\partial\xi} + \left[l(l+1) - \frac{m^2}{1-\xi^2}\right]\psi_l^m = 0 \qquad (12\text{-}12)$$

The operators $(\mathcal{L}_x \pm i\mathcal{L}_y)$ are similarly written in terms of ξ:

$$(\mathcal{L}_x \pm i\mathcal{L}_y)\psi_l^m = \pm \exp(\pm i\phi)\hbar\left[-(1-\xi^2)^{1/2}\frac{\partial}{\partial\xi} \mp m\xi(1-\xi^2)^{1/2}\right]\psi_l^m$$

Therefore

$$\psi_l^{m-1} = \frac{(\mathcal{L}_x - i\mathcal{L}_y)\psi_l^m}{\hbar[(l+m)(l-m+1)]^{1/2}} = $$
$$= \exp(-i\phi)\frac{[(1-\xi^2)^{1/2}(\partial/\partial\xi) - m\xi(1-\xi^2)^{-1/2}]\psi_l^m}{[(l+m)(l-m+1)]^{1/2}}$$

$$\psi_l^{m+1} = \frac{(\mathcal{L}x + i\mathcal{L}_y)\psi_l^m}{\hbar[(l-m)(l+m+1)]^{1/2}} = $$
$$= \exp(i\phi)\frac{[-(1-\xi^2)^{1/2}(\partial/\partial\xi) - m\xi(1-\xi^2)^{-1/2}]\psi_l^m}{[(l-m)(l+m+1)]^{1/2}}$$

and hence

$$[(l-m)(l+m+1)]^{1/2}\exp(-i\phi)\psi_l^{m+1} + $$
$$+ [(l+m)(l-m+1)]^{1/2}\exp(i\phi)\psi_l^{m-1} = 2m\xi(1-\xi^2)^{-1/2}\psi_l^m$$

Therefore, the following relation exists between three adjacent rungs of the same ladder (same l):

$$(1-\xi^2)^{1/2}\{[(l-m)(l+m+1)]^{1/2}\exp(-i\phi)\psi_l^{m+1} + $$
$$+ [(l+m)(l-m+1)]^{1/2}\exp(i\phi)\psi_l^{m-1}\} = 2m\xi\psi_l^m \qquad (12\text{-}13)$$

With the aid of Rodrigues's formula some relationships are now derived between spherical harmonics having different values of l, that is, between different ladders:

$$\begin{aligned}
\psi_{l-1}^0 &= \frac{1}{2^{l-1}(l-1)!}\left(\frac{2l-1}{4\pi}\right)^{1/2} \frac{d^{l-1}}{d\xi^{l-1}}(\xi^2-1)^{l-1} \\
\frac{d\psi_{l-1}^0}{d\xi} &= \frac{1}{2^{l-1}(l-1)!}\left(\frac{2l-1}{4\pi}\right)^{1/2} \frac{d^{l}}{d\xi^{l}}(\xi^2-1)^{l-1} \\
\psi_{l+1}^0 &= \frac{1}{2^{l+1}(l+1)!}\left(\frac{2l+3}{4\pi}\right)^{1/2} \frac{d^{l+1}}{d\xi^{l+1}}(\xi^2-1)^{l+1} = \\
&= \frac{1}{2^l l!}\left(\frac{2l+3}{4\pi}\right)^{1/2} \frac{d^{l}}{d\xi^{l}}[\xi(\xi^2-1)^l]
\end{aligned} \tag{12-14}$$

Therefore

$$\begin{aligned}
\frac{d\psi_{l+1}^0}{d\xi} &= \frac{1}{2^l l!}\left(\frac{2l+3}{4\pi}\right)^{1/2} \frac{d^{l}}{d\xi^{l}}[(\xi^2-1)^l + 2l\xi^2(\xi^2-1)^{l-1}] = \\
&= \frac{1}{2^l l!}\left(\frac{2l+3}{4\pi}\right)^{1/2} \frac{d^{l}}{d\xi^{l}}\{(\xi^2-1)^{l-1}[(2l+1)\xi^2-1]\}
\end{aligned} \tag{12-15}$$

Equation (12-14) can be rewritten

$$\frac{d\psi_{l-1}^0}{d\xi} = \frac{1}{2^l l!}\left(\frac{2l-1}{4\pi}\right)^{1/2} \frac{d^{l}}{d\xi^{l}}[2l(\xi^2-1)^{l-1}] \tag{12-16}$$

Both sides of Eq. (12-15) are divided by $(2l+3)^{1/2}$ and those of Eq. (12-16) by $(2l-1)^{1/2}$; when the resulting equations are subtracted from each other,

$$\frac{1}{(2l+3)^{1/2}}\frac{d\psi_{l+1}^0}{d\xi} - \frac{1}{(2l-1)^{1/2}}\frac{d\psi_{l-1}^0}{d\xi} = \frac{2l+1}{2^l l!(4\pi)^{1/2}}\frac{d^l}{d\xi^l}(\xi^2-1)^l$$

Application of Rodrigues's formula to the right-hand side of this last equation produces

$$\frac{1}{(2l+3)^{1/2}}\frac{d\psi_{l+1}^0}{d\xi} - \frac{1}{(2l-1)^{1/2}}\frac{d\psi_{l-1}^0}{d\xi} = (2l+1)^{1/2}\psi_l{}^0 \tag{12-17}$$

Equation (12-17) relates functions having $m = 0$ in adjacent ladders. This equation will now be generalized to functions having any value not exceeding the range $-l \leq m \leq l$ in adjacent ladders, by differentiating it $(m-1)$ times:

$$\frac{1}{(2l+3)^{1/2}}\frac{d^m\psi_{l+1}^0}{d\xi^m} - \frac{1}{(2l-1)^{1/2}}\frac{d^m\psi_{l-1}^0}{d\xi^m} = (2l+1)^{1/2}\frac{d^{m-1}\psi_l{}^0}{d\xi^{m-1}} \tag{12-18}$$

According to Eq. (12-9), replacing l by $(l + 1)$,

$$\frac{d^m\psi_{l+1}^0}{d\xi^m} = \exp(-im\phi)\sqrt{\frac{(l+m+1)!}{(l-m+1)!}}(1-\xi^2)^{-m/2}\psi_{l+1}^m$$

$$\frac{d^m\psi_{l-1}^0}{d\xi^m} = \exp(-im\phi)\sqrt{\frac{(l+m-1)!}{(l-m-1)!}}(1-\xi^2)^{-m/2}\psi_{l-1}^m$$

$$\frac{d^{m-1}\psi_l^0}{d\xi^{m-1}} = \exp[-i(m-1)\phi]\sqrt{\frac{(l+m-1)!}{(l-m+1)!}}(1-\xi^2)^{-(m-1)/2}\psi_l^{m-1}$$

These three expressions are substituted into Eq. (12-18):

$$\left[\frac{(l+m+1)(l+m)}{(2l+1)(2l+3)}\right]^{1/2}\psi_{l+1}^m - \left[\frac{(l-m+1)(l-m)}{(2l-1)(2l+1)}\right]^{1/2}\psi_{l-1}^m = \exp(i\phi)(1-\xi^2)^{1/2}\psi_l^{m-1} \quad (12\text{-}19)$$

Equations (12-13) and (12-19) constitute the recursion formulas that will be used in the next section in deriving the selection rules in l.

12-6 Selection rules for the central field. The condition for the appearance of a spectral line (see Chap. 5) can be written, in terms of the central-field wave functions,

$$\oint q(\psi_l^m)_1^*(\psi_l^m)_2\,dq \neq 0$$

where the subscripts 1 and 2 refer to two different states, having in general different sets of quantum numbers l and m.

We shall show in this section that there are restrictions on the changes in both m and l for transitions in a central-field system. Since all wave functions having a given value of l are degenerate, transitions involving changes in m are usually masked. However, this degeneracy can be removed by the presence of a magnetic field, because the energy of the system increases with increasing angle between the angular momentum and the magnetic field. Therefore selection rules for m can be observed when a magnetic field is superimposed on the central-field system.

The radiation absorbed (or emitted) by a system may be polarized in any of the three cartesian directions, or it may have components in two or three cartesian directions. The condition for the appearance of a spectral line is therefore that at least one of the following equations holds:

$$\left.\begin{aligned}\oint x(\psi_l^m)_1^*(\psi_l^m)_2\,d\tau \neq 0\\ \oint y(\psi_l^m)_1^*(\psi_l^m)_2\,d\tau \neq 0\\ \oint z(\psi_l^m)_1^*(\psi_l^m)_2\,d\tau \neq 0\end{aligned}\right\} \quad \text{where } d\tau \text{ is a differential volume element}$$

Since we are here interested only in transitions involving changes in m and l, and are not concerned about radial motion, we need integrate only over the angles θ and ϕ. Then $d\tau = \sin\theta\, d\theta\, d\phi$.

Substituting for x, y, and z, the expressions (10-19) to (10-21), we get the following conditions:

$$\int_0^{2\pi}\int_0^{\pi} (\psi_l^m)_1^*(\psi_l^m)_2 \sin^2\theta \cos\phi\, d\theta\, d\phi \neq 0$$

$$\int_0^{2\pi}\int_0^{\pi} (\psi_l^m)_1^*(\psi_l^m)_2^* \sin^2\theta \sin\phi\, d\theta\, d\phi \neq 0$$

$$\int_0^{2\pi}\int_0^{\pi} (\psi_l^m)_1^*(\psi_l^m)_2 \sin\theta \cos\theta\, d\theta\, d\phi \neq 0$$

Since $\psi_l^m = F_l^m(r,\theta) \exp im\phi$, where $F_l^m(r,\theta)$ is a function independent of ϕ,

$$\int_0^{2\pi}\int_0^{\pi} (\psi_l^m)_1^*(\psi_l^m)_2 \sin^2\theta \cos\phi\, d\theta\, d\phi =$$
$$= \int_0^{\pi} (F_l^m)_1^*(F_l^m)_2 \sin^2\theta\, d\theta \int_0^{2\pi} \exp i(m_2 - m_1)\phi \cos\phi\, d\phi \tag{12-20}$$

$$\int_0^{2\pi}\int_0^{\pi} (\psi_l^m)_1^*(\psi_l^m)_2 \sin^2\theta \sin\phi\, d\theta\, d\phi =$$
$$= \int_0^{\pi} (F_l^m)_1^*(F_l^m)_2 \sin^2\theta\, d\theta \int_0^{2\pi} \exp i(m_2 - m_1)\phi \sin\phi\, d\phi \tag{12-21}$$

$$\int_0^{2\pi}\int_0^{\pi} (\psi_l^m)_1^*(\psi_l^m)_2 \sin\theta \cos\theta\, d\theta\, d\phi =$$
$$= \int_0^{\pi} (F_l^m)_1^*(F_l^m)_2 \sin\theta \cos\theta\, d\theta \int_0^{2\pi} \exp i(m_2 - m_1)\phi\, d\phi \tag{12-22}$$

Therefore transitions involving dipole radiation certainly will *not* occur under the following conditions:

For the X component,

$$\int_0^{2\pi} \exp i(m_2 - m_1)\phi \cos\phi\, d\phi = 0$$

For the Y component,

$$\int_0^{2\pi} \exp i(m_2 - m_1)\phi \sin\phi\, d\phi = 0$$

For the Z component,

$$\int_0^{2\pi} \exp i(m_2 - m_1)\phi\, d\phi = 0$$

Since

$$\int_0^{2\pi} \exp i(m_2 - m_1)\phi \cos \phi \, d\phi =$$
$$= \tfrac{1}{2}\left[\int_0^{2\pi} \exp i(m_2 - m_1 + 1)\phi \, d\phi + \int_0^{2\pi} \exp i(m_2 - m_1 - 1)\phi \, d\phi\right]$$

transitions for the X and Y components can only occur when

$$m_2 - m_1 = \pm 1$$

The condition for the appearance of a spectral line for the Z component becomes similarly

$$\int_0^{2\pi} \exp i(m_2 - m_1)\phi \, d\phi \neq 0, \qquad \text{i.e.,} \qquad m_2 = m_1$$

Therefore, regardless of the changes in l, no lines appear in the spectrum unless the following relations between m_1 and m_2 are satisfied:

For the X and Y components,

$$m_2 - m_1 = \pm 1$$

For the Z component,

$$m_2 - m_1 = 0$$

Therefore transitions involving a decrease in orbital angular momentum but conservation of its Z component (decrease in l, but constant m), result in the emission of radiation polarized in the Z direction. Conversely, transitions involving a change in the Z component of angular momentum do not involve a Z component of polarized radiation. This polarization of spectral lines of atoms in an external magnetic field was first observed by Zeeman.

In addition to constraints on changes in the quantum number m, there are constraints on changes in l. These constraints are derived with the aid of the recursion relations between normalized spherical harmonics derived in the previous section. Substitution of the definition $\xi \equiv \cos \theta$ and of the appropriate relations just found between m_1 and m_2 together with Eqs. (12-20) to (12-22) imposes the following restrictions on changes in l:

X and Y components,

$$\int_{-1}^{1} (F_{l_1}{}^{m_1})^*(F_{l_2}{}^{m_1 \pm 1})(1 - \xi^2)^{1/2} \, d\xi \neq 0$$

Z component,

$$\int_{-1}^{1} (F_{l_1}{}^{m_1})^*(F_{l_2}{}^{m_1})\xi \, d\xi \neq 0$$

Since $F_l{}^m = \psi_l{}^m \exp -im\phi$,

For X and Y components,

$$\int_{-1}^{1} (\psi_{l_1}{}^{m_1})^* \exp (\mp i\phi)\psi_{l_2}{}^{m_1 \pm 1}(1 - \xi^2)^{1/2} \, d\xi \neq 0 \quad \text{[inequality (12-1)]}$$

For Z component,

$$\int_{-1}^{1} (\psi_{l_1}{}^{m_1})^*(\psi_{l_2}{}^{m_1})\xi \, d\xi \neq 0$$

By substituting Eq. (12-13) into inequality (12-1),

$$[(l + m)(l - m + 1)]^{1/2} \int_{-1}^{1} (\psi_{l_1}{}^{m_1})^* \exp (i\phi)\psi_{l_2}{}^{m_1 - 1}(1 - \xi^2)^{1/2} \, d\xi +$$
$$+ [(l - m)(l + m + 1)]^{1/2} \int_{-1}^{1} (\psi_{l_1}{}^{m_1})^* \exp (-i\phi)\psi_{l_2}{}^{m_1 + 1}(1 - \xi^2)^{1/2} \, d\xi \neq 0$$
$$\text{[inequality (12-2)]}$$

Since inequality (12-1) is a necessary condition for inequality (12-2), we need only concern ourselves with the former. When Eq. (12-19) is substituted into inequality (12-1) (taking only the upper signs in this inequality),

$$\int_{-1}^{1} (\psi_{l_1}{}^{m_1})^* \exp (i\phi)\psi_{l_2}{}^{m_1 - 1}(1 - \xi^2)^{1/2} \, d\xi =$$
$$= \left[\frac{(l_2 + m_1 + 1)(l_2 + m_1)}{(2l_2 + 1)(2l_2 + 3)}\right]^{1/2} \int_{-1}^{1} (\psi_{l_1}{}^{m_1})^* \psi_{l_2+1}^{m_1} \, d\xi +$$
$$- \left[\frac{(l_2 - m_1 + 1)(l_2 - m_1)}{(2l_2 - 1)(2l_1 + 1)}\right]^{1/2} \int_{-1}^{1} (\psi_{l_1}{}^{m_1})^* \psi_{l_2-1}^{m_1} \, d\xi \neq 0$$
$$\text{[inequality (12-3)]}$$

Since the functions $\psi_{l_1}{}^{m_1}$, $\psi_{l_2+1}^{m_1}$, $\psi_{l_2-1}^{m_1}$ are eigenfunctions of the Hermitian operator $\mathfrak{L}^2$, and are nondegenerate as long as $l_1 \neq l_2 + 1$ and $l_1 \neq l_2 - 1$, the integrals in inequality (12-3) vanish under those conditions. Therefore the only condition under which a spectral line may appear is when $l_1 = l_2 \pm 1$, that is, between adjacent ladders.

---

problem 12-2. Show that the same restrictions as above are also imposed when the lower signs in inequalities (12-1) are used. [*Hint:* Absorb the exponential function into the first factor, and apply Eq. (12-19) to the first resulting factor in the integral.]

We conclude, therefore, that only those spectral lines can occur that satisfy *both* of the following conditions:

$$\Delta l = \pm 1$$

and

$$\begin{aligned} \Delta m &= \pm 1 \qquad \text{for } X \text{ and } Y \text{ components of polarization} \\ &= 0 \qquad \text{for the } Z \text{ component of polarization} \end{aligned}$$

12-7 The rotational spectra of diatomic molecules. The constraints just found for the motions of electrons around an atomic nucleus are equally valid for the rotation of a molecule around its center of mass. For a diatomic molecule, transitions, involving radiation, occur only for $\Delta J = \pm 1$. When a molecule having the angular-momentum quantum number J is raised to the next higher rotational level, as it would be in the absorption of radiation, the frequency of the spectral line, using Eqs. (1-1) and (11-31), is:

$$\nu = \frac{\Delta E}{h} = [(J+1)(J+2) - J(J+1)]\frac{\hbar^2}{h}\overline{\frac{1}{2\mu r^2}} = (J+1)\hbar\overline{\frac{1}{2\pi\mu r^2}}$$

The frequency interval $(\nu_1 - \nu_2)$ between the two adjacent absorption lines will be $(\hbar/2\pi\mu)\overline{(1/r^2)}$, and hence independent of J. Since the molecules of a gas have J values 0, 1, 2, 3, . . . , the rotational spectrum of a gas composed of (absorbing) diatomic molecules consists of equally spaced lines. Since $(\nu_1 - \nu_2)/c = (1/\lambda_1 - 1/\lambda_2)$, where λ is the wavelength of a line, measurement of the wavelengths of two adjacent lines of the rotational spectrum permits calculation of $\overline{1/r^2}$. (μ is calculated from the atomic masses of the two atoms composing the molecule.)

In practice slight deviations from equal spacing are observed. The intervals between lines becomes smaller toward the shorter wavelength region, or the spacing becomes less for larger J values. Thus $\overline{1/r^2}$ decreases with increasing J. Such behavior is compatible with the fact that the interatomic distance becomes greater as the molecules rotate faster (larger J).

---

problem 12-3. The rotational spectrum of a gas consisting of diatomic species shows a series of equally spaced (in terms of frequencies) lines. The wavelengths of one pair of adjacent lines are, respectively, 85.7 and 100 microns. The molecules of the gas have a reduced mass μ, of 2×10^{-24} g.

(*a*) Find the interatomic distance for these molecules.

(*b*) Correlate the two spectral lines with the proper J values.

The molecules involved in Prob. 12-3 are the same as those involved in Prob. 10-16; one observes that the radiation resulting from transitions due to changes in rotational motion and those due to changes in vibrational motion occur in different parts of the electromagnetic spectrum, so that it is possible to isolate the study of the rotational motion from the study of vibratory motion.

12-8 Summary. We have proved the equivalence of the eigenfunctions of $\mathcal{L}^2$ and $\mathcal{L}_z$, with the spherical harmonics. We have further derived some recursion relations between functions on adjacent ladders and on adjacent rungs in one ladder. With the aid of these recursion relations we have shown that only those spectral lines occur that correspond to transitions from one ladder to another ladder having a value of l differing from the original one by one unit. The value of the Z component of orbital angular momentum must either remain unchanged or change by exactly $\hbar$ as the result of a transition. The selection rule for m can only be observed in the presence of a magnetic field parallel to the Z axis.

radial dependence of wave functions in a coulomb field

chapter 13

13-1 Introduction. In Chap. 11 we found the angular dependence of the wave functions corresponding to any central-field potential. It was pointed out that the radial dependence of these wave functions depends on the form of the central field. In this chapter, we use the operator method to derive the radial dependence of the wave function when the central field is coulombic, such as is encountered by an electron in the field of a proton (hydrogen atom) or in the field of an α particle (singly charged helium ion). Such a field is described by the potential-energy function

$$V(r) = -\frac{Ze^2}{r} \tag{13-1}$$

Here, e is the elementary charge on an electron and r the distance from the nuclear particle to the electron. Z is proportional to the ratio of the charge on the nucleus to that of a proton, that is, to the atomic number of the element under consideration. The units of Z are those of reciprocal dielectric constant and depend on the system of units (mks, cgs, etc.) employed.

In Chaps. 11 and 12 we have found eigenfunctions of the $\mathcal{L}^2$ and $\mathcal{L}_z$ operators, in the knowledge that any wave function can be expanded in terms of these eigenfunctions. In the present chapter we shall seek eigenfunctions of the energy operator; in other words we shall look for the stationary wave functions, because any wave function can be expanded in terms of all stationary ones. Thus we shall find the radial dependence of the wave function for a coulomb field. We shall here confine ourselves to the "bound" states of the electron, i.e., those states whose energy nowhere exceeds the potential energy of the ionized hydrogen atom.

13-2 Solution of Schroedinger's equation for a coulomb field. Substitution of Eq. (13-1) into Eq. (11-29) produces

$$r^2 \frac{\partial^2 \psi_{nl}{}^m}{\partial r^2} + 2r \frac{\partial \psi_{nl}{}^m}{\partial r} + \frac{2\mu Z e^2}{\hbar^2} r\psi_{nl}{}^m + \frac{2\mu E_n r^2}{\hbar^2} \psi_{nl}{}^m = l(l+1)\psi_{nl}{}^m \qquad (13\text{-}2)$$

where $\psi_{nl}{}^m$ is an eigenfunction of the operators $\mathcal{L}_z$, $\mathcal{L}^2$, and $\mathcal{H}$.

Since the quantum number m does not occur explicitly in Eq. (13-2), the radial dependence of the wave function is independent of m. Therefore

$$\psi_{nl}{}^m = R_{nl}(r)F_l{}^m(\phi,\theta)$$

where $R_{nl}(r)$ is independent of the quantum number m and the angles ϕ and θ, and $F_l{}^m$ describes the eigenfunctions of $\mathcal{L}^2$ and $\mathcal{L}_z$ found in Chap. 11. Substitution into Eq. (13-2) then gives the following differential equation for R_{nl}:

$$r^2 \frac{d^2 R_{nl}}{dr^2} + 2r \frac{dR_{nl}}{dr} + \frac{2\mu Z e^2}{\hbar^2} rR_{nl} + \frac{2\mu E_n r^2}{\hbar^2} R_{nl} = l(l+1)R_{nl} \qquad (13\text{-}3)$$

The zero of potential energy has been chosen at infinite r, so that the potential energy is never positive, so that E_n is never positive.

To solve Eq, (13.3), we make the following coordinate transformation:

$$u \equiv \hbar^{-1}(-2\mu E_n)^{1/2} r \qquad (13\text{-}4)$$

We further define

$$K_n \equiv \frac{Ze^2\mu^{1/2}}{\hbar(-2E_n)^{1/2}} \qquad (13\text{-}5)$$

so that

$$u = \frac{Ze^2\mu}{K_n\hbar^2} r \qquad (13\text{-}6)$$

Then Eq. (13-3) becomes

$$u^2 \frac{d^2R_{nl}}{du^2} + 2u \frac{dR_{nl}}{du} + 2K_n u R_{nl} - u^2 R_{nl} = l(l+1)R_{nl} \quad (13\text{-}7)$$

13-3 Generation of the eigenfunctions of the Hamiltonian operator. Equation (13-7) is solved by the same type of procedure as was used for the LHO in Chap. 10 and for the eigenfunctions of $\mathcal{L}_z$ in Chap. 11. The particular factoring method for Eq. (13-7) is due to Schroedinger.† In analogy with the procedures followed in Chaps. 10 and 11, this equation should be factored in terms of operators containing derivatives of no higher than the first order. It would then be in the general form

$$\left(u \frac{d}{du} + au + b\right)\left(u \frac{d}{du} + cu + f\right) R_{nl} = gR_{nl} \quad (13\text{-}8)$$

where a, b, c, f, and g are constants to be determined such that Eqs. (13-7) and (13-8) are identical. Expansion of Eq. (13-8) produces

$$u^2 \frac{d^2R_{nl}}{du^2} + (1 + b + f)u \frac{dR_{nl}}{du} + (a + c)u^2 \frac{dR_{nl}}{du} + (af + bc + c)uR_{nl} + acu^2R_{nl} = (g - bf)R_{nl} \quad (13\text{-}9)$$

$$\begin{aligned} 2 &= 1 + b + f & l(l+1) &= g - bf \\ 0 &= a + c & 2K_n &= af + bc + c \\ -1 &= ac \end{aligned}$$

Three of these five relations are of second order and hence give two sets of solutions:

$$\begin{aligned} a &= \pm 1 & f &= 1 \pm K_n \\ c &= \mp 1 & g &= l(l+1) - K_n(K_n \pm 1) \\ b &= \mp K_n \end{aligned}$$

By substituting both sets of solutions into Eq. (13-8), the following

† Erwin Schroedinger, "A Method of Determining Quantum Mechanical Eigenvalues and Eigenfunctions," *Proc. Roy. Irish Acad.*, **46A,** 9–16 (1940).

are the two ways in which Eq. (13-7) may be rewritten

$$\left(u\frac{d}{du} + u - K_n\right)\left(u\frac{d}{du} - u + 1 + K_n\right)R_{nl} = \\ = [l(l+1) - K_n(K_n+1)]R_{nl} \qquad (13\text{-}10a)$$

$$\left(u\frac{d}{du} - u + K_n\right)\left(u\frac{d}{du} + u + 1 - K_n\right)R_{nl} = \\ = [(l(l+1) - (K_n-1)K_n]R_{nl} \qquad (13\text{-}10b)$$

Any solution of Eq. (13-7) is therefore an eigenfunction of the operator

$$\left(u\frac{d}{du} + u - K_n\right)\left(u\frac{d}{du} - u + 1 + K_n\right)$$

with eigenvalue $l(l+1) - K_n(K_n+1)$ and at the same time an eigenfunction of the operator

$$\left(u\frac{d}{du} - u + K_n\right)\left(u\frac{d}{du} + u + 1 - K_n\right)$$

with eigenvalue $l(l+1) - (K_n - 1)K_n$. As before, the solution of Eqs. (13-10a) and (13-10b) is accomplished in two steps: first a method is developed for generating all solutions in terms of one particular solution and then this particular solution is found. Finally, it will be shown that the "ladder" of solutions thus generated contains all possible solutions.

The following notation will be used:

$$\mathcal{U}_{nl} \equiv u\frac{d}{du} + u - K_n \qquad (13\text{-}11)$$

$$\mathcal{V}_{nl} \equiv u\frac{d}{du} - u + K_n \qquad (13\text{-}12)$$

Equations (13-10a) and (13-10b) may then be written

$$\mathcal{U}_{nl}(\mathcal{V}_{nl}+1)R_{nl} = [l(l+1) - K_n(K_n+1)]R_{nl} \qquad (13\text{-}13a)$$

$$\mathcal{V}_{nl}(\mathcal{U}_{nl}+1)R_{nl} = [l(l+1) - (K_n-1)K_n]R_{nl} \qquad (13\text{-}13b)$$

These equations are valid for any value of n; hence, for instance, for adjacent stationary states,

$$(\mathcal{U}_{n+1,l})(\mathcal{V}_{n+1,l}+1)R_{n+1,l} = \\ = [l(l+1) - K_{n+1}(K_{n+1}+1)]R_{n+1,l} \quad (13\text{-}14a)$$

$$(\mathcal{V}_{n+1,l})(\mathcal{U}_{n+1,l}+1)R_{n+1,l} = \\ = [l(l+1) - (K_{n+1}-1)K_{n+1}]R_{n+1,l} \quad (13\text{-}14b)$$

and

$$(\mathcal{U}_{n-1,l})(\mathcal{V}_{n-1,l}+1)R_{n-1,l} = \\ = [l(l+1) - K_{n-1}(K_{n-1}+1)]R_{n-1,l} \quad (13\text{-}15a)$$

$$(\mathcal{V}_{n-1,l})(\mathcal{U}_{n-1,l}+1)R_{n-1,l} = \\ = [l(l+1) - (K_{n-1}-1)K_{n-1}]R_{n-1,l} \quad (13\text{-}15b)$$

Apply the operator $(\mathcal{V}_{nl}+1)$ to both sides of Eq. (13-13a):

$$(\mathcal{V}_{nl}+1)\mathcal{U}_{nl}(\mathcal{V}_{nl}+1)R_{nl} = \\ = [l(l+1) - K_n(K_n+1)](\mathcal{V}_{nl}+1)R_{nl} \quad (13\text{-}16)$$

This last equation can be identified with Eq. (13-14b) under the following conditions:

$$\mathcal{V}_{nl}+1 = \mathcal{V}_{n+1,l} \quad (13\text{-}17)$$

$$\mathcal{U}_{nl} = \mathcal{U}_{n+1,l}+1 \quad (13\text{-}18)$$

$$(\mathcal{V}_{nl}+1)R_{nl} = R_{n+1,l} \quad (13\text{-}19)$$

$$K_n = K_{n+1}-1 \quad (13\text{-}20)$$

Let us examine each of these four conditions in turn. According to the definition of $\mathcal{V}_{nl}$,

$$\mathcal{V}_{n+1,l} = u\frac{d}{du} - u + K_{n+1}$$

Equation (13-17) is therefore satisfied if $K_n + 1 = K_{n+1}$, so that the conditions expressed by Eqs. (13-17) and (13-20) are certainly consistent. Furthermore, from the definition of $\mathcal{U}_{nl}$,

$$\mathcal{U}_{n+1,l} = u\frac{d}{du} + u - K_{n+1}$$

so that Eq. (13-18) is satisfied also if Eq. (13-20) is. Therefore, we have proved the following theorem:

***theorem* 13-1a.** If R_{nl} is a solution of Schroedinger's stationary wave equation corresponding to the nth stationary state and if $R_{n+1,l}$

is a solution of the same equation corresponding to the $(n+1)$st stationary state, then these functions are related as follows:

$$R_{n+1,l} = (\mathcal{V}_{nl} + 1)R_{nl} \tag{13-19}$$

Furthermore, the eigenvalues of these two functions are related:

$$K_{n+1} = K_n + 1 \tag{13-20}$$

Thus the operator $(\mathcal{V}_{nl} + 1)$ has been shown to transform the nth eigenfunction of the Hamiltonian operator into its $(n+1)$st eigenfunction. We are therefore finding once more a "ladder" of eigenfunctions. Equation (13-20) can be rewritten in terms of the energy with the aid of Eq. (13-5):

$$\frac{1}{(-2E_{n+1})^{1/2}} = \frac{1}{(-2E_n)^{1/2}} + \frac{\hbar}{Ze^2\mu^{1/2}} \tag{13-21}$$

In order to transform the nth eigenfunction of the Hamiltonian operator into its $(n-1)$st eigenfunction, we apply the operator $(\mathcal{U}_{nl} + 1)$ to both sides of Eq. (13-13b), and attempt to identify the resulting equation with Eq. (13-15a). The result is

$$(\mathcal{U}_{nl} + 1)\mathcal{V}_{nl}(\mathcal{U}_{nl} + 1)R_{nl} = [l(l+1) - (K_n - 1)K_n](\mathcal{U}_{nl} + 1)R_{nl}$$

and hence

$$\begin{aligned} \mathcal{U}_{nl} + 1 &= \mathcal{U}_{n-1,l} \\ \mathcal{V}_{nl} &= \mathcal{V}_{n-1,l} + 1 \\ (\mathcal{U}_{nl} + 1)R_{nl} &= R_{n-1,l} \\ K_n - 1 &= K_{n-1} \end{aligned}$$

These four conditions are consistent with the definitions of $\mathcal{U}_{nl}$ and $\mathcal{V}_{nl}$, so that we have proved the following theorem.

***theorem* 13-1b.** If R_{nl} is a solution of Schroedinger's stationary wave equation corresponding to the nth stationary state, and if $R_{n-1,l}$ is a solution of the same equation corresponding to the $(n-1)$st stationary state, then these functions are related as follows:

$$R_{n-1,l} = (\mathcal{U}_{nl} + 1)R_{nl} \tag{13-22}$$

Furthermore, the eigenvalues of these two functions are related:

$$K_{n-1} = K_n - 1 \tag{13-23}$$

Theorems 13-1a and 13-1b can be summarized as follows:

$$R_{n\pm1,l} = \left(u\frac{d}{du} \mp u \pm K_n + 1\right)R_{nl} \tag{13-24}$$

$$K_{n\pm1} = K_n \pm 1 \tag{13-25}$$

Repeated application of these operators generates the complete ladder of eigenfunctions; it should be noted that in this case the operator depends on K_n, and hence is increased by unity each time that n is increased by a unit and is decreased by unity whenever n is decreased by a unit.

13-4 Termination of the generating procedure. The generating procedure described by Eq. (13-24) is terminated when a value of n, say n', is found so that

$$u\frac{dR_{n',l}}{du} \mp uR_{n',l} = -(1 \pm K_{n'})R_{n',l}$$

or

$$d(\ln R_{n',l}) = \pm du - (1 \pm K_{n'})d(\ln u)$$

and

$$R_{n'l} = C_{n',l}\frac{e^{\pm u}}{u^{1\pm K_{n}'}} \tag{13-26}$$

where $C_{n'l}$ is independent of u and can be determined by normalization.

Of these two functions only the one with the negative sign could possibly be properly behaved: therefore the $(\mathcal{V}_n + 1)$ operator can be applied indefinitely without termination.

The $(\mathcal{U}_n + 1)$ operator produces zero when

$$R_{n',l} = C_{n',l}u^{K_{n'}-1}e^{-u} \tag{13-27}$$

Equation (13-27) is not always properly behaved, for when $K_{n'}$ is negative, a singularity occurs at $u = 0$ that violates the requirement of proper behavior. Therefore $K_{n'}$ may not be negative.

The function $R_{n'l}$ was defined by the equation

$$(\mathcal{U}_{n',l} + 1)R_{n',l} = 0$$

When this equation is substituted into Eq. (13-13b), the left-hand side of that equation vanishes. Therefore, its right-hand side also vanishes, and

$$l(l+1) = (K_{n'} - 1)K_{n'}$$

Therefore, either $K_{n'} = l + 1$ or $K_{n'} = -l$.

Since $K_{n'}$ may not be negative, the second possibility can occur only when l equals zero. If $K_{n'}$ is zero, however, then according to Eq. (13-5), E_n equals minus infinity, and the coordinate transformation given by Eq. (13-6) would be invalidated. Therefore, we must consider $K_{n'} = -l$ an extraneous root.

Since l is a nonnegative integer, K_n must be an integer greater than zero, whose lowest value for a given value of the angular momentum equals $(l + 1)$. When $K_n = l + 1$, Eq. (13-27) becomes

$$R_{l+1,l} = C_{l+1,l}u^l e^{-u} \tag{13-28}$$

This function represents the bottom rung of a ladder. In general, $K_n = n$, where n is an integer greater than l. From Eq. (13-5) it follows that the eigenvalues of the Hamiltonian are

$$E_n = -\frac{Z^2e^4\mu}{2\hbar^2n^2} \tag{13-29}$$

and from Eqs. (13-25), (13-27), and (13-28), it follows that its unnormalized eigenfunctions are

$$R_{n,l} = \prod_{k=l+2}^{n} \left(u\frac{d}{du} - u + k\right) R_{l+1,l} \tag{13-30}$$

for instance,

$$R_{l+2,l} = \left(u\frac{d}{du} - u + l + 2\right) u^l e^{-u} = 2(l + 1 - u)u^l e^{-u} \tag{13-30a}$$

The constant $Z^2e^4\mu/2\hbar^2$ in Eq. (13-29) is recognized as Rydberg's constant (see Chap. 1).

---

problem 13-1. Find the radial and angular dependences of the wave functions for the following states of an electron in a coulombic field (the initial numeral indicates the value of n): $1s$; $2p$; $3d$; $4s$.

---

problem 13-2. Plot the radial dependence of each of the four functions found in Prob. (13-1) vs. u. To do so, determine the following:

(*a*) Where the curves cross the axes
(*b*) Where the functions have maxima and minima
(*c*) Their behavior when u is very large

The functions generated by the use of Eqs. (13-28) and (13-30) are known as the Laguerre polynomials.†

13-5 Uniqueness of the ladders. We have shown that Eq. (13-30) represents a set of eigenfunctions of the Hamiltonian operator with a coulombic potential. In this section we shall show that the set of functions generated by Eq. (13-30) represents *all* eigenfunctions of the Hamiltonian operator corresponding to bound states, so that any functions that do not belong to the set generated by Eq. (13-30) are not eigenfunctions of this Hamiltonian operator. To demonstrate this, we use the following theorem.

***theorem* 13-2.** The operator $\mathcal{V}_{nl}(\mathcal{U}_{nl} + 1)$ can have no positive eigenvalues.

***proof of theorem* 13-2.** For any functions $f(u)$ and $g(u)$ it follows from the definition of $\mathcal{V}_{nl}$, Eq. (13-12),

$$\int_0^\infty f\mathcal{V}_{nl}g\,du = \int_0^\infty f\cdot u\frac{dg}{du}\,du - \int_0^\infty f\cdot(u - K_n)g\,du$$

Integration of the first term by parts gives

$$\int_0^\infty f\cdot u\frac{dg}{du}\,du = ufg\Big|_0^\infty - \int_0^\infty g\left(u\frac{df}{du} + f\right)du$$

---

† L. Pauling and E. B. Wilson. Jr., "Introduction to Quantum Mechanics," chap. V, McGraw-Hill Book Company, Inc., New York, 1935.
H. Eyring, J. Walter, and G. E. Kimball, "Quantum Chemistry," chaps. IV and VI, John Wiley & Sons, Inc., New York, 1944.

Therefore

$$\int_0^\infty f\mathcal{V}_{nl}g\,du = ufg\Big|_0^\infty - \int_0^\infty g\left(u\frac{d}{du} + 1 - K_n + u\right)f\,du \qquad (13\text{-}31)$$

If the functions $f(u)$ and $g(u)$ obey the rules of proper behavior for wave functions, then the product ufg vanishes when $u \to \infty$ because functions f and g must vanish sufficiently fast. As singularities at $u = 0$ are also excluded, the product ufg also vanishes for $u = 0$.

From Eq. (13-31) and the definition of $\mathcal{U}_{nl}$, we conclude that

$$\int_0^\infty f\mathcal{V}_{nl}g\,du = -\int_0^\infty g(\mathcal{U}_{nl} + 1)f\,du \qquad (13\text{-}32)$$

This relation between $\mathcal{V}_{nl}$ and $(\mathcal{U}_{nl} + 1)$ is reminiscent of the Hermitian property of operators. To complete the proof of Theorem 13-2, we apply Eq. (13-32) for the following particular functions $f(u)$ and $g(u)$:

$$f(u) = R_{nl}u^2 \qquad g(u) = (\mathcal{U}_{nl} + 1)R_{nl}$$

Then (recall that $dq = 4\pi r^2\,dr \propto u^2\,du$)

$$\int_0^\infty R_{nl}\mathcal{V}_{nl}(\mathcal{U}_{nl} + 1)R_{nl}u^2\,du = -\int_0^\infty [(\mathcal{U}_{nl} + 1)R_{nl}]^2u^2\,du + \\ - 2\int_0^\infty (\mathcal{U}_{nl} + 1)R_{nl}\cdot R_{nl}u^2\,du \qquad (13\text{-}33)$$

Since $(\mathcal{U}_{nl} + 1)R_{nl} = R_{n-1,l}$, and $R_{n-1,l}$ is orthogonal to R_{nl} (both are nondegenerate eigenfunctions of $\mathcal{H}$), the second integral on the right-hand side of Eq. (13-30) vanishes. According to Eq. (13-13*b*), R_{nl} is an eigenfunction of the operator $\mathcal{V}_{nl}(\mathcal{U}_{nl} + 1)$, with eigenvalue $[l(l + 1) - (K_n - 1)K_n]$. Since the right-hand side of Eq. (13-33) cannot be positive because the integrand in the first term is nowhere negative, we conclude that the eigenvalue of the operator $\mathcal{V}_{nl}(\mathcal{U}_{nl} + 1)$ cannot be positive.

We know that for the set of eigenfunctions given by Eq. (13-30) K_n equals the integer n. If we had a function R_{nl} *not* belonging to the set defined by Eq. (13-30), then according to Eq. (13-13*b*), it would be necessary that $\mathcal{V}_{nl}(\mathcal{U}_{nl} + 1)R_{nl} = [l(l + 1) - (K_n - 1)K_n]R_{nl}$, where K_n is *not* an integer. According to Theorem (13-1*b*), there would also exist an eigenfunction of the Hamiltonian $R_{n-1,l} = (\mathcal{U}_{nl} + 1)R_{nl}$, whose eigenvalue equals $[l(l + 1) - (K_{n-1} - 1)K_{n-1}]$.

In addition, Theorem 10-13*b* gives $K_{n-1} = K_n - 1$, so that the eigenvalue of $R_{n-1,l}$ would actually be $[l(l+1) - (K_n - 2)(K_n - 1)]$, which equals $[l(l+1) - (K_n - 1)K_n] + 2(K_n - 1)$. Thus the eigenvalue of $R_{n-1,l}$ is greater than that of $R_{n,l}$. Repeated application of the $(\mathfrak{U}_{nl} + 1)$ operator would produce functions $R_{n-2,l}R_{n-3,l}$, etc., which have eigenfunctions successively higher in the ladder. The generating procedure could only terminate when $K_n = l + 1$, but that would make K_n equal to an integer and R_{nl} part of the set generated by Eq. (13-30). If R_{nl} is *not* to be part of that set, and therefore K_n not an integer, then the generating procedure could be continued indefinitely, so that eventually positive eigenvalues of the operator $\mathfrak{V}_{nl}(\mathfrak{U}_{nl} + 1)$ would be attained. This, however, violates Theorem 13-2, so that we conclude that only the functions belonging to the set defined by Eq. (13-30) are properly behaved wave functions.

---

problem 13-3. Plot, on a vertical scale, the relative values of the energies of the states of a singly ionized helium atom characterized by the following sets of quantum numbers:

(*a*) $n = 1, l = 0, m = 0$
(*b*) $n = 2, l = 1, m = 0$
(*c*) $n = 2, l = 0, m = 0$
(*d*) $n = 3, l = 2, m = 1$
(*e*) $n = 4, l = 1, m = -1$
(*f*) $n = 20, l = 15, m = 12$
(*g*) $n = \infty, l = 100, m = 90$

---

problem 13-4. Find the degeneracy of the energy level having $n = 5$, listing all possible combinations of values of l and m.

13-6 Some low-energy states of the hydrogen atom; comparison with Bohr's model. The lowest value of the quantum number n equals $l + 1$; the lowest value of l equals zero. Therefore, the lowest value of n equals unity. Since E_n increases monotonically with n [see Eq. (13-29)], the lowest energy is that of the state having $n = 1, l = 0$, that is, of the 1*s* state. Since l equals zero, m also equals zero for this state, so that the wave function is independent of the angles ϕ and θ (see Chap. 11). Whenever $n = l + 1$, the radial dependence of the wave function having $n = l + 1$ is found from Eq. (13-27):

$$R_{l+1,l} = C'_{l+1,l}u^{n-1}e^{-u}$$

where $C'_{l+1,l}$ is a normalization constant independent of u. Substitute Eqs. (13-4) and (13-5):

$$R_{l+1,l} = C_{l+1,l}r^{n-1} \exp - \frac{Ze^2\mu}{\hbar^2 n} r \tag{13-34}$$

where
$$C_{l+1,l} = \left[\frac{Ze^2\mu}{\hbar^2(l+1)}\right]^l C'_{l+1,l}$$

Define $a_0 \equiv \hbar^2/e^2\mu$; then $u = (Z/na_0)r$, so that,

when $n = 1, l = 0,$

$$R_{1s} = C_{1s} = \exp \frac{-Zr}{a_0}$$

when $n = 2, l = 1,$

$$R_{2p} = C_{2p}r \exp \frac{-Zr}{2a_0}$$

when $n = 3, l = 2,$

$$R_{3d} = C_{3d}r^2 \exp \frac{-Zr}{3a_0}$$

when $n = 4, l = 3,$

$$R_{4f} = C_{4f}r^3 \exp \frac{-Zr}{4a_0}$$

.
.
.

etc.

When $n = l + 2$, Eq. (13-30a) produces

$$R_{l+2,l} = C_{l+2,l}\left[l + 1 - \frac{Zr}{(l+2)a_0}\right] r^l \exp \frac{-Zr}{(l+2)a_0} \tag{13-35}$$

Hence:

When $n = 2, l = 0,$

$$R_{2s} = C_{2s}\left(1 - \frac{Zr}{2a_0}\right) \exp \frac{-Zr}{2a_0}$$

When $n = 3, l = 1,$

$$R_{3p} = C_{3p}\left(2 - \frac{Zr}{3a_0}\right) r \exp \frac{-Zr}{3a_0}$$

When $n = 4, l = 2,$

$$R_{4d} = C_{4d}\left(3 - \frac{Zr}{4a_0}\right)r^2 \exp\frac{-Zr}{4a_0}$$

$$\vdots$$

etc.

---

problem 13-5. Find the values of l and n for the wave functions given in Probs. 7-5*a* and 7-5*b*.

---

problem 13-6. (*a*) Starting with R_{2s}, given above, find R_{3s}, and plot R_{3s}, R_{3p}, and R_{3d} vs. r.

(*b*) How many roots does each of these functions have, that is, for how many values of r does each function vanish?

(*c*) How many roots does *any* function R_{nl} have?

---

problem 13-7. Normalize the wave function for the electron in a coulomb field, whose quantum numbers are: $n = 3$, $l = 2$, $m = 2$. (*Hint:* recall that $-\pi \leq \phi \leq \pi$, $0 \leq \theta \leq \pi$ and the differential volume element in spherical coordinates is $r^2 \sin\theta\, d\theta\, d\phi\, dr$.)

The expression for the quantized energy values in a coulombic field as given by Eq. (13-29) agrees exactly with the energy values found by Bohr; in terms of a_0, $E_n = -Z^2/2n^2a_0$. Bohr also predicted exact values for the radii of the circular orbits of electrons around the nucleus: $r_n = n^2\hbar^2/Ze^2m_e = (n^2/Z)a_0$ (see Chap. 1). In other words, the quantity a_0 defined above equals Bohr's calculated value of the radius of an electron orbit in a hydrogen atom ($Z = 1$) in its ground state ($n = 1$). Its numerical value is 0.529A. According to the postulates of wave mechanics, an exact specification of the location of an electron is not possible; wave mechanics can only yield statistical results such as the most probable location of an electron, or its expected location. (According to the results of Prob. 7-5, these two locations are not generally identical.) It will be of interest to compare Bohr's values for the dimensions of electronic orbits with the statistical values derived from the postulates of wave mechanics. To do so, we shall look for the relative maxima in the probability density, or more exactly, for those values of r for which the probability of finding an electron within a spherical shell of radius r, width dr, is a maximum. The probability of finding an electron in such a shell is $4\pi(rR_{nl})^2\,dr$, where R_{nl}^2 is the probability density, and $4\pi r^2\,dr$ is the volume of the shell. This probability has an extremum when

$$\frac{d}{dr}(rR_{nl})^2 = 0$$

that is, when

$$2rR_{nl}\left(r\frac{dR_{nl}}{dr} + R_{nl}\right) = 0$$

The solution $r = 0$ is trivial, and the solution $R_{nl} = 0$ always corresponds to a minimum in the probability. Maxima occur therefore when

$$\frac{dR_{nl}}{dr} = -\frac{R_{nl}}{r}$$

When $n = l + 1$ [see Eq. (13-34)],

$$\frac{dR_{nl}}{dr} = \frac{R_{nl}}{r}\left[l - \frac{Zr}{a_0(l+1)}\right]$$

so that the most probable nucleus-electron distance for all states having $n = l + 1$ is

$$r_{mp} = \frac{(l+1)^2}{Z}a_0 = \frac{n^2}{Z}a_0 \qquad (13\text{-}36)$$

This expression is exactly that found by Bohr for the radius of an electron orbit; for the case $n = l + 1$ the wave mechanical model gives the same value for *the most probable* nucleus-electron distance as Bohr's model gives for *the* nucleus-electron distance.

For states having $n = l + 2$ the most probable nucleus-electron distance is found from the equation

$$\frac{dR_{l+2,l}}{dr} = -\frac{R_{l+2,l}}{r}$$

By a procedure similar to that followed for $n = l + 1$ it is found that

$$r_{mp} = n[(n - \tfrac{1}{2}) \pm (n - \tfrac{3}{4})^{\frac{1}{2}}]Z^{-1}a_0 \qquad \text{for } n = l + 2 \quad (13\text{-}37)$$

While states having $n = l + 1$ have only *one* most probable nucleus-electron distance, those with $n = l + 2$ have two relative maxima in the probability distribution.

Below are found the most probable values of the nucleus-electron distance for some particular states:

For 1*s* state,

$$r_{mp} = \frac{a_0}{Z}$$

For 2*s* state,

$$r_{mp} = \frac{(3 \pm \sqrt{5})a_0}{Z}$$

For 2*p* state,

$$r_{mp} = \frac{4a_0}{Z}$$

The probability distributions as a function of the radial coordinate are sketched for some particular states in Fig. 13-1.

---

problem 13-8. How many relative maxima does the probability distribution over the radial distance have for a hydrogen atom in a state for which $n = l + k$, where k is a positive integer?

---

problem 13-9. (*a*) Compare the expectation value of the nucleus-electron distance with the most probable nucleus-electron distance for the 1*s*, 2*s*, and 2*p* states.

(*b*) For each of these states find the standard deviations from each of the values found under (*a*).

(*c*) Plot the results of this problem on Fig. 13-1.

---

problem 13-10. (*a*) Find the expectation value of the kinetic energy for the 2*s* state of the hydrogen atom in units of $e^2/2a_0$. [*Hint:* First find $\overline{(1/r)}$.]

(*b*) Find in units of $e^2/2a_0$, the expectation value of the kinetic energy associated with radial motion only, for a hydrogen atom in a 2*p* state. [*Hint:* See Sec. 11-13; note that $\overline{1/r^2} \neq 1/\overline{(r^2)}$, here.]

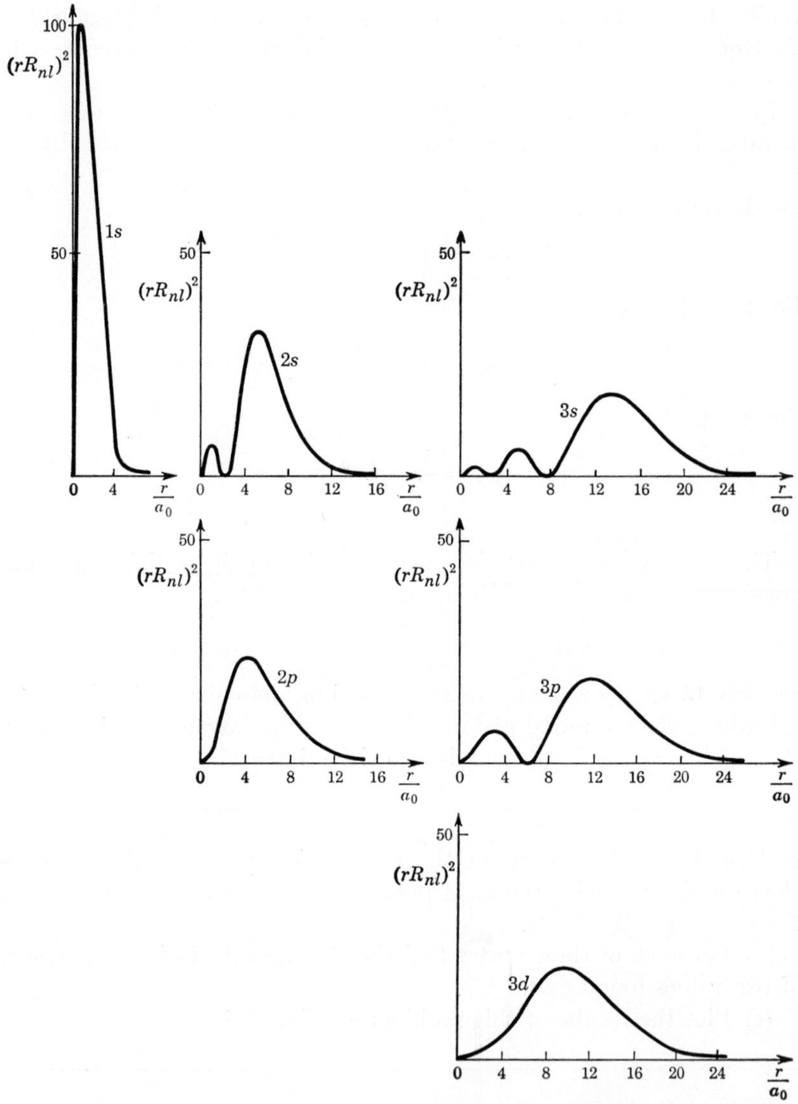

fig. 13-1 probability densities as functions of the radial coordinate for six states of the hydrogen atom. (*After G. Herzberg, "Atomic Spectra," Dover Publications, New York, 1944, by permission.*)

problem 13-11. (*a*) Find the fraction of all hydrogen atoms in their ground states having a nucleus-electron distance less than the most probable distance.

(*b*) Find the fraction of atoms having an electron closer to the nucleus than the expected nucleus-electron distance.

13-7 Selection rules. There are no restrictions on the possible changes in the value of n. For example, the Lyman series of the spectrum of the hydrogen atom involves transitions from states having $n > 1$ to the ground state ($n = 1$); the Balmer series corresponds to all transitions from states having $n > 2$ to the $n = 2$ state. The selection rules for l and m (Chap. 12) do, of course, restrict the spectrum of hydrogen-like atoms.

problem 13-12. Find the number of distinct spectral lines that one may expect to observe as a result of all allowed transitions from a $4d$ state of the hydrogen atom to lower states. Explain briefly. (Assume that there are no external fields that perturb the spherical symmetry of the potential function.)

problem 13-13. Find the θ, ϕ, and r dependence of the wave function of He^+ having the following quantum numbers: $n = 3$, $l = 1$, and $m = 1$.

13-8 Summary. The operator method of Chaps. 10 and 11 has been extended to find the radial dependence of wave functions in a coulombic field. A semi-infinite ladder of eigenfunctions of the Hamiltonian operator was generated, whose eigenvalues represent the allowed determinate energy levels. These energy values were found to be of the form $-\mathfrak{R}/n^2$, ranging from $-\mathfrak{R}$ to zero. It was found that electrons in such systems do not follow discrete orbits, but that the most probable nucleus-electron distance increases with increasing energy and increasing quantum number n, so that there is considerable justification in referring to electrons having small values of n as "inner electrons," to those having large valuse of n as "outer electrons." In Table 13-1 we summarize the variables whose eigenfunctions were found in Chaps. 11 and 13, and their eigenvalues. We conclude that for a given value of n the states with maximum value of $l(= n - 1)$ have highly directed (angularly dependent) wave functions, with a single extremum in their radial distribution. For a given value of n, states with lower values of l have fewer "lobes" in the angular wave functions, but more nodes in the radial wave function.

Since the appearance of "nodes" and "lobes" essentially increases $\nabla^2\psi$—the operator ∇^2 is sometimes said to indicate the "waviness" of a wave function—these nodes and lobes are associated with radial and angular kinetic energies, respectively. States with relatively large values of $(n - l)$ therefore have a higher radial kinetic energy than those with the minimum value of $(n - l)$, namely, unity. While the energy was shown to depend explicitly on n only, and not on l, it would be a mistake to imagine that the total energy is independent of angular momentum. Indeed, the quantum number n depends implicitly on angular momentum, because its minimum value equals $l + 1$. Thus we conclude that when n equals $l + 1$, much of the energy is associated with angular motion, and that when n exceeds $l + 1$, more radial motion contributes to the total energy.

The energy levels of the hydrogen atom appear to be highly degenerate. When we take into account small interactions neglected so far, such as the interaction between the electron's magnetic dipoles with the dipole caused by the electron's orbital motion, and the interaction with the proton's magnetic dipole, these degeneracies are partially removed. When high resolution is used to examine the spectrum of the hydrogen atom, a fine structure of the spectral lines is revealed; the structure is the result of the removal of the degeneracy due to the interaction of the two dipoles. We shall further discuss the magnetic dipole associated with the electron in Chap. 16.

table 13-1

relations between variables and quantum numbers

variable	permitted determinate values	quantum numbers
L_z	$m\hbar$	m = integer; $\|m\| \leq l$
L	$\sqrt{l(l+1)}\hbar$	l = integer
E	$Z^2e^4\mu/2\hbar^2n^2$	n = integer, $n \geq l + 1$

the hydrogen molecule-ion

chapter

14

14-1 Introduction. In Chap. 11 we considered the rotation of diatomic molecules, and we pointed out that the rotational and vibrational motions of such a molecule cannot properly be separated, although as an approximation we can find the expectation value of the interatomic distance and treat the rotation as if this distance were held fixed. In the present chapter we shall examine the vibrational motion for a simple example, namely, the hydrogen molecule-ion. The hydrogen molecule-ion consists of two protons and an electron. We shall consider a mechanism by which the electron overcompensates the repulsion between the two protons, and thus demonstrate the principle of molecular binding. In so doing we derive the splitting of energy levels to which we referred in the discussion of energy bands (Chap. 8).

14-2 The Hamiltonian for the hydrogen molecule-ion. Figure 14-1 represents the hydrogen molecule-ion, with $\mathbf{r}_{AB}$ joining proton A to proton B, and $\mathbf{r}_A$ and $\mathbf{r}_B$ joining the respective protons to the electron. We shall assume that the vibration of the system, that is, the motion of the protons toward each other, is essentially independent of the motion of the electron in the field of the

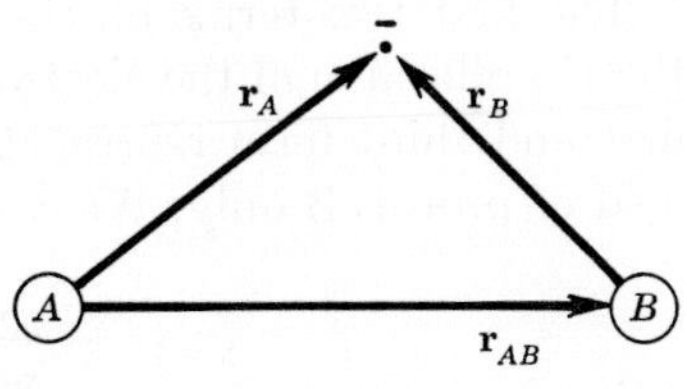

fig. 14-1 the hydrogen molecule-ion

protons, that is to say that we shall consider $\mathbf{r}_{AB}$ a fixed parameter of the system. Our results will be expressed as functions of this parameter $\mathbf{r}_{AB}$, and we shall finally study how these results are affected by changing $\mathbf{r}_{AB}$. This procedure is analogous to that used in isolating the rotational and vibrational motions of a diatomic molecule. Mathematically, our assumption is that the wave function of the electron is a certain function of $\mathbf{r}_{AB}$, and that the *form* of this function remains the same as the value of $\mathbf{r}_{AB}$ is changed.

The potential energy of the hydrogen molecule-ion is

$$V = \frac{e^2}{r_{AB}} - \frac{e^2}{r_A} - \frac{e^2}{r_B} \tag{14-1}$$

so that the Hamiltonian is

$$\mathcal{H} = \frac{\mathcal{P}^2}{2\mu_A} + \frac{\mathcal{P}^2}{2\mu_B} + \frac{\mathcal{P}^2}{2\mu_e} - \frac{e^2}{r_A} - \frac{e^2}{r_B} + \frac{e^2}{r_{AB}}$$

Since the distance r_{AB} is being held constant, the term e^2/r_{AB} does not need to be included in the Hamiltonian, and since the kinetic energy of the protons may be neglected, compared to that of the electrons, the Hamiltonian for the system reduces to

$$\mathcal{H} = \frac{\mathcal{P}^2}{2\mu_e} - \frac{e^2}{r_A} - \frac{e^2}{r_B} \tag{14-2}$$

---

problem 14-1. Where is the arbitrary zero point of energy chosen when the potential is given by Eq. (14-1)? Where is it chosen when the term e^2/r_{AB} is not included in the Hamiltonian? How does a constant term in the Hamiltonian affect the wave function?

The first two terms on the right-hand side of Eq. (14-2) represent the Hamiltonian of the electron in the field of proton A only, while the first and third term represent the Hamiltonian of the electron in the field of proton B only. We can rewrite Eq. (14-2) as follows:

$$\mathcal{H} = \mathcal{H}_A{}^0 + \mathcal{H}'_A \tag{14-3a}$$

$$\mathcal{H} = \mathcal{H}_B{}^0 + \mathcal{H}'_B \tag{14-3b}$$

$$\mathcal{H}_A{}^0 \equiv \frac{\mathcal{P}^2}{2\mu_e} - \frac{e^2}{r_A} \tag{14-4a}$$

$$\mathcal{H}_B{}^0 \equiv \frac{\mathcal{P}^2}{2\mu_e} - \frac{e^2}{r_B} \tag{14-4b}$$

$$\mathcal{H}'_A \equiv -\frac{e^2}{r_B} \tag{14-5a}$$

$$\mathcal{H}'_B \equiv -\frac{e^2}{r_A} \tag{14-5b}$$

As usual, we shall look for some stationary wave functions of the system: Schroedinger's equation can be written in two equivalent forms, using either Eq. (14-3*a*) or Eq. (14-3*b*),

$$\mathcal{H}_A{}^0\psi + \mathcal{H}'_A\psi = E\psi \tag{14-6a}$$
$$\mathcal{H}_B{}^0\psi + \mathcal{H}'_B\psi = E\psi \tag{14-6b}$$

Here, E represents the energy of a system of two protons and an electron for a fixed distance between the protons, where the interaction of the protons is not included.

If $\mathcal{H}'_A$ were zero, that is, if r_B were infinite, the Eq. (14-6*a*) would reduce to the relation for the hydrogen atom made up of proton A and the electron. Similarly, if $\mathcal{H}'_B$ were zero, then Eq. (14-6*b*) would reduce to that for the hydrogen atom made up of proton B and the electron. In the former case the function ψ would equal what we shall call $\psi_A{}^0$, in the latter it would equal $\psi_B{}^0$, where

$$\mathcal{H}_A{}^0\psi_A{}^0 = E^0\psi_A{}^0 \tag{14-7a}$$
$$\mathcal{H}_B{}^0\psi_B{}^0 = E^0\psi_B{}^0 \tag{14-7b}$$

and E^0 is an allowed energy of the hydrogen atom. The functions $\psi_A{}^0$ and $\psi_B{}^0$ differ from each other only by a displacement in space.

14-3 Solution of Schroedinger's equation. To find ψ, try a wave function of the hydrogen molecule-ion that is a linear combination of the atomic wave functions $\psi_A{}^0$ and $\psi_B{}^0$:

$$\psi \exp(-i\hbar^{-1}Et) = C_A(t)\psi_A{}^0 \exp(-i\hbar^{-1}E^0t) + C_B(t)\psi_B{}^0 \exp(-i\hbar^{-1}E^0t) \tag{14-8}$$

Here C_A and C_B are independent of coordinates, but may be dependent on time. Equation (14-8) was chosen intuitively as a trial function because at some times $C_A(t)$ might be nearly unity and $C_B(t)$ nearly zero, at which time the electron would be near proton A, forming a hydrogen atom slightly perturbed by proton B, while at another moment, the electron might be similarly situated near proton B to form a hydrogen atom. We shall, in a later section, study the behavior of the wave function as a function of time. First, however, we shall substitute Eq. (14-8) into Schroedinger's equation to see whether expressions can be found for $C_A(t)$ and $C_B(t)$ that make the function given by Eq. (14-8) a satisfactory stationary wave function.

When $\mathcal{H}$ operates on the right-hand side of Eq. (14-8), there results, since $\mathcal{H}$ is independent of time,

$$\begin{aligned} C_A(t) \exp(-i\hbar^{-1}E^0t)\mathcal{H}\psi_A{}^0 + C_B(t) \exp(-i\hbar^{-1}E^0t)\mathcal{H}\psi_B{}^0 \\ = E[C_A(t) \exp(-i\hbar^{-1}E^0t)\psi_A{}^0 + C_B(t) \exp(-i\hbar^{-1}E^0t)\psi_B{}^0] \end{aligned}$$

With the use of Eqs. (14-3*a*) and (14-7*a*), we write

$$\mathcal{H}\psi_A{}^0 = \mathcal{H}^0\psi_A{}^0 + \mathcal{H}'_A\psi_A{}^0 = E^0\psi_A{}^0 + \mathcal{H}'_A\psi_A{}^0 \tag{14-9a}$$

and similarly with the aid of Eqs. (14-3*b*) and (14-7*b*)

$$\mathcal{H}\psi_B{}^0 = \mathcal{H}^0\psi_B{}^0 + \mathcal{H}'_B\psi_B{}^0 = E^0\psi_B{}^0 + \mathcal{H}'_B\psi_B{}^0 \tag{14-9b}$$

Therefore

$$\begin{aligned} C_A(t) \exp(-i\hbar^{-1}E^0t)(E^0 + \mathcal{H}'_A - E)\psi_A{}^0 \\ + C_B(t) \exp(-i\hbar^{-1}E^0t)(E^0 + \mathcal{H}'_B - E)\psi_B{}^0 = 0 \end{aligned}$$

Dividing both sides of the last equation by $\exp -i\hbar^{-1}E^0t$ and multiplying the result in turn by $\overset{*}{\psi}{}_A^0$ and by $\overset{*}{\psi}{}_B^0$, we obtain the following two equivalent equations:

$$C_A(t)\overset{*}{\psi}{}_A^0(E^0 + \mathcal{H}'_A - E)\psi_A{}^0 + C_B(t)\overset{*}{\psi}{}_A^0(E^0 + \mathcal{H}'_B - E)\psi_B{}^0 = 0$$
$$C_A(t)\overset{*}{\psi}{}_B^0(E^0 + \mathcal{H}'_A - E)\psi_A{}^0 + C_B(t)\overset{*}{\psi}{}_B^0(E^0 + \mathcal{H}'_B - E)\psi_B{}^0 = 0$$

Integrating over all coordinates of the electron, gives

$$\begin{aligned} C_A(t)[(E^0 - E)\oint\overset{*}{\psi}{}_A^0\psi_A{}^0\,dq + \oint\overset{*}{\psi}{}_A^0\mathcal{H}'_A\psi_A{}^0\,dq] + \\ + C_B(t)[(E^0 - E)\oint\overset{*}{\psi}{}_A^0\psi_B{}^0\,dq + \oint\overset{*}{\psi}{}_A^0\mathcal{H}'_B\psi_B{}^0\,dq] = 0 \end{aligned} \tag{14-10a}$$

$$\begin{aligned} C_A(t)[(E^0 - E)\oint\overset{*}{\psi}{}_B^0\psi_A{}^0\,dq + \oint\overset{*}{\psi}{}_B^0\mathcal{H}'_A\psi_A{}^0\,dq] + \\ + C_B(t)[(E^0 - E)\oint\overset{*}{\psi}{}_B^0\psi_B{}^0\,dq + \oint\overset{*}{\psi}{}_B^0\mathcal{H}'_B\psi_B{}^0\,dq] = 0 \end{aligned} \tag{14-10b}$$

In these two equations there are six integrals that bear important relationships to each other. These relationships are derived by remembering that $\psi_A{}^0$ and $\psi_B{}^0$ differ from each other only by a translation in space. Therefore, upon integration over *all* of space,

$$\oint \overset{*}{\psi}{}_A^0 \psi_B{}^0 \, dq = \oint \overset{*}{\psi}{}_B^0 \psi_A{}^0 \, dq \equiv \Delta \qquad (14\text{-}11)$$

$$\oint \overset{*}{\psi}{}_A^0 \mathcal{H}'_A \psi_A{}^0 \, dq = \oint \overset{*}{\psi}{}_B^0 \mathcal{H}'_B \psi_B{}^0 \, dq \equiv J \qquad (14\text{-}12)$$

$$\oint \overset{*}{\psi}_A \mathcal{H}'_B \psi_B{}^0 \, dq = \oint \overset{*}{\psi}{}_B^0 \mathcal{H}'_A \psi_A{}^0 \, dq \equiv K \qquad (14\text{-}13)$$

Furthermore, we shall assume $\psi_A{}^0$ and $\psi_B{}^0$ normalized:

$$\oint \overset{*}{\psi}{}_A^0 \psi_A{}^0 \, dq = \oint \overset{*}{\psi}{}_B^0 \psi_B{}^0 \, dq = 1$$

---

problem 14-2. If $\psi_A{}^0$ and $\psi_B{}^0$ represent ground states of the hydrogen atom, plot in one diagram the values of $\psi_A{}^0$ and of $\psi_B{}^0$ as a function of distance from A and B in any plane that contains both A and B.

Show that $\psi_A{}^0$ and $\psi_B{}^0$ are generally not orthogonal. For what value of r_{AB} are they orthogonal? What physical structure results when r_{AB} approaches zero? Show the Bohr radius in your drawing. (*Hint:* Consult Chap. 13 for the form of $\psi_A{}^0$ and the Bohr radius.)

When Eqs. (14-11) to (14-13) are substituted in Eqs. (14-10*a*) and (14-10*b*),

$$C_A(t)[(E^0 - E) + J] + C_B(t)[(E^0 - E)\,\Delta + K] = 0 \qquad (14\text{-}14a)$$

$$C_A(t)[(E^0 - E)\,\Delta + K] + C_B(t)[(E^0 - E) + J] = 0 \qquad (14\text{-}14b)$$

If C_A and C_B do not equal zero, the determinant of their coefficients must vanish:

$$(E^\circ - E) + J = \pm[(E^\circ - E)\Delta + K]$$

Therefore

$$(E^\circ - E)(1 \mp \Delta) = -J \pm K$$

and

$$E = E^\circ + \frac{J \mp K}{1 \mp \Delta} \qquad (14\text{-}15)$$

Thus we find that there are two stationary states, both differing in energy from E^0.

Since $\mathcal{H}'_A$ and $\mathcal{H}'_B$ represent the attraction between electron and proton, J and K are negative. Consequently, the lowest energy of the hydrogen molecule-ion is lower than that of the hydrogen atom. It should be recalled, however, that the energy given by Eq. (14-15) does not include the repulsion between the protons. In the next section we shall include this repulsion to find the energies of H_2^+ as a function of r_{AB}. We shall see that the net energy is negative for a large range of r_{AB} values so that the hydrogen molecule-ion is more stable than the hydrogen atom.

14-4 Energy as a function of proton-proton distance. When the integrals for J, K, and Δ are evaluated,† using for $\psi_A{}^0$ and $\psi_B{}^0$ the ground-state wave functions of the hydrogen atoms,

$$\begin{aligned} J &= -\frac{e^2}{a_0}\left[\frac{a_0}{r_{AB}} - \left(1 + \frac{a_0}{r_{AB}}\right)\exp - \frac{2r_{AB}}{a_0}\right] \\ K &= -\frac{e^2}{a_0}\left(1 + \frac{r_{AB}}{a_0}\right)\exp - \frac{r_{AB}}{a_0} \\ \Delta &= \left(1 + \frac{r_{AB}}{a_0} + \frac{r_{AB}{}^2}{3a_0{}^2}\right)\exp - \frac{r_{AB}}{a_0} \end{aligned}$$

where a_0 is the Bohr radius for the ground state of the hydrogen atom. When we analyze the various terms in Eq. (14-15), we recognize in E^0 the energy of the electron in the ground state of the hydrogen atom and in J the coulomb attraction of the electron in a hydrogen atom for a second proton. The integral K, which gives the hydrogen molecule-ion additional stability, has no classical interpretation; it expresses the fact that the electron might equally well be associated with proton A as with proton B. Δ represents the effect of the overlapping of ψ_A and ψ_B; except as $r_{AB} \to \infty$, Δ is not zero, since $\psi_A{}^0$ and $\psi_B{}^0$ are positive over the range r_{AB}.

Table 14-1 gives the values of the parameters of Eq. (14-15) for different values of r_{AB}/a_0. Figure 14-2 shows how both E_+ and E_- change for different fixed values of r_{AB}. The zero of energy is here chosen as the energy of the hydrogen atom in its ground state, namely, as $-e^2/2a_0$. The E_+ state is seen to be the more stable; in fact, it is more stable than the ground state of H, for a large range of r_{AB} values. The minimum in the E_+ curve corresponds to the equilibrium internuclear distance of H_2^+, $r_{AB} = 2.5\ a_0$; this is the internuclear distance

† See H. Eyring, J. Walker and G. E. Kimball, "Quantum Chemistry," pp. 196, 197, John Wiley & Sons, Inc., New York, 1954.

for which H_2^+ is most stable. The E_- curve, on the other hand, has no minimum; whenever a H_2^+ is formed corresponding to that electronic energy and internuclear distance, it will have only a transitory existence.

Since E^0 represents the energy of a hydrogen atom in its ground state, it also represents the energy of a proton and a normal hydrogen atom at an infinite distance apart; these two species may be considered

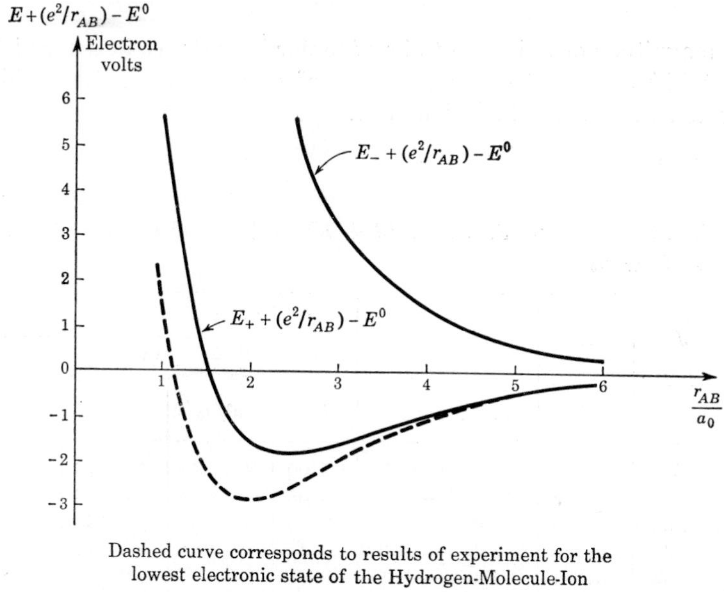

fig. 14-2 energy of the hydrogen molecule-ion as a function of r_{AB}/a_0

to be the dissociation products of H_2^+. The difference between the values of the ordinate for the equilibrium value of r_{AB} and for r_{AB} equal to infinity, gives the dissociation energy of H_2^+ into H^+ and H; the dissociation energy of H_2^+ is thus 1.77 ev.

When the change of the electron cloud of a hydrogen atom by the proximity of a proton is included in the analysis, a more complicated wave function results; a treatment similar to that used above gives a dissociation energy of 2.789 ev (instead of 1.77 ev); the equilibrium internuclear distance is found to be $2a_0$ (instead of 2.5 a_0). The calculated values using the more detailed wave function are in agreement with the results of experiment. The simple wave function used, nevertheless gives a strikingly good approximation, as is observed in Fig. 14-2. The agreement is particularly good for the equilibrium distance when it is recalled that according to the uncertainty principle the standard deviation from the equilibrium distance is considerable.

problem 14-3. Using the numerical data of Table 14-1, fit a parabola to the region near the minimum of the $(E_+ + e^2/r_{AB} - E^0)$ curve of Fig. 14-2. Having thus approximated this region by a linear harmonic oscillator, estimate the standard deviation in r_{AB}. (Refer to Chap. 5 for the standard deviation from the equilibrium position of a LHO).

The magnitude of K is seen to be of major importance in determining the stability of the H_2^+ for all values of r_{AB}; no stable H_2^+ could be expected without the inclusion of K.

table 14-1

calculated values of J, K, Δ, $(J + K)/(1 + \Delta)$, e^2/r_{AB} for different values of r_{AB}/a_0

$\dfrac{r_{AB}}{a_0}$	J	K	Δ	$\dfrac{J+K}{1+\Delta}$	$\dfrac{e^2}{r_{AB}}$	$\dfrac{J+K}{1+\Delta} + \dfrac{e^2}{r_{AB}} = E_+ + \dfrac{e^2}{r_{AB}} - E_0$		
	e^2/a_0	e^2/a_0	......	e^2/a_0	e^2/a_0	e^2/a_0	$e^2/2a_0$	ev
1	−0.730	−0.736	0.858	−0.791	+1.00	+0.209	+0.418	+5.7
2	−0.4725	−0.405	0.584	−0.554	+0.05	−0.054	−0.108	−1.46
2.5	−0.3905	−0.288	0.458	−0.465	+0.40	−0.065	−0.130	−1.77
3	−0.330	−0.200	0.350	−0.392	+0.33	−0.062	−0.124	−1.69
4	−0.250	−0.0915	0.189	−0.288	+0.25	−0.038	−0.076	−1.03
5	−0.200	−0.0404	0.0863	−0.220	+0.20	−0.020	−0.040	−0.543
6	−0.1667	−0.0174	0.045	−0.176	+0.167	−0.009	−0.018	−0.245
30	−0.033	-2.83×10^{-12}	3.02×10^{-11}					
∞	0	0	0	0	0	0	0	0

Each curve in Fig. 14-2 represents the change in energy with nuclear separation for a given electronic excitation of the H_2^+ molecule, and so gives a representation of $V(r)$. Note that the curves are not parabolas, as would be the case if the molecule behaved as a LHO. It is only near the region of the equilibrium nuclear distance that the potential function approaches that of the LHO.

problem 14-4. Calculate the ionization potential of H_2^+ using the Born cycle. [The dissociation energy of H_2^+ is 2.789 ev; the dissociation energy of H_2 is 4.478 ev, and the ionization potential of H is 13.56 ev.]

14-5 The stationary wave functions. The condition for non-vanishing $C_A(t)$ and $C_B(t)$ is given by Eq. (14-15); as long as Eq. (14-15) holds, Eqs. (14-14*a*) and (14-14*b*) both give the following relation between C_A and C_B:

$$C_A = \mp C_B \equiv C \tag{14-16}$$

When Eqs. (14-15) and (14-16) are substituted into Eq. (14-8), the following expression is obtained for the wave function of the hydrogen molecule-ion:

$$\psi \exp\left[-i\hbar^{-1}\left(E^0 + \frac{J \mp K}{1 \mp \Delta}\right)t\right] = $$
$$= C(t)[\psi_A{}^0 \exp(-i\hbar^{-1}E^0 t) \mp \psi_B{}^0 \exp(i\hbar^{-1}E^0 t)]$$

therefore $\quad \psi = C(t) \exp\left(i\hbar^{-1}\dfrac{J \mp K}{1 \mp \Delta}t\right)(\psi_A{}^0 \mp \psi_B{}^0)$

Since ψ, $\psi_A{}^0$, and $\psi_B{}^0$ have been defined as independent of time,

$$C(t) \propto \exp\left(-i\hbar^{-1}\frac{J \mp K}{1 \mp \Delta}t\right)$$

To normalize ψ, choose the proportionality constant such that

$$C(t) = \frac{1}{\sqrt{2(1 \mp \Delta)}} \exp\left(-i\hbar^{-1}\frac{J \mp K}{1 \mp \Delta}t\right)$$

Thus $\quad \psi = \dfrac{1}{\sqrt{2(1 \mp \Delta)}}(\psi_A{}^0 \mp \psi_B{}^0) \qquad (14\text{-}17)$

and using Eq. (14-15),

$$\Psi = \frac{1}{\sqrt{2(1 \mp \Delta)}}(\psi_A{}^0 \mp \psi_B{}^0) \exp -i\hbar^{-1}\left(E^0 + \frac{J \mp K}{1 \mp \Delta}\right)t \tag{14-18}$$

that is,

$$\Psi_+ = \frac{1}{\sqrt{2(1 + \Delta)}}(\psi_A{}^0 + \psi_B{}^0) \exp -i\hbar^{-1}\left(E^0 + \frac{J + K}{1 + \Delta}\right)t \tag{14-18+}$$

$$\Psi_- = \frac{1}{\sqrt{2(1 - \Delta)}}(\psi_A{}^0 - \psi_B{}^0) \exp -i\hbar^{-1}\left(E^0 + \frac{J - K}{1 - \Delta}\right)t \tag{14-18−}$$

Thus, two wave functions are necessary to describe the proposed model of the $H_2{}^+$; Ψ_+ represents the state with the lowest energy E_+.

---

problem 14-5. Prove that, if $\psi_A{}^0$ and $\psi_B{}^0$ are normalized, Eqs. (14-18+) and (14-18−) represent normalized wave functions.

In Fig. 14-3 we have sketched the probability density for both stationary states as a function of position along the axis connecting proton A and proton B, on the assumption that $\psi_A{}^0$ and $\psi_B{}^0$ represent

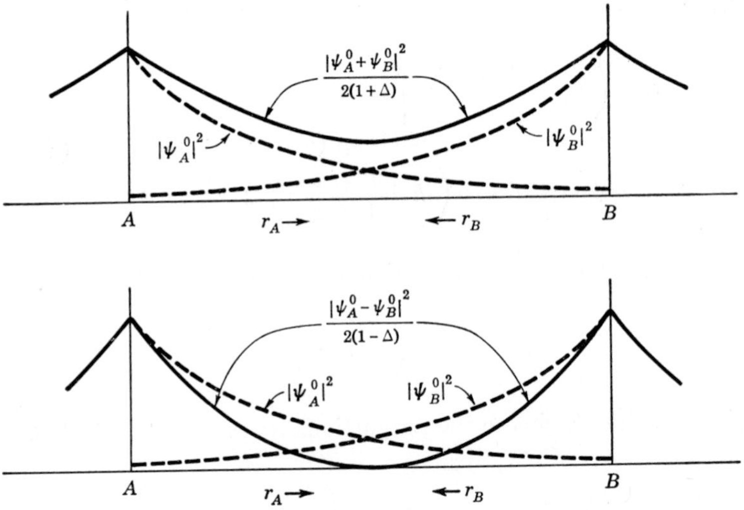

fig. 14-3 probability density for two different states of the electron in the hydrogen molecule-ion

the ground state of a hydrogen atom. It is observed that halfway between the two protons, where $r_A = r_B$, $\psi_A{}^0 = \psi_B{}^0$. Therefore, the probability of finding the electron halfway between the protons, is zero for the higher-energy state, while for the lower-energy state the probability is finite. In the lower-energy state the two protons are shielded from each other by the electron, while in the higher-energy state the protons are not shielded from one another. In Fig. 14-3 we have also shown by dotted lines the probability densities of the electron in a normal hydrogen atom. Note that in the two stationary states of the hydrogen molecule-ion the probability densities halfway between the protons are respectively greater than and less than that for an electron of a hydrogen atom at the same distance from the proton. It is not surprising, therefore, that one of the states of the molecule-ion is more, the other less, stable than the ground state of the hydrogen atom. The state represented by Ψ_+ has a greater negative charge between the nuclei than has the state represented by Ψ_-, and this charge may be said to shield the protons from one another. The attraction between this negative charge and the proton charges may be considered as effecting the stability of the Ψ_+ state. The two stationary states are sometimes referred to as "bonding" and "antibonding" states of the hydrogen molecule-ion.

14-6 Time-dependent wave functions of the hydrogen molecule-ion. We can find the behavior of the wave function as a function of time for nonstationary states if we give a single initial condition. Let us suppose that before time $t = 0$ proton B were placed at an infinite distance from a hydrogen atom A in its ground state. At time $t = 0$ proton B is brought to a distance r_{AB} from the proton of atom A. We assume that the proton B does not have enough kinetic energy to raise the electron in the atom to its first excited ($2s$) state, so that $\Psi(t = 0) = \psi_A{}^0$.

This assumption is reasonable because at least 10 ev are required to excite the electron into its $2s$ state, while only about 3 ev are sufficient for removal of a proton from a hydrogen molecule-ion (see Sec. 13-6 and Fig. 14-2).

Therefore, when we expand $\Psi(t)$ in terms of the stationary wave functions, only two states, namely the lowest bonding and antibonding states of the hydrogen molecule-ion need be considered:

$$\Psi(t) = \phi_+\Psi_+ + \phi_-\Psi_- = \frac{\phi_+}{\sqrt{2(1+\Delta)}}(\psi_A{}^0 + \psi_B{}^0)\exp(-i\hbar^{-1}E_+t) + $$
$$+ \frac{\phi_-}{\sqrt{2(1-\Delta)}}(\psi_A{}^0 - \psi_B{}^0)\exp -(i\hbar^{-1}E_-t)$$

Since $\Psi(t = 0) = \psi_A{}^0$, we find

$$\psi_A{}^0 = \frac{\phi_+}{\sqrt{2(1+\Delta)}}(\psi_A{}^0 + \psi_B{}^0) + \frac{\phi_-}{\sqrt{2(1-\Delta)}}(\psi_A{}^0 - \psi_B{}^0)$$

Equating coefficients of $\psi_A{}^0$ and $\psi_B{}^0$ on both sides of this last equation gives

$$1 = \frac{\phi_+}{\sqrt{2(1+\Delta)}} + \frac{\phi_-}{\sqrt{2(1-\Delta)}}$$
$$0 = \frac{\phi_+}{\sqrt{2(1+\Delta)}} - \frac{\phi_-}{\sqrt{2(1-\Delta)}}$$
$$\phi_+ = \sqrt{\frac{1+\Delta}{2}} \quad (14\text{-}19+); \qquad \phi_- = \sqrt{\frac{1-\Delta}{2}} \quad (14\text{-}19-)$$

Therefore

$$\Psi(t) = \frac{\psi_A{}^0 + \psi_B{}^0}{2} \exp(-i\hbar^{-1}E_+t) + \frac{\psi_A{}^0 - \psi_B{}^0}{2} \exp(i\hbar^{-1}E_-t) \quad (14\text{-}20)$$

It will now be interesting to determine at what time, if any, $|\Psi|$ might equal $|\psi_B{}^0|$. We would then solve the following equation for t_B:

$$\psi_B{}^0 = \frac{\psi_A{}^0 + \psi_B{}^0}{2} \exp(-i\hbar^{-1}E_+t_B) + \frac{\psi_A{}^0 - \psi_B{}^0}{2} \exp(-i\hbar^{-1}E_-t_B)$$

Equating coefficients of $\psi_A{}^0$ on both sides of the equation gives

$$0 = \tfrac{1}{2} \exp(-i\hbar^{-1}E_+t_B) + \tfrac{1}{2} \exp(-i\hbar^{-1}E_-t_B)$$
$$\exp[-i\hbar^{-1}(E_+ - E_-)t_B] = -1$$

and $(E_+ - E_-)t_B = (2n + 1)\pi\hbar$, where n is an integer.

Therefore $$t_B = \frac{(2n+1)\pi\hbar}{E_+ - E_-}$$

It can similarly be shown that $|\Psi| = |\psi_A{}^0|$ whenever $t = t_A$, where

$$t_A = \frac{2n\pi\hbar}{E_+ - E_-}$$

Thus $|\Psi|$ alternately equals $|\psi_A{}^0|$ and $|\psi_B{}^0|$, oscillating between them with a period equal to $2(t_A - t_B) = 2\pi\hbar/(E_- - E_+) = h/(E_- - E_+)$.

14-7 The interaction of electromagnetic radiation with $H_2{}^+$. Let us consider two models for the interaction between electromagnetic radiation and hydrogen molecule-ions. The first is that of Chap. 5, where we considered the admixture of two stationary states to form a nonstationary state. It was shown there that if we consider a frequency E/h to be associated with every stationary state whose energy is E, then the admixture of stationary states may create an oscillating dipole, whose frequency of oscillation is just the "beat frequency" between the admixed stationary states. In the case of the hydrogen molecule-ion there are two low-energy states, one with a frequency E_-/h, the other with a frequency E_+/h; the "beat frequency" is $(E_- - E_+)/h$. In the presence of radiation of just this frequency, resonance would occur, and radiation energy would be transferred to the $H_2{}^+$.

Another model for the interaction between radiation and H_2^+ is concerned directly with the behavior of the electron. In Sec. 14-6 we showed that an electron which is initially near proton A will oscillate between the protons with a frequency $(E_- - E_+)/h$. Thus an oscillating dipole moment could be associated with the oscillating electron; since the natural frequency of the oscillation is $(E_- - E_+)/h$, resonance would occur here if radiation of just this frequency is present.

Since the state with energy E_- is unstable for all values of r_{AB}, absorption of the radiation, for either model, would cause dissociation of a hydrogen molecule-ion into a hydrogen atom and a proton. This process of photodecomposition is quite common for molecular systems.

---

problem 14-6. Show that selection rules do not preclude the transition from a bonding to an antibonding state. (*Hint:* Determine whether the wave functions are even or odd functions of the distance from a point halfway between the protons.)

---

problem 14-7. Show that Ψ_+ and Ψ_-, as given by Eqs. (14-18+) and (14-18−), are orthogonal to each other.

---

problem 14-8. (*a*) Find the expectation value and the standard deviation of the energy in terms of the ground-state energy of the hydrogen atom, and of J, K, and Δ, for the state whose wave function is given by Eq. (14-20). [*Hint:* Remember the equation

$$\bar{f} = \frac{\sum_n |\phi_n|^2 f_n}{\sum_n |\phi_n|^2}$$

and Eq. (14-19).]

(*b*) Calculate the magnitude of the standard deviation for $r_{AB}/a_0 = 2$; for $r_{AB}/a_0 = 30$.

(*c*) Show in a diagram: $\bar{E}$, E_-, E_+ for $r_{AB}/a_0 = 2$; for $r_{AB}/a_0 = 30$.

(*d*) Draw conclusions from your diagrams about the probability of the electron jumping from one proton to the other and of the electron leaving both protons.

14-8 The limiting case of very large proton-proton distance. When r_{AB} is made to go to infinity,

$$\lim_{r_{AB}\to\infty} J = 0 \qquad \lim_{r_{AB}\to\infty} K = 0 \qquad \lim_{r_{AB}\to\infty} \Delta = 0$$

Therefore $\lim E_+ = \lim E_- = E^0$, so that removal of the proton from a H_2^+ to infinity simply leaves a hydrogen atom in its ground state. When E_+ and E_- approach E^0, then Eq. (14-20) reduces to

$$\Psi(t) = \psi_A{}^0 \exp i\hbar^{-1}E^0t \tag{14-21}$$

which is just the stationary hydrogen-atom wave function. Also the frequency with which the electron oscillates between the protons decreases as r_{AB} is increased, that is as E_+ and E_- approach each other. For a large value of r_{AB} the electron will only oscillate very slowly between A and B, and as r_{AB} increases to infinity, the electron no longer oscillates between A and B and H_2^+ as such no longer exists.

---

problem 14-9. Estimate the period of oscillation of the electron in the hydrogen molecule-ion for the following cases:

(*a*) $r_{AB} = \frac{1}{2}a_0$
(*b*) $r_{AB} = a_0$
(*c*) $r_{AB} = 2.5a_0$
(*d*) $r_{AB} = 8a_0$
(*e*) $r_{AB} = 30a_0$

Plot the period of oscillation as a function of (r_{AB}/a_0).

14-9 Resonance energy: the double-well potential. When a molecular system may have more than one equally probable configuration (different locations of the electrons with respect to one another and/or the nuclei), then the molecular system resonating between these various configurations is more stable than any of the individual configurations. In the case of H_2^+, the two equivalent configurations are shown in Fig. 14-4. The system may be said to "resonate"

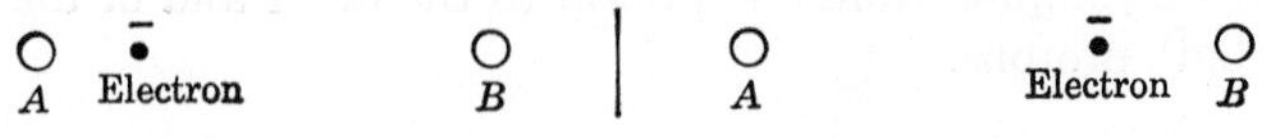

fig. 14-4 two equivalent configurations of the hydrogen molecule-ion

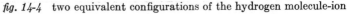

between these configurations with the frequencies calculated above. As r_{AB} is decreased to near a_0, the probability of the passage of the electron from one nucleus to the other becomes appreciable and the original single-valued energy level, E^0, is split into two levels, E_+ and E_-, one level with energy higher than E^0, the other with energy lower than E^0. This is a general feature of systems in which resonance occurs.

It should be noted that except for the illustrative sketches, we have not used the specific form of the functions $\psi_A{}^0$ and $\psi_B{}^0$ in this chapter. Therefore the discussion should be applicable to any system capable of being in two or more stationary states whose wave functions differ only by a displacement in space. Another example of such a system is the ammonia molecule, NH_3. Here the nitrogen atom is stable on either side of a triangle of protons and is able to "jump through" this triangle from a stable position on one side to a stable position on the other side. The molecule is like an umbrella that is being inverted; when the nitrogen and hydrogens are coplanar, the potential-energy function is at a maximum. The beat frequency between the two lowest-energy states of the NH_3 molecule lies in the microwave region and is very sharp and reproducible. Therefore this frequency is used as a standard of time ("ammonia clock").

Both in the hydrogen molecule-ion and in the ammonia molecule, there are two degenerate configurations for which the potential energy is a minimum; to pass from one configuration to another, the molecule passes through a potential-maximum. For this reason this type of system is often referred to as a "double-well" system.

In Chap. 8 we noted that electrons in an infinite linear array of identical wells have an "infinite" number of energy levels in a finite range of allowed energies. At that time we pointed out that a finite array of identical wells has a finite number of energy levels for each energy level in an isolated well. This statement has now been demonstrated for the case of two wells.

14-10 Summary. We have dealt with the principle of bonding atoms together to form molecules. We found that a proton can be bound to a hydrogen atom by the phenomenon of resonance of the electron between the two protons. The stability of the hydrogen molecule-ion has been related to the oscillation of its electron between its two protons. The question might be asked whether three protons plus an electron would be more stable than the hydrogen molecule-ion; while the calculation of the stability would be beyond the scope of this text, a negative answer must be given. The additional proton-proton repulsions would overcome the additional resonance energy.

the separation of variables

chapter

15

15-1 Introduction. In Chaps. 10, 11, and 13 we considered the motion of a single particle in three dimensions. In later chapters we shall discuss the motion of several particles that constitute an atomic system. In each case, Schroedinger's equation is a partial differential equation, containing several independent variables. Both in the example of the three-dimensional harmonic oscillator and in that of the spherical coulomb field we reduced the multidimensional problem to a combination of single-dimensional problems, and in each case a quantum number resulted from each single-dimensional problem. We saw that in the case of the isotropic three-dimensional harmonic oscillator, the problem could be separated into that of three degenerate linear oscillators with the quantum numbers n_x, n_y, and n_z, but that it could also be solved as a central-field problem, with the quantum numbers l, m, and another quantum number for the radial motion. In view of the multiparticle problems that are to be considered in later chapters, we shall devote the present chapter to a review of the separation of independent variables used in chaps. 10, 11, and 13 and then generalize this procedure for application to more complex systems.

15-2 Eigenfunctions and separation of variables. It should be recalled that in the discussion of the central field we first found eigenfunctions of the $\mathcal{L}_z$ operator. Since the $\mathcal{L}_z$ operator depends only on the spherical coordinate ϕ, the condition that a wave function be an eigenfunction of $\mathcal{L}_z$ imposes a restriction only on the ϕ dependence of the wave function, which can be valid for any properly behaved function of the coordinates r and θ. Thus, we found that if ψ is an eigenfunction of $\mathfrak{L}_z$, then $\psi = F(r,\theta) \exp im\phi$, where m is an integer and $F(r,\theta)$ is any properly behaved function of r and θ. By requiring the wave function to be an eigenfunction of $\mathfrak{L}_z$, we isolated the problem of determining its ϕ dependence. The assumption that ψ be an eigenfunction of $\mathfrak{L}_z$ necessarily implies that ψ can be expressed as the product of a function that is independent of ϕ and a function that depends on ϕ only. Similarly, the requirement that ψ be an eigenfunction of $\mathfrak{L}^2$ and the fact that the operator $\mathfrak{L}^2$ depends on the coordinates θ and ϕ only, but not on r, produced the factorization $\psi = R(r)G(\theta,\phi)$. Since $\mathfrak{L}^2$ and $\mathfrak{L}_z$ commute and therefore can have a common set of eigenfunctions, the two expressions $\psi = F(r,\theta) \exp im\phi$ and $\psi = R(r)G(\theta,\phi)$ were combined, and led to the conclusion that all wave functions that are eigenfunctions of both $\mathfrak{L}_z$ and $\mathfrak{L}^2$ can be factored into a function of r only, a function of θ only, and a function of ϕ only.

Wave functions are not necessarily eigenfunctions of $\mathfrak{L}^2$ and $\mathfrak{L}_z$. Since $\mathfrak{L}^2$ and $\mathfrak{L}_z$ are Hermitian, however, their eigenfunctions provide an orthogonal set into which any wave function can be expanded. Consider as an example the wave function for the $2s$ and $2p$ states of an electron in a central field, together with the four $2s2p^3$ hybrid orbitals. The angular dependences of the wave functions $\psi_{nl}{}^m$ are as follows (see Chap. 11):

$$\left.\begin{aligned} \psi_{20}{}^0 &= 1 \\ \psi_{21}{}^1 &= \sin\theta \exp i\phi \\ \psi_{21}{}^0 &= \cos\theta \\ \psi_{21}{}^{-1} &= \sin\theta \exp -i\phi \end{aligned}\right\} \quad \text{(unnormalized)} \qquad (15\text{-}1)$$

and for the four sp^3 orbitals they are of the form:

$$\psi_{2s2p^3} = a\psi_{20}{}^0 + b\psi_{21}{}^1 + c\psi_{21}{}^0 + d\psi_{21}{}^{-1} \qquad (15\text{-}2)$$

where a, b, c, and d are independent of the angles θ and ϕ. Each sp^3 orbital is described by a different set of values of a, b, c, and d.

The functions $\psi_{20}{}^0$, $\psi_{21}{}^1$, $\psi_{21}{}^0$ and $\psi_{21}{}^{-1}$ are all eigenfunctions of $\mathfrak{L}_z$ and $\mathfrak{L}^2$; in each of these functions the variables θ and ϕ are separated into separate factors. The hybrid wave functions are *not* eigenfunctions of $\mathfrak{L}_z$, and in these wave functions the variables θ and ϕ are *not* separated into separate factors, as can be seen by substituting

Eq. (15-1) into Eq. (15-2):

$$\begin{aligned}\psi_{2s2p^3} &= a + b \sin\theta \exp i\phi + c\cos\theta + d\sin\theta \exp -i\phi \\ &= a + c\cos\theta + \sin\theta(b \exp i\phi + d \exp -i\phi)\end{aligned}$$

The wave functions describing the sp^3 hybrid orbitals are thus examples in which *each term* is separable into a factor independent of ϕ and a factor independent of θ, but where the coordinates are not separated in the *wave function itself.*

Another example of the separation of variables is the system of eigenfunctions of the energy operator. It was shown (Chap. 5) that any wave function can be expressed in terms of eigenfunctions of $\mathcal{E}$ and that each eigenfunction of $\mathcal{E}$ is a stationary function. In stationary wave functions (of the form ψT, see Chapters 2 and 5) the time occurs in only one of the two factors and not in the other one. Nonstationary wave functions can be expanded as linear combinations of stationary functions, but the time is not separated out in nonstationary wave functions themselves (see Prob. 2-16).

The procedure followed so far for solving Schroedinger's equation in several independent variables is summarized in the following steps:

1. We found operators that commute with the Hamiltonian operator, but contain fewer independent variables. For example, in the three-dimensional harmonic oscillator we found the three Hamiltonians for the three independent linear oscillators; for the central field, we found $\mathcal{L}_z$ and $\mathcal{L}^2$.
2. We found the eigenfunctions of these operators.
3. We combined the functions found in step 2 into a wave function.

In Sec. 15-3 we shall deal with a particularly important special case of the separation of variables, namely, the case in which an operator containing several independent variables can be written as the sum of operators, each of which contains only a fraction of all independent variables.

---

problem 15-1. A particle is free to move inside a rectangular box whose sides are respectively, 1 A, 2 A, and 3 A long. The particle is restricted to this box, .o.w., the probability of finding it anywhere outside the box is identically zero.

(*a*) Write Schroedinger's time-dependent equation for this particle.

(*b*) Separate the independent variables.

(*c*) Find an expression for all stationary-state energy values of this particle. How many quantum numbers are needed for this expression?

(*d*) Find the kinetic energy associated with the motion of the particle in directions parallel to the edges of the box, and compare these energy values with the result of *c*.

(*e*) Write the most general expression for a wave function describing the motion of this particle.

15-3 Separation of variables in an operator. In the case of the three-dimensional harmonic oscillator, the Hamiltonian operator was written as the sum of three terms:

$$\begin{aligned}\mathcal{H} &= -\frac{\hbar^2}{2\mu}\nabla^2 + V = -\frac{\hbar^2}{2\mu}\left(\frac{\partial^2}{\partial x^2} + \frac{\partial^2}{\partial y^2} + \frac{\partial^2}{\partial z^2}\right) + \\ &\quad + \tfrac{1}{2}(k_x x^2 + k_y y^2 + k_z z^2) = \left(-\frac{\hbar^2}{2\mu}\frac{\partial^2}{\partial x^2} + \frac{1}{2}k_x x^2\right) + \\ &\quad + \left(-\frac{\hbar^2}{2\mu}\frac{\partial^2}{\partial y^2} + \tfrac{1}{2}k_y y^2\right) + \left(-\frac{\hbar^2}{2\mu}\frac{\partial^2}{\partial z^2} + \frac{1}{2}k_z z^2\right) \equiv \\ &\equiv \mathcal{H}_x + \mathcal{H}_y + \mathcal{H}_z\end{aligned}$$

---

problem 15-2. (*a*) Show that $\mathcal{H}$, $\mathcal{H}_x$, $\mathcal{H}_y$, and $\mathcal{H}_z$ all commute with each other.

(*b*) Show that all eigenfunctions of $\mathcal{H}_x$ are nondegenerate.

Since $\mathcal{H}$ commutes with each of $\mathcal{H}_x$, $\mathcal{H}_y$, and $\mathcal{H}_z$, and all eigenfunctions of $\mathcal{H}_x$ are nondegenerate, all eigenfunctions of $\mathcal{H}_x$, (and similarly of $\mathcal{H}_y$ and $\mathcal{H}_z$), are eigenfunctions of $\mathcal{H}$. It was shown in Sec. 10-11 that the product of eigenfunctions of $\mathcal{H}_x$, $\mathcal{H}_y$, and $\mathcal{H}_z$, respectively, is an eigenfunction of $\mathcal{H}$. We shall now generalize this statement.

***theorem* 15-1.** If $\mathfrak{F}$ is an operator containing a number of independent variables, and $\mathfrak{F}_1, \mathfrak{F}_2, \ldots, \mathfrak{F}_i, \ldots$ are operators such that $\mathfrak{F} = \sum_i \mathfrak{F}_i$, and such that no independent variable occurs in more than one of the operators $\mathfrak{F}_i$, then the product of respective eigenfunctions of the operators $\mathfrak{F}_i$ is an eigenfunction of $\mathfrak{F}$.

***proof of theorem* 15-1.** If each function ψ_i is an eigenfunction of an operator $\mathfrak{F}_i$, then $\mathfrak{F}_i\psi_i = \bar{\bar{f}}_i\psi_i$, where ψ_i is *independent* of all independent variables that do *not* occur in $\mathfrak{F}_i$.

Define ψ as the product of all functions ψ_i:

$$\psi = \prod_i \psi_i$$

Then

$$\begin{aligned}\mathfrak{F}\psi &= \mathfrak{F}\prod_i \psi_i = \Big[\sum_i \mathfrak{F}_i\Big]\Big[\prod_i \psi_i\Big] \\ &= (\mathfrak{F}_1 + \mathfrak{F}_2 + \cdots + \mathfrak{F}_i + \cdots)(\psi_1\psi_2\psi_3 \cdots) \\ &= \mathfrak{F}_1(\psi_1\psi_2\psi_3 \cdots) + \mathfrak{F}_2(\psi_1\psi_2\psi_3 \cdots) + \cdots + \mathfrak{F}_i(\psi_1\psi_2\psi_3 \cdots) \\ &= \sum_i [\mathfrak{F}_i\psi]\end{aligned}$$

Since the independent variables occurring in $\mathfrak{F}_1$ only occur in ψ_1, but not in ψ_2, ψ_3, etc., and similar statements apply to $\mathfrak{F}_2$, $\mathfrak{F}_3$, etc.,

$$\begin{aligned}\mathfrak{F}_1\psi &= \mathfrak{F}_1\psi_1\psi_2\psi_3 \cdots = (\psi_2\psi_3 \cdots)\mathfrak{F}_1\psi_1 = (\psi_2\psi_3 \cdots)\bar{\bar{f}}_1\psi_1 \\ &= \bar{\bar{f}}_1\psi_1\psi_2\psi_3 \cdots = \bar{\bar{f}}_1\psi\end{aligned}$$

and similarly in general,

$$\mathfrak{F}_i\psi = \bar{\bar{f}}_i\psi$$

Therefore

$$\mathfrak{F}\psi = \sum_i \mathfrak{F}_i\psi = \sum_i \bar{\bar{f}}_i\psi = \Big(\sum_i \bar{\bar{f}}_i\Big)\psi$$

and hence $\psi = \prod_i \psi_i$ is an eigenfunction of $\mathfrak{F} = \sum_i \mathfrak{F}_i$.

corollary. The eigenvalue of ψ is $\sum_i \bar{\bar{f}}_i$.

---

problem 15-3. Two particles are confined to move along a straight line. The particles do not exert forces on each other, and are not subject to external forces. Write Schroedinger's equation for this two-particle system, separate variables, and write a wave function describing this system.

---

problem 15-4. Two particles move in three dimensions. They are not subject to external forces, but there is a harmonic force between the particles. [If the particles are at positions located by vectors $\mathbf{r}_1$ and $\mathbf{r}_2$, then the potential energy of their interaction is $\frac{1}{2}k(\mathbf{r}_1 - \mathbf{r}_2)^2$.]

(*a*) Write Schroedinger's equation for this system.
(*b*) How many independent variables are there?
(*c*) Are these variables separable?
(*d*) Using the following coordinate transformation (m_1 and m_2 are the masses of the two particles, respectively):

$$x = \frac{m_1 x_1 + m_2 x_2}{m_1 + m_2} \qquad q_x = x_2 - x_1 \qquad \text{etc.}$$

write the Hamiltonian in terms of the new coordinates, and separate the new independent variables. (x represents the location of the center of mass of the two particles, and q_x the distance between the particles.)
(*e*) Reduce the resulting problem to that solved in Chap. 10.

Problem 15-4 demonstrates that by suitable coordinate transformations one may transform a problem in which variables are *not* separable, into one in which the variables *are* separable. It illustrates how the translational motion of a diatomic molecule may be separated from its rotational and vibrational motion. We have already seen in Sec. (11-10) that the rotational motion cannot be completely uncoupled from the vibrational motion in a diatomic molecule.

15-4 Summary. The procedure of separating independent variables was related to that of finding eigenfunctions of appropriate operators each of which contains as few independent variables as possible. It was shown that when an operator can be written as a sum of operators, each of which contains fewer independent variables than did the original operator, then an eigenfunction of the original operator can be correspondingly factored. These results will be used in Chaps. 16 and 17.

electron spin and the exclusion principle

chapter

16

16-1 Introduction. The hypothesis that an electron in an atom is endowed with an intrinsic magnetic moment in addition to its charge and mass has led to a systematization of atomic and molecular structure. This hypothesis was proposed by Goudsmit and Uhlenbeck; it helped explain the increase in the number of spectral lines observed when an emitting atom is placed in a strong magnetic field (Zeeman effect), and it also helped explain the quantized traces observed when a stream of atoms moves through a strongly inhomogeneous magnetic field and is collected on a receiver (Stern-Gerlach experiment). Both types of experiment, as well as the theory later developed by Dirac, agree with the model of an electron spinning with an angular momentum whose component along the magnetic-field direction is $\pm\frac{1}{2}\hbar$ and with a resulting magnetic dipole whose dipole moment has a component in the field direction equal to $\pm$ one Bohr magneton ($\pm e\hbar/2m_e$).

In this chapter we shall use operator algebra to derive the properties of the spin vector first for a single valence electron in an atom. Next we shall extend the method to two valence electrons.

16-2 The spin operators, their eigenfunctions and eigenvalues. Since the experimental results could be explained on the assumption that the electron is a body of finite mass that can rotate, we define an operator $\boldsymbol{\sigma}$ that represents the angular momentum of the spinning electron. We distinguish the angular momentum due to the spin from that due to the motion of the electron around the nucleus by the terms "spin angular momentum" and "orbital angular momentum." It is proposed that the operator $\boldsymbol{\sigma}$ have certain analogies with the orbital-angular-momentum operator $\mathfrak{L}$, particularly, that their cartesian components have the same commutation properties. If $\boldsymbol{\sigma} = \hat{\mathbf{i}}\sigma_x + \hat{\mathbf{j}}\sigma_y + \hat{\mathbf{k}}\sigma_z$,

$$\begin{aligned} \sigma_x\sigma_y - \sigma_y\sigma_x &= i\hbar\sigma_z \\ \sigma_y\sigma_z - \sigma_z\sigma_y &= i\hbar\sigma_x \\ \sigma_z\sigma_x - \sigma_x\sigma_z &= i\hbar\sigma_y \end{aligned} \tag{16-1}$$

We derive the following relationships between the cartesian components of $\boldsymbol{\sigma}$, in a manner similar to that used in Chap. 11 for the $\mathfrak{L}$ operator:

$$\sigma_z(\sigma_x \pm i\sigma_y) = (\sigma_x \pm i\sigma_y)(\sigma_z \pm \hbar) \tag{16-2}$$

$$\sigma^2 = (\sigma_x + i\sigma_y)(\sigma_x - i\sigma_y) - \hbar\sigma_z + \sigma_z^2 \tag{16-3a}$$

$$\sigma^2 = (\sigma_x - i\sigma_y)(\sigma_x + i\sigma_y) + \hbar\sigma_z + \sigma_z^2 \tag{16-3b}$$

The operator for *spin* angular momentum differs from that of *orbital* angular momentum in one very important aspect. Since the spinning electron can exist only in *two* distinct states, the operator σ^2 can have no more than two distinct eigenfunctions, for if σ^2 had more than two eigenfunctions, then we would have to be able to distinguish as many separate states. We shall call α and β the two eigenfunctions of σ^2. Since σ^2 commutes with σ_z, we can define α and β as being also eigenfunctions of σ_z:

$$\sigma_z\alpha = A\alpha \tag{16-4a}$$

$$\sigma_z\beta = B\beta \tag{16-4b}$$

Since the commutation properties for $\boldsymbol{\sigma}$ are identical with those for $\mathfrak{L}$, a theorem analogous to Theorem 11-1 exists:

***theorem* 16-1.** If α is an eigenfunction of σ_z with eigenvalue A, then $(\sigma_x - i\sigma_y)\alpha$ is also an eigenfunction of σ_z, but with eigenvalue $(A - \hbar)$; similarly, if β is an eigenfunction of σ_z with eigenvalue B, then $(\sigma_x + i\sigma_y)\beta$ is also an eigenfunction of σ_z, but with eigenvalue $(B + \hbar)$.

---

problem 16-1. Prove Theorem 16-1.

According to Theorem 16-1 there are four eigenfunctions of σ_z, namely, α, β, $(\sigma_x - i\sigma_y)\alpha$, and $(\sigma_x + i\sigma_y)\beta$. Since σ_z has only two *independent* eigenfunctions, two of these functions must be linearly related to the other two. There are two possibilities:

$$\begin{aligned}(\sigma_x - i\sigma_y)\alpha &\propto \alpha \\ (\sigma_x + i\sigma_y)\beta &\propto \beta\end{aligned} \qquad \text{or} \qquad \begin{aligned}(\sigma_x - i\sigma_y)\alpha &\propto \beta \\ (\sigma_x + i\sigma_y)\beta &\propto \alpha\end{aligned}$$

The first pair of equations implies that α is an eigenfunction of $(\sigma_x - i\sigma_y)$ and β of $(\sigma_x + i\sigma_y)$. Since $(\sigma_x \pm i\sigma_y)$ does not commute with σ_z and since α and β are eigenfunctions of σ_z, we would not expect α or β to be eigenfunctions of $(\sigma_x \pm i\sigma_y)$. Therefore we eliminate the first pair of equations and conclude that

$$(\sigma_x - i\sigma_y)\alpha = C_{\alpha\beta}\beta \tag{16-5a}$$
$$(\sigma_x + i\sigma_y)\beta = C_{\beta\alpha}\alpha \tag{16-5b}$$

where $C_{\alpha\beta}$ and $C_{\beta\alpha}$ are independent of the spin coordinate. We have not expressed the spin operators in terms of the spin coordinates, but base our approach on the commutation properties of the spin operator rather than on an explicit differential form of the spin operators.

Since α and β are the *only* eigenfunctions of σ_z, one of them must terminate the generation of eigenfunctions by the $(\sigma_x + i\sigma_y)$ operator, the other the generating procedure using the $(\sigma_x - i\sigma_y)$ operator. We shall call α the "top" of the ladder, β the "bottom" of the ladder, as defined by the following equations:

$$(\sigma_x + i\sigma_y)\alpha = 0 \tag{16-6a}$$
$$(\sigma_x - i\sigma_y)\beta = 0 \tag{16-6b}$$

We use Eqs. (16-3*a*), and (16-3*b*) to find the eigenvalues of the σ^2 operator:

$$\sigma^2\alpha = (\sigma_x - i\sigma_y)(\sigma_x + i\sigma_y)\alpha + \hbar\sigma_z\alpha + \sigma_z^2\alpha = (\hbar A + A^2)\alpha \tag{16-7a}$$
$$\sigma^2\beta = (\sigma_x + i\sigma_y)(\sigma_x - i\sigma_y)\beta - \hbar\sigma_z\beta + \sigma_z^2\beta = (-\hbar B + B^2)\beta \tag{16-7b}$$

In analogy with Theroem 11-2, which was derived from the fact that $\mathcal{L}^2$ commutes with $\mathcal{L}_x$ and $\mathcal{L}_y$, we have Theorem 16-2.

***theorem* 16-2.** If α is an eigenfunction of σ^2 with eigenvalue $\mathcal{S}^2$, then $(\sigma_x - i\sigma_y)\alpha$ is also an eigenfunction of σ^2 with eigenvalue $\mathcal{S}^2$. Similarly, if β is an eigenfunction of σ^2 with the same eigenvalue $\mathcal{S}^2$, then $(\sigma_x + i\sigma_y)\beta$ is also an eigenfunction of σ^2 with eigenvalue $\mathcal{S}^2$.

From Theorem 16-2 and Eqs. (16-7*a*) and (16-7*b*),

$$\hbar A + A^2 = -\hbar B + B^2 \tag{16-8}$$

From Theorem 16-1 and the identification of α with $(\sigma_x + i\sigma_y)\beta$ we conclude that $B = A - \hbar$. When this is substituted in Eq. (16-8),

$$A = \tfrac{1}{2}\hbar \tag{16-9}$$

and hence

$$B = -\tfrac{1}{2}\hbar \tag{16-10}$$

Substituting the results of Eqs. (16-9) and (16-10) into Eqs. (16-4*a*) and (16-4*b*), we see that the Z component of spin angular momentum of an electron is quantized in units of $\hbar$, just as is the Z component of orbital momentum. However, unlike the Z component of orbital momentum, the Z component of spin angular momentum never equals zero, but equals a half integer multiple of $\hbar$.

When Eqs. (16-9) and (16-10) are substituted into Eqs. (16-7*a*) and (16-7*b*), it is found that

$$\sigma^2\alpha = \tfrac{3}{4}\hbar^2\alpha \tag{16-11a}$$

and

$$\sigma^2\beta = \tfrac{3}{4}\hbar^2\beta \tag{16-11b}$$

In analogy with orbital angular momentum, we can write $\sigma^2\alpha = s(s+1)\hbar^2\alpha$ and $\sigma^2\beta = s(s+1)\hbar^2\alpha$, where the quantum number s always equals $\frac{1}{2}$. Therefore the value of the square of the spin angular momentum equals $s(s+1)\hbar^2$. Similarly, we say that the Z component of spin angular momentum equals $m_s\hbar$, where $m_s = \pm\frac{1}{2}$. The quantization of spin angular momentum is shown in Fig. 16-1. It is not too surprising that the total spin angular momentum has only one allowed value, for an electron is an elementary particle, and has a definite spin just as it has a definite charge and mass. By analogy with orbital angular momentum the number of allowed orientations of spin angular momentum is $(2s + 1)$; since experiments indicated that only two states exist for the spin of the electron, we conclude that $2s + 1 = 2$, that is, $s = \frac{1}{2}$, which agrees with the result derived above.

16-3 The orthonormality of α and β. Since σ_z is defined in analogy with $\mathfrak{L}_z$, it should be Hermitian. Since α and β are nondegenerate eigenfunctions of the Hermitian operator σ_z, they must be orthogonal:

$$\oint \alpha^*\beta\, d\omega = 0 \tag{16-12}$$

where ω denotes the spin coordinate.

In Eqs. (16-5a) and (16-5b) we defined two constants $C_{\alpha\beta}$ and $C_{\beta\alpha}$; these can be determined such that α and β each are normalized. If

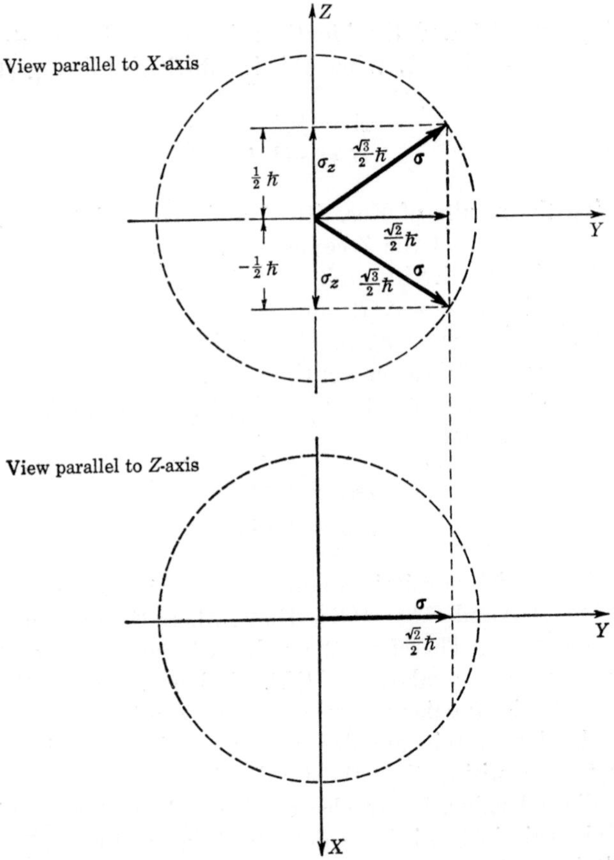

fig. 16-1 space quantization of spin angular momentum

α is to be normalized, then

$$\oint \alpha^* \alpha \, d\omega = 1 \tag{16-13a}$$

From Eq. (16-5b) it then follows that

$$\begin{aligned} 1 &= |C_{\beta\alpha}|^{-2} \oint [(\sigma_x + i\sigma_y)\beta]^* [(\sigma_x + i\sigma_y)\beta] \, d\omega = \\ &= |C_{\beta\alpha}|^{-2} \oint [(\sigma_x + i\sigma_y)\beta][(\sigma_x + i\sigma_y)\beta]^* \, d\omega = \\ &= |C_{\beta\alpha}|^{-2} [\oint (\sigma_x + i\sigma_y)\beta\sigma_x^*\beta^* \, d\omega - i\oint (\sigma_x + i\sigma_y)\beta\sigma_y^*\beta^* \, d\omega] \end{aligned}$$

Since σ_x and σ_y are Hermitian,

$$\begin{aligned} 1 &= |C_{\beta\alpha}|^{-2}[\oint \beta^* \sigma_x(\sigma_x + i\sigma_y)\beta \, d\omega - i\oint \beta^* \sigma_y(\sigma_x + i\sigma_y)\beta \, d\omega] = \\ &= |C_{\beta\alpha}|^{-2}[\oint \beta^*(\sigma_x - i\sigma_y)(\sigma_x + i\sigma_y)\beta \, d\omega] \end{aligned}$$

From Eqs. (16-3*b*), (16-4*b*), (16-10), and (16-11*b*)

$$(\sigma_x - i\sigma_y)(\sigma_x + i\sigma_y)\beta = \sigma^2\beta - \hbar\sigma_z\beta - \sigma_z{}^2\beta = \hbar^2\beta$$

Hence, $|C_{\beta\alpha}| = \hbar$, and similarly it can be proved that $|C_{\alpha\beta}| = \hbar$. We can summarize the relationships between α and β as follows:

$$\oint \alpha^*\beta \, d\omega = 0 \tag{16-12}$$
$$\oint \alpha^*\alpha \, d\omega = 1 \tag{16-13a}$$
$$\oint \beta^*\beta \, d\omega = 1 \tag{16-13b}$$
$$\sigma_z\alpha = \tfrac{1}{2}\hbar\alpha \tag{16-14a}$$
$$\sigma_z\beta = -\tfrac{1}{2}\hbar\beta \tag{16-14b}$$
$$\sigma^2\alpha = \tfrac{3}{4}\hbar^2\alpha \tag{16-11a}$$
$$\sigma^2\beta = \tfrac{3}{4}\hbar^2\beta \tag{16-11b}$$
$$(\sigma_x + i\sigma_y)\alpha = 0 \tag{16-6a}$$
$$(\sigma_x - i\sigma_y)\beta = 0 \tag{16-6b}$$
$$(\sigma_x - i\sigma_y)\alpha = \hbar\beta \tag{16-15a}$$
$$(\sigma_x + i\sigma_y)\beta = \hbar\alpha \tag{16-15b}$$

16-4 Systems of two electrons. Since each electron has two possible spin states, an atomic system containing two electrons must have four possible spin states. If the interaction between electrons is assumed to be entirely electrostatic, so that magnetic dipole interactions are neglected (see Prob. 16-2), then the Hamiltonian for the system is independent of the electron spin. According to the arguments of Chap. 15, the spin wave function may therefore be factored into individual spin wave functions of the separate electrons.†

† Large external magnetic fields (>20,000 gauss for the Zeeman effect, and fields with a gradient >100,000 gauss/cm for the Stern-Gerlach effect) are required to observe the presence of net electronic spin in an atomic system. In Prob. 16-2 it is shown that the interaction between electrons in an atom is almost entirely electrostatic, the magnetic-dipole interaction being comparatively small. Nevertheless, a spectrograph of only moderate resolution reveals the interaction of the magnetic dipole due to electron spin with the magnetic dipole due to the orbital motion of the electron ($l > 0$), as is evidenced by the observation of the sodium doublet. The sodium doublet is due to two nondegenerate states of the valence electron, one having the electron spin aligned with the orbital angular momentum, while in the other the electron spin is directed opposite to the orbital angular momentum.

---

problem 16-2. Calculate and compare the relative magnitudes of the repulsive energy due to their electrostatic interaction and the energy due to their magnetic dipole interaction of the two 1*s* electrons in the helium atom. (Assume that the two electrons are 0.6 A apart, and that this is the distance through which both effects manifest themselves. The interaction energy of two dipoles of magnetic moment μ separated by a distance r equals $k_\mu \mu^2/r^3$, where k_μ is the permeability of the medium. The magnetic moment due to the spin of electron is $2[s(s+1)]^{1/2}$ Bohr magnetons.)

The four spin functions for the two electrons would be

$$\alpha(1)\alpha(2) \qquad \alpha(1)\beta(2) \qquad \beta(1)\alpha(2) \qquad \beta(1)\beta(2)$$

where $\alpha(1)$ and $\beta(1)$ are the spin functions of the first electron, and $\alpha(2)$ and $\beta(2)$ are the spin functions of the second electron. To find the total spin and its components for the combined system of two electrons, consider the effect of the spin operators on these four spin wave functions. The total spin operator of the system would be $\boldsymbol{\sigma} = \boldsymbol{\sigma}_1 + \boldsymbol{\sigma}_2$, where $\boldsymbol{\sigma}_1$ and $\boldsymbol{\sigma}_2$ are the spin operators of the individual electrons. In Table 16-1 are listed the results of having the operators σ^2 and σ_z operate on the four spin functions.

To derive Table 16-1, the following operator algebra is used:

$$\sigma^2 = (\boldsymbol{\sigma}_1 + \boldsymbol{\sigma}_2)^2 = (\boldsymbol{\sigma}_1 + \boldsymbol{\sigma}_2) \cdot (\boldsymbol{\sigma}_1 + \boldsymbol{\sigma}_2) = \sigma_1^2 + \sigma_2^2 + \boldsymbol{\sigma}_1 \cdot \boldsymbol{\sigma}_2 + \boldsymbol{\sigma}_2 \cdot \boldsymbol{\sigma}_1$$

The operators $\boldsymbol{\sigma}_1$ and $\boldsymbol{\sigma}_2$ commute because they involve independent coordinates. Therefore

$$\sigma^2 = \sigma_1^2 + \sigma_2^2 + 2\boldsymbol{\sigma}_1 \cdot \boldsymbol{\sigma}_2 = \sigma_1^2 + \sigma_2^2 + (\sigma_x + i\sigma_y)_1(\sigma_x - i\sigma_y)_2 + \\ + (\sigma_x - i\sigma_y)_1(\sigma_x + i\sigma_y)_2 + 2\sigma_{z_1}\sigma_{z_2}$$

$$\sigma_z = \sigma_{z_1} + \sigma_{z_2}$$

$$\sigma_z\alpha(1)\alpha(2) = \sigma_{z_1}\alpha(1)\alpha(2) + \sigma_{z_2}\alpha(1)\alpha(2) = \tfrac{1}{2}\hbar\alpha(1)\alpha(2) + \tfrac{1}{2}\hbar\alpha(1)\alpha(2) = \\ = \hbar\alpha(1)\alpha(2)$$

$$\sigma_z\alpha(1)\beta(2) = \sigma_{z_1}\alpha(1)\beta(2) + \sigma_{z_2}\alpha(1)\beta(2) = \tfrac{1}{2}\hbar\alpha(1)\beta(2) - \tfrac{1}{2}\hbar\,\alpha(1)\beta(2) = \\ = 0$$

etc.

$$(\sigma_x + i\sigma_y)_1(\sigma_x - i\sigma_y)_2\alpha(1)\alpha(2) = (\sigma_x + i\sigma_y)_1\alpha(1)(\sigma_x - i\sigma_y)_2\alpha(2) = \\ = 0 \cdot \hbar\beta(2) = 0$$

$$2\sigma_{z_1}\sigma_{z_2}\alpha(1)\beta(2) = 2(\tfrac{1}{2}\hbar)\alpha(1)(-\tfrac{1}{2}\hbar)\beta(2) = -\tfrac{1}{2}\hbar^2\alpha(1)\beta(2)$$

etc.

table 16-1

effect of spin operators on spin wave functions for two-electron systems

operator	spin wave function			
	$\alpha(1)\alpha(2)$	$\alpha(1)\beta(2)$	$\beta(1)\alpha(2)$	$\beta(1)\beta(2)$
$\sigma_z = \sigma_{z_1} + \sigma_{z_2}$	$\hbar\alpha(1)\alpha(2)$	0	0	$-\hbar\beta(1)\beta(2)$
σ_1^2	$\frac{3}{4}\hbar^2\alpha(1)\alpha(2)$	$\frac{3}{4}\hbar^2\alpha(1)\beta(2)$	$\frac{3}{4}\hbar^2\beta(1)\alpha(2)$	$\frac{3}{4}\hbar^2\beta(1)\beta(2)$
σ_2^2	$\frac{3}{4}\hbar^2\alpha(1)\alpha(2)$	$\frac{3}{4}\hbar^2\alpha(1)\beta(2)$	$\frac{3}{4}\hbar^2\beta(1)\alpha(2)$	$\frac{3}{4}\hbar^2\beta(1)\beta(2)$
$(\sigma_x + i\sigma_y)_1(\sigma_x - i\sigma_y)_2$	0	0	$\hbar^2\alpha(1)\beta(2)$	0
$(\sigma_x - i\sigma_y)_1(\sigma_x + i\sigma_y)_2$	0	$\hbar^2\beta(1)\alpha(2)$	0	0
$2\sigma_{z_1}\sigma_{z_2}$	$\frac{1}{2}\hbar^2\alpha(1)\alpha(2)$	$-\frac{1}{2}\hbar^2\alpha(1)\beta(2)$		
σ^2	$2\hbar^2\alpha(1)\alpha(2)$	$\hbar^2[\alpha(1)\beta(2) + \beta(1)\alpha(2)]$	$\hbar^2[\alpha(1)\beta(2) + \beta(1)\alpha(2)]$	$2\hbar^2\beta(1)\beta(2)$

---

problem 16-3. Derive the remaining entries in Table 16-1.

16-5 Vector representation for the spin functions $\alpha(1)\alpha(2)$ and $\beta(1)\beta(2)$. From Table 16-1 it follows that all four spin wave functions are eigenfunctions of σ_z, having eigenvalues $\hbar$, 0, 0, and $-\hbar$. However, only $\alpha(1)\alpha(2)$ and $\beta(1)\beta(2)$ are eigenfunctions of σ^2, each with eigenvalue $2\hbar^2$. For a state described by the spin wave function $\alpha(1)\ \alpha(2)$ two spin-momentum vectors, each with Z component $\frac{1}{2}\hbar$ and magnitude $\frac{1}{2}\sqrt{3}\,\hbar$ are added to give a total spin momentum of Z component $\hbar$ and magnitude $\sqrt{2}\,\hbar$. The angle between the two spin vectors may be found as follows:

$$\sigma^2 = \sigma_1^2 + \sigma_2^2 + 2\sigma_1\sigma_2 \cos(\boldsymbol{\sigma}_1,\boldsymbol{\sigma}_2)$$

since $\sigma^2 = 2\hbar^2$ and $\sigma_1^2 = \sigma_2^2 = \frac{3}{4}\hbar^2$,

$$\cos(\boldsymbol{\sigma}_1,\boldsymbol{\sigma}_2) = \tfrac{1}{3}$$

The projections of the individual and resultant spin momenta on the XY plane are found from the relation $\sigma_x^2 + \sigma_y^2 = \sigma^2 - \sigma_z^2$:

$$(\sigma_x^2 + \sigma_y^2)_1 = (\sigma_x^2 + \sigma_y^2)_2 = \tfrac{3}{4}\hbar^2 - \tfrac{1}{4}\hbar^2 = \tfrac{1}{2}\hbar^2$$
$$\sigma_x^2 + \sigma_y^2 = 2\hbar^2 - \hbar^2 = \hbar^2$$

Therefore

$$(\sigma_x^2 + \sigma_y^2)_1 + (\sigma_x^2 + \sigma_y^2)_2 = \sigma_x^2 + \sigma_y^2$$

It follows that the individual spins combine in such a way that the projection of one on the XY plane is perpendicular to the projection of the other on the XY plane. Their Z components are aligned parallel to each other. This vector addition is illustrated in Fig. 16-2*a* and *b*. It should be noted that in these figures it is immaterial which of the two electrons is labeled 1 and which 2. Only the relative directions of the electron spins are determinate; their orientation with respect to the X and Y axis is not.

16-6 Vector representation of the spin functions $\alpha(1)\beta(2)$ and $\beta(1)\alpha(2)$. The functions $\alpha(1)\beta(2)$ and $\beta(1)\alpha(2)$ are *not* eigenfunctions of the σ^2 operator, but *are* eigenfunctions of the σ_z operator, with eigenvalues of zero. Therefore for states described by these two spin wave functions the Z components of the individual spins line up antiparallel. The net spin must therefore be perpendicular to the Z axis, in other words, lie in the XY plane. Since the functions $\alpha(1)\beta(2)$ and $\beta(1)\alpha(2)$ are not eigenfunctions of the σ^2 operator, the magnitude of the net spin is indeterminate. If the two spins would line up in the XY plane with their spins parallel, then the magnitude of the total spin would be given by $\sigma_{xy} = (\sigma_1)_{xy} + (\sigma_2)_{xy} = \sqrt{2}\,\hbar$; on the other hand, if they

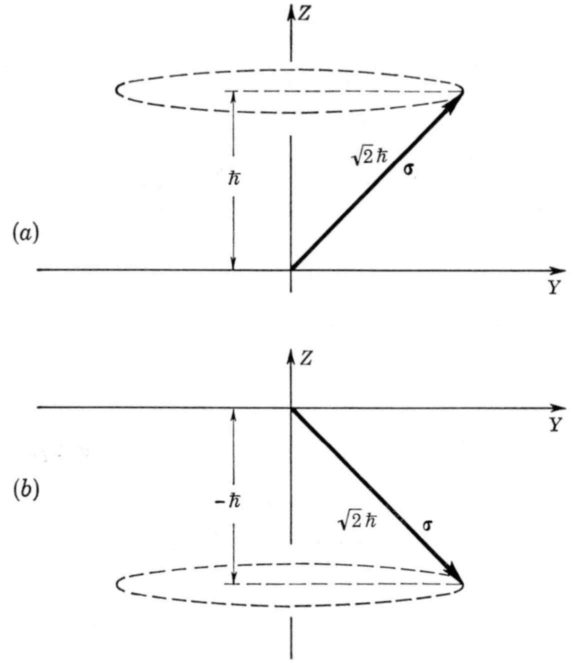

fig. 16-2a resultant spin vector for the spin function $\alpha(1)\alpha(2)$
fig. 16-2b resultant spin vector for the spin function $\beta(1)\beta(2)$

were aligned antiparallel, then the net spin would be zero. At any time however, the angle between the two spin vectors may have any value between and including 0^0 and 180^0, so that the vector sum of the spin vectors has a magnitude between zero and $\sqrt{2}\,\hbar$. Some of the relative orientations are shown in Fig. 16-3. In this figure one of the electron spins is held "fixed," that is, the "camera" is in each case oriented such that one of the spins always is in the same orientation. The expectation value of the magnitude of σ is found as follows:

$$\boldsymbol{\sigma} = \boldsymbol{\sigma}_1 + \boldsymbol{\sigma}_2 = \hat{\mathbf{i}}(\sigma_{x_1} + \sigma_{x_2}) + \hat{\mathbf{j}}(\sigma_{y_1} + \sigma_{y_2}) + \hat{\mathbf{k}}(\sigma_{z_1} + \sigma_{z_2})$$

Since $\sigma_{z_1} + \sigma_{z_2} = 0$,

$$\boldsymbol{\sigma} = \hat{\mathbf{i}}(\sigma_{x_1} + \sigma_{x_2}) + \hat{\mathbf{j}}(\sigma_{y_1} + \sigma_{y_2})$$
$$\sigma^2 = (\sigma_{x_1} + \sigma_{x_2})^2 + (\sigma_{y_1} + \sigma_{y_2})^2 =$$
$$= \sigma_{x_1}{}^2 + \sigma_{x_2}{}^2 + \sigma_{y_1}{}^2 + \sigma_{y_2}{}^2 + 2\sigma_{x_1}\sigma_{x_2} + 2\sigma_{y_1}\sigma_{y_2}$$

Since

$$\sigma_{x_1}{}^2 + \sigma_{y_1}{}^2 = \sigma_1{}^2 - \sigma_{z_1}{}^2 = \tfrac{3}{4}\hbar^2 - \tfrac{1}{4}\hbar^2 = \tfrac{1}{2}\hbar^2$$

and

$$\sigma_{x_2}{}^2 + \sigma_{y_2}{}^2 = \qquad = \tfrac{1}{2}\hbar^2,$$
$$\sigma^2 = \hbar^2 + 2(\sigma_{x_1}\sigma_{x_2} + \sigma_{y_1}\sigma_{y_2})$$

If we define θ_{xy} as the angle between the projections of $\boldsymbol{\sigma}_1$ and $\boldsymbol{\sigma}_2$ on the

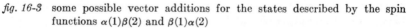

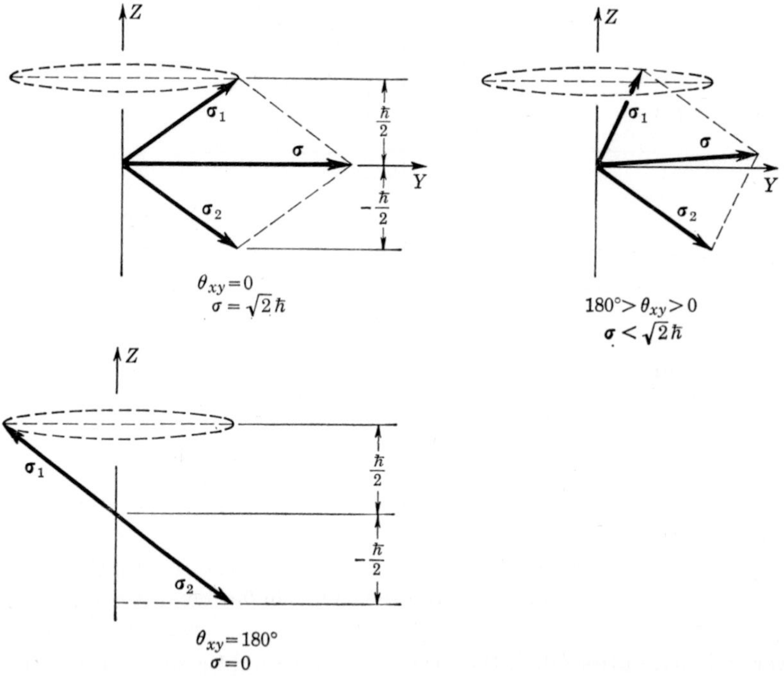

fig. 16-3 some possible vector additions for the states described by the spin functions $\alpha(1)\beta(2)$ and $\beta(1)\alpha(2)$

XY plane, then

$$\sigma_{x_1}\sigma_{x_2} + \sigma_{y_1}\sigma_{y_2} = \sigma_1\sigma_2 \cos\theta_{xy}$$

Therefore $\sigma^2 = \hbar^2 + 2\sigma_1\sigma_2\cos\theta_{xy} = \hbar^2 + 2(\tfrac{1}{2}\hbar\sqrt{3})(\tfrac{1}{2}\hbar\sqrt{3})\cos\theta_{xy}$

$$\overline{\sigma^2} = \hbar^2 + \tfrac{3}{2}\hbar^2\,\overline{\cos\theta_{xy}} \tag{16-16}$$

From the third postulate we find the expectation value of σ^2 for the state with spin wave function $\alpha(1)\beta(2)$;

$$\overline{\sigma^2} = \oint \alpha^*(1)\beta^*(2)\sigma^2\alpha(1)\beta(2)\, d\omega_1\, d\omega_2$$

From the last row of Table 16-1 we get the expression for $\sigma^2\alpha(1)\beta(2)$, and obtain upon substitution

$$\begin{aligned}\overline{\sigma^2} &= \hbar^2\oint\alpha^*(1)\beta^*(2)\alpha(1)\beta(2)\, d\omega_1\, d\omega_2 + \hbar^2\oint\alpha^*(1)\beta^*(2)\beta(1)\alpha(2)\, d\omega_1\, d\omega_2 = \\ &= \hbar^2\oint\alpha^*(1)\alpha(1)\, d\omega_1\oint\beta^*(1)\beta(2)\, d\omega_2 + \\ &\qquad + \hbar^2\oint\alpha^*(1)\beta(1)\, d\omega_1\oint\beta^*(2)\alpha(2)\, d\omega_2\end{aligned}$$

Since α and β form an orthornormal set, $\overline{\sigma^2} = \hbar^2$. The same result is obtained for the spin wave function $\beta(1)\alpha(2)$. When those results are compared with Eq. (16-16), it follows that $\overline{\cos\theta_{xy}} = 0$, so that the cosine of the angle between projections of the vectors $\boldsymbol{\sigma}_1$ and $\boldsymbol{\sigma}_2$ on the XY plane is as often positive as negative.

From the vector analysis performed on the spin angular momentum for the four states whose wave functions are listed in Table 16-1, we draw the following conclusions. The functions $\alpha(1)\alpha(2)$ and $\beta(1)\beta(2)$ describe two states in which the individual spins align their respective Z components parallel to each other (respectively, parallel and antiparallel to the Z axis), and their respective projections in the XY plane perpendicular to each other. The individual Z components and the resultant Z component are determinate (see Fig. 16-2*a* and *b*). The magnitudes of the projections of the individual spins and of the resultant spin on the XY plane are also determinate. On the other hand, their orientation within the XY plane is indeterminate.

The states described by $\alpha(1)\beta(2)$ or $\beta(1)\alpha(2)$ have no determinate resultant spin momentum. It is possible, however, to take linear combinations of $\alpha(1)\beta(2)$ and $\beta(1)\alpha(2)$ which are eigenfunctions of σ^2; the states described by these eigenfunctions are discussed in Sec. 16-7.

16-7 The four eigenfunctions of σ^2. In Sec. 16-4 it was shown that $\alpha(1)\alpha(2)$ and $\beta(1)\beta(2)$ are eigenfunctions of σ^2 with eigenvalues $2\hbar^2$ (see Table 16-1), and that $\alpha(1)\beta(2)$ and $\beta(1)\alpha(2)$ are not eigenfunctions of σ^2. Let us investigate here which linear combinations of $\alpha(1)\beta(2)$ and $\beta(1)\alpha(2)$ would be eigenfunctions of σ^2. From Table 16-1 it follows that the functions $\alpha(1)\beta(2) + \beta(1)\alpha(2)$ and $\alpha(1)\beta(2) - \beta(1)\alpha(2)$ are both eigenfunctions of σ^2, with respective eigenvalues $2\hbar^2$ and 0.

problem 16-4. Show that the following four functions are normalized:

$$\alpha(1)\beta(2);\ \beta(1)\beta(2);\ \frac{1}{\sqrt{2}}\,[\alpha(1)\beta(2) \pm \beta(1)\alpha(2)]$$

In Table 16-2 we summarize some of the properties of the four eigenfunctions of σ^2. The addition of spins for the functions $\alpha(1)\alpha(2)$ and $\beta(1)\beta(2)$ has, of course, already been shown in Fig. 16-2*a* and *b*,

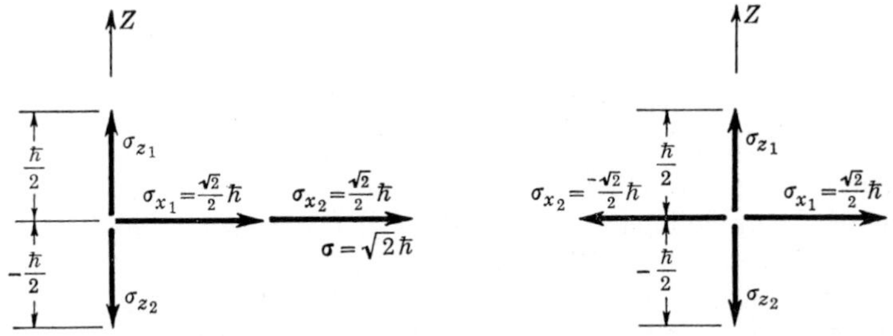

(*a*) Spin wave function: $\frac{1}{\sqrt{2}}[\alpha(1)\beta(2)+\beta(1)\alpha(2)]$

(*b*) Spin wave function: $\frac{1}{\sqrt{2}}[\alpha(1)\beta(2)-\beta(1)\alpha(2)]$

fig. 16-4 vector addition of spins (components)

respectively. The addition of spins for $(1/\sqrt{2})\ [\alpha(1)\beta(2) \pm \beta(1)\alpha(2)]$ is shown in Fig. 16-4; it is observed that this figure corresponds to two of the vector diagrams in Fig. 16-3.

problem 16-5. Derive the entries of Table 16-2.

problem 16-6. What angle does the $\boldsymbol{\sigma}$ vector make with the Z axis for the spin wave functions:

(*a*) $\alpha(1)\alpha(2)$
(*b*) $\beta(1)\alpha(2)$
(*c*) $\alpha(1)\beta(2) + \beta(1)\alpha(2)$

What is the angle between the $\boldsymbol{\sigma}_1$ and $\boldsymbol{\sigma}_2$ vectors for the spin functions:

(*d*) $\alpha(1)\alpha(2)$
(*e*) $\alpha(1)\beta(2) - \beta(1)\alpha(2)$

table 16-2

eigenfunctions and eigenvalues of σ_z, σ_1^2, σ_2^2 and σ^2

eigen-functions / operators	$\alpha(1)\alpha(2)$	$\frac{1}{\sqrt{2}}[\alpha(1)\beta(2) + \beta(1)\alpha(2)]$	$\beta(1)\beta(2)$	$\frac{1}{\sqrt{2}}[\alpha(1)\beta(2) - \beta(2)\alpha(2)]$
σ_z	$\hbar\alpha(1)\alpha(2)$	0	$-\hbar\beta(1)\beta(2)$	0
σ_1^2	$\frac{3}{4}\hbar^2\alpha(1)\alpha(2)$	$\frac{3}{4}\hbar^2 \frac{1}{\sqrt{2}}[\alpha(1)\beta(2) + \beta(1)\alpha(2)]$	$\frac{3}{4}\hbar^2\beta(1)\beta(2)$	$\frac{3}{4}\hbar^2 \frac{1}{\sqrt{2}}[\alpha(1)\beta(2) - \beta(1)\alpha(2)]$
σ_2^2	$\frac{3}{4}\hbar^2\alpha(1)\alpha(2)$	$\frac{3}{4}\hbar^2 \frac{1}{\sqrt{2}}[\alpha(1)\beta(2) + \beta(1)\alpha(2)]$	$\frac{3}{4}\hbar^2\beta(1)\beta(2)$	$\frac{3}{4}\hbar^2 \frac{1}{\sqrt{2}}[\alpha(1)\beta(2) - \beta(1)\alpha(2)]$
σ^2	$2\hbar^2\alpha(1)\alpha(2)$	$2\hbar^2 \frac{1}{\sqrt{2}}[\alpha(1)\beta(2) + \beta(1)\alpha(2)]$	$2\hbar^2\beta(1)\beta(2)$	$0 \cdot \frac{1}{\sqrt{2}}[\alpha(1)\beta(2) - \beta(1)\alpha(2)]$

problem 16-7. A two-electron system is described by the spin wave function $\alpha(1)\beta(2)$. Find the angle between the vector $\boldsymbol{\sigma}_1$ and the vector $\boldsymbol{\sigma}_2$ at the instant when $\sigma^2 = \hbar^2$.

16-8 Indistinguishability of electrons. In Sec. 16-6 we discussed some of the properties of the functions $\alpha(1)\beta(2)$ and $\beta(1)\alpha(2)$, and we dealt with their linear combinations, $(1/\sqrt{2})\ [\alpha(1)\beta(2) \pm \beta(1)\alpha(2)]$, in Sec. 16-7. These two sets of spin wave functions differ from each other in that the angle between individual spins is indeterminate for $\alpha(1)\beta(2)$ or $\beta(1)\alpha(2)$ but is determinate for

$$\frac{1}{\sqrt{2}}\ [\alpha(1)\beta(2) \pm \beta(1)\alpha(2)]$$

In the former cases the individual spins precess around the Z axis in an uncorrelated manner, while in the latter the individual spins precess in such a manner that they are always coplanar with the Z axis, and hence are correlated. In Fig. 16-5, we show the resultant spin vectors

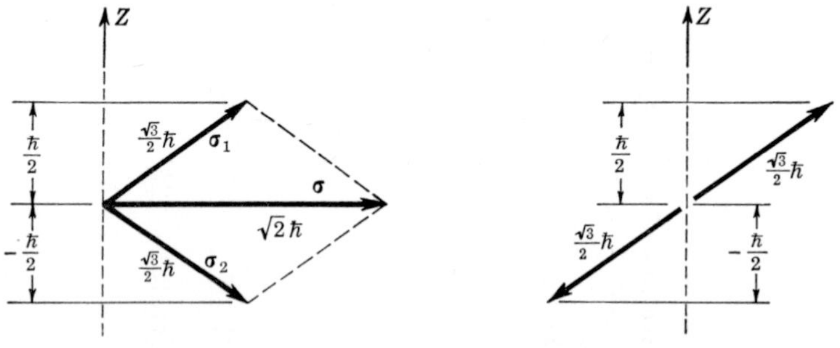

(*a*) Spin wave function: $\frac{1}{\sqrt{2}}[\alpha(1)\beta(2)+\beta(1)\alpha(2)]$

(*b*) Spin wave function: $\frac{1}{\sqrt{2}}[\alpha(1)\beta(2)-\beta(1)\alpha(2)]$

fig. 16-5 vector addition of spins (resultants)

of the two electrons explicitly, together with their vector sum. When the two spins precess in a correlated manner, their sum has a determinate magnitude, whereas when the precessions are not correlated, the magnitude of the total spin is indeterminate. This is the physical interpretation of the fact that neither $\alpha(1)\beta(2)$ nor $\beta(1)\alpha(2)$ are eigenfunctions of σ^2, but that the functions

$$\frac{1}{\sqrt{2}} [\alpha(1)\beta(2) \pm \beta(1)\alpha(2)]$$

are. Since we have consistently looked for eigenfunctions of the operators representing physical quantities of the system under examination, the functions $(1/\sqrt{2})$ $[\alpha(1)\beta(2) \pm \beta(1)\alpha(2)]$ are the ones in which we are interested. These functions have another advantage over the functions $\alpha(1)\beta(2)$ and $\beta(1)\alpha(2)$, which we shall now discuss.

The fact that $\alpha(1)\beta(2)$ is not necessarily equal to $\beta(1)\alpha(2)$ indicates that the states $\alpha(1)\beta(2)$ and $\beta(1)\alpha(2)$ describe distinct physical states. For instance, in the state described by $\alpha(1)\beta(2)$, electron 1 has a spin whose Z component is positive, while in the state corresponding to $\beta(1)\alpha(2)$ this same electron has a negative Z component of spin. The implication is that it is possible to distinguish experimentally between a state in which electron 1 points its spin upward while electron 2 points its spin downward, and one in which these two electrons interchange their spin directions. Such an experimental distinction can be made only if the two electrons are experimentally distinguishable. Since electrons are elementary particles, they are all identical, for there are no building blocks that could be put together in different ways to form different kinds of electrons. In nature, different "particles" such as atoms, molecules, dust particles, etc., are distinct only when they are built up out of different numbers or different combinations of elementary particles. To say that two electrons or neutrons are experimentally distinguishable, however, would be equivalent to denying that these particles are elementary. Therefore the wave functions $\alpha(1)\beta(1)$ and $\beta(1)\alpha(2)$ both describe states that are experimentally indistinguishable. In wave mechanics, one does not admit the existence of a state that cannot, in principle, be observed. Therefore we must reject $\alpha(1)\beta(2)$ and $\beta(1)\alpha(2)$, as suitable wave functions.

The functions $(1/\sqrt{2})$ $[\alpha(1)\beta(2) \pm \beta(1)\alpha(2)]$ are not objectionable from the point of view of the last paragraph, for interchange of the coordinates of the two electrons, at most, alters the sign of the wave function. It has been pointed out several times that the sign of a wave function has no physical significance. Therefore both the function $(1/\sqrt{2})$ $[\alpha(1)\beta(2) + \beta(1)\beta(2)]$ and $(1/\sqrt{2})$ $[\alpha(1)\beta(2) - \beta(1)\alpha(2)]$ describe states in which it is immaterial to which electron we attach the label 1 and to which we attach the label 2. The two states described by these two functions are, of course, physically distinct, for we have already seen that the former corresponds to a total spin angular momentum $\hbar\sqrt{2}$, the latter to a spin angular momentum of zero. In replacing the functions $\alpha(1)\beta(2)$ and $\beta(1)\alpha(2)$ by the functions $(1/\sqrt{2})\,[\alpha(1)\beta(2) \pm \beta(1)\alpha(2)]$ we have thus produced a pair of functions that is more satisfactory than the original set from two points of view: in the first place the new functions are eigenfunctions of σ^2 and hence represent states with determinate magnitude of total spin angular momentum, and in the second place the new functions are unaffected, except possibly in their sign, by interchange of the electrons.

16-9 The orbital wave functions of a two-electron system. In Sec. 16-8 we found that for a two-electron system there are four eigenfunctions of the spin operators σ^2 and σ_z, namely, $\alpha(1)\alpha(2)$, $\beta(1)\beta(2)$, $(1/\sqrt{2})[\alpha(1)\beta(2) + \beta(1)\alpha(2)]$ and $(1/\sqrt{2})[\alpha(1)\beta(2) - \beta(1)\alpha(2)]$. Of these four functions the first three are unchanged when electrons 1 and 2 are interchanged; such functions are said to be "symmetrical" in the coordinates of the two electrons. The fourth function experiences a change of sign when the two electrons are interchanged; such a function is called "antisymmetrical." Let us consider as an example of a two-electron system the helium atom, and consider the dependence of the wave function on the space as well as on the spin coordinates. As a first approximation let us neglect the repulsion between the two electrons. In that case the Hamiltonian of the system is simply the sum of the Hamiltonians of the two electrons.

According to Chap. 15, the wave function of the helium atom can be factored into one factor that depends on the coordinates of one electron only and another one depending only on those of the other electron, as long as we neglect the electrostatic interaction between the electrons:

$$\psi(\mathbf{r}_1,\mathbf{r}_2,\omega_1,\omega_2) = C_{ab}(\omega_1,\omega_2)\psi_a(\mathbf{r}_1)\psi_b(\mathbf{r}_2) \qquad (16\text{-}17)$$

where C_{ab} is independent of $\mathbf{r}_1$ and $\mathbf{r}_2$, but may depend on spin coordinates.

---

problem 16-8. Express the energy of the ground state of a helium atom in terms of the energy of the ground state of a hydrogen atom, neglecting electron repulsion.

---

problem 16-9. Apply the principle of the separation of variables to the helium atom without neglecting electron repulsion. How many independent variables are there? Can this principle be of use here? Explain.

While Eq. (16-17) represents a mathematically satisfactory wave function, it violates the indistinguishability of the electrons, for we assume here that electron 1 is in state a and electron 2 in state b. There is no way in which such a state can be experimentally distinguished from one having electron 1 in state b and electron 2 in state a; the same state could therefore be described by Eq. (16-18):

$$\psi(\mathbf{r}_1,\mathbf{r}_2,\omega_1,\omega_2) = C_{ba}(\omega_1,\omega_2)\psi_b(\mathbf{r}_1)\psi_a(\mathbf{r}_2) \tag{16-18}$$

where C_{ba} is independent of $\mathbf{r}_1$ and $\mathbf{r}_2$.

Since we may not have two distinct wave functions describing the same state, neither Eq. (16-17) nor Eq. (16-18) is a satisfactory wave function, although a linear combination of them may be

$$\psi(\mathbf{r}_1,\mathbf{r}_2,\omega_1,\omega_2) = \frac{1}{\sqrt{2}}[C_{ab}(\omega_1,\omega_2)\psi_a(\mathbf{r}_1)\psi_b(\mathbf{r}_2) + C_{ba}(\omega_1,\omega_2)\psi_b(\mathbf{r}_1)\psi_a(\mathbf{r}_2)] \tag{16-19}$$

(The factor $\sqrt{2}$ is introduced to preserve normalization.)

When we interchange the two electrons, the result is

$$\psi(\mathbf{r}_2,\mathbf{r}_1,\omega_2,\omega_1) = \frac{1}{\sqrt{2}}[C_{ab}(\omega_2,\omega_1)\psi_b(\mathbf{r}_1)\psi_a(\mathbf{r}_2) + C_{ba}(\omega_2,\omega_1)\psi_a(\mathbf{r}_1)\psi_b(\mathbf{r}_2)] \tag{16-20}$$

Since we require that interchange of electrons does not alter the wave function except for possible change of sign of the wave function,

$$C_{ba}(\omega_1,\omega_2) = \pm C_{ab}(\omega_2,\omega_1)$$
$$C_{ba}(\omega_2,\omega_1) = \pm C_{ab}(\omega_1,\omega_2)$$

In Sec. 16-8 we found that there are four ways in which the wave function can depend on the two spin coordinates, so that

$$C_{ab}(\omega_1,\omega_2) = \begin{cases} \alpha(1)\alpha(2) \\ \beta(1)\beta(2) \\ \dfrac{1}{\sqrt{2}}[\alpha(1)\beta(2) + \beta(1)\alpha(2)] \\ \dfrac{1}{\sqrt{2}}[\alpha(1)\beta(2) - \beta(1)\alpha(2)] \end{cases}$$

Accordingly,

$$C_{ab}(\omega_2,\omega_1) = \begin{cases} \alpha(1)\alpha(2) \\ \beta(1)\beta(2) \\ \dfrac{1}{\sqrt{2}}[\alpha(1)\beta(2) + \beta(1)\alpha(2)] \\ -\dfrac{1}{\sqrt{2}}[\alpha(1)\beta(2) - \beta(1)\alpha(2)] \end{cases}$$

When these expressions are substituted in Eq. (16-19), the following possibilities result:

$$\psi(\mathbf{r}_1,\mathbf{r}_2,\omega_1,\omega_2) = \begin{cases} \alpha(1)\alpha(2)\,\dfrac{1}{\sqrt{2}}[\psi_a(\mathbf{r}_1)\psi_b(\mathbf{r}_2) \pm \psi_b(\mathbf{r}_1)\psi_a(\mathbf{r}_2)] & (16\text{-}21a) \\ \beta(1)\beta(2)\,\dfrac{1}{\sqrt{2}}[\psi_a(\mathbf{r}_1)\psi_b(\mathbf{r}_2) \pm \psi_b(\mathbf{r}_1)\psi_a(\mathbf{r}_2)] & (16\text{-}21b) \\ \tfrac{1}{2}[\alpha(1)\beta(2) + \beta(1)\alpha(2)][\psi_a(\mathbf{r}_1)\psi_b(\mathbf{r}_2) + \\ \qquad \pm \psi_b(\mathbf{r}_1)\psi_a(\mathbf{r}_2)] & (16\text{-}21c) \\ \tfrac{1}{2}[\alpha(1)\beta(2) - \beta(1)\alpha(2)][\psi_a(\mathbf{r}_1)\psi_b(\mathbf{r}_2) + \\ \qquad \pm \psi_b(\mathbf{r}_1)\psi_a(\mathbf{r}_2)] & (16\text{-}21d) \end{cases}$$

We conclude that for each state a and each state b there are eight different states in which the electrons are indistinguishable. We observe, however, that if $a = b$ [for instance, if both electrons are in the 1s (ground) state] then four of the wave functions vanish, so that only four possible states remain.

---

problem 16-10. (*a*) Write all possible wave functions for the helium atom if each electron is in the ground state.

(*b*) Repeat Prob. 16-10*a* for the state where one electron is in the 1*s*, the other in the $2p_0$ state.

[In (*a*) and (*b*) use ψ_{1s}, ψ_{2s}, ψ_{2p_1}, ψ_{2p_0}, $\psi_{2p_{-1}}$, etc., to denote the hydrogen-like wave functions.]

(*c*) Find the energy for each of these states, neglecting electron repulsion.

---

problem 16-11. (*a*) Which of the following wave functions satisfy the principle of indistinguishability of electrons?

(1) $\psi_{1s}(1)\psi_{2s}(2)\alpha(1)\beta(2)$

(2) $\frac{1}{\sqrt{2}}\psi_{1s}(1)\psi_{2s}(2)[\alpha(1)\beta(2) + \beta(1)\alpha(2)]$

(3) $\frac{1}{2}[\psi_{1s}(1)\psi_{2s}(2) - \psi_{2s}(1)\psi_{1s}(2)][\alpha(1)\beta(2) + \beta(1)\alpha(2)]$

(4) $\frac{1}{\sqrt{2}}[\psi_{1s}(1)\psi_{2s}(2)\alpha(1)\beta(2) - \psi_{2s}(1)\psi_{1s}(2)\beta(1)\alpha(2)]$

(5) $\psi_{2s}(1)\psi_{1s}(2)\beta(1)\alpha(2)$

(6) $\frac{1}{\sqrt{2}}[\psi_{1s}(1)\psi_{2s}(2) + \psi_{2s}(1)\psi_{1s}(2)]\alpha(1)\beta(2)$

(7) $\frac{1}{2}[\psi_{1s}(1)\psi_{2s}(2) - \psi_{2s}(1)\psi_{1s}(2)][\alpha(1)\beta(2) - \beta(1)\alpha(2)]$

(8) $\frac{1}{2}[\psi_{1s}(1)\psi_{2s}(2)\beta(1)\alpha(2) - \psi_{2s}(1)\psi_{1s}(2)\alpha(1)\beta(2)]$

(*b*) Which of the functions listed are eigenfunctions of the σ^2 operator?

(*c*) Find the expectation value of σ^2 for those functions listed under (*a*) that satisfy the principle of indistinguishability.

---

problem 16-12. Which of the following functions are symmetric, antisymmetric, or neither, in the coordinates of particles 1 and 2?

(*a*) $\alpha(1)\beta(2)$
(*b*) $\beta(1)\alpha(2)$
(*c*) $r_{12} \exp - (r_1 + r_2)$
(*d*) $\alpha(1)\beta(2) - \beta(1)\beta(2)$
(*e*) $\cos(x_1 + y_2) + \sin(x_2 - y_1)$
(*f*) $\psi_{1s}(1)\psi_{2s}(2)\alpha(1)\beta(2) - \psi_{2s}(1)\psi_{1s}(2)\beta(1)\alpha(2)$
(*g*) $[\psi_{1s}(1)\psi_{2s}(2) - \psi_{2s}(1)\psi_{1s}(2)]\alpha(1)\alpha(2)$
(*h*) $[\psi_{1s}(1)\psi_{2s}(2) + \psi_{2s}(1)\psi_{1s}(2)][\alpha(1)\beta(2) - \beta(1)\alpha(2)]$
(*i*) $\psi_{1s}(1)\psi_{1s}(2)\alpha(1)\alpha(2)$
(*j*) $\psi_{2s}(1)\psi_{2s}(2)[\alpha(1)\beta(2) + \beta(1)\alpha(2)]$
(*k*) $\psi_{1s}(1)\psi_{2s}(2)\beta(1)\beta(2)$

16-10 The fourth postulate: the exclusion principle. The principle of indistinguishability of electrons is not in itself sufficient to explain the spectra of atoms and their chemical behaviour. For instance, in Sec. 16-9 we found that there would be four possible states available to two electrons both in their ground state; yet spectroscopic and chemical experiments indicate that only one such state is available. If in Eqs. (16-21a) to (16-21d) we set $\psi_a = \psi_{1s}$ and $\psi_b = \psi_{1s}$, and eliminate all wave functions that would consequently be zero, we have the following possible wave functions:

$$\psi = \alpha(1)\alpha(2)\psi_{1s}(1)\psi_{1s}(2)$$
$$\psi = \beta(1)\beta(2)\psi_{1s}(1)\psi_{1s}(2)$$
$$\psi = \frac{1}{\sqrt{2}}[\alpha(1)\beta(2) + \beta(1)\alpha(2)]\psi_{1s}(1)\psi_{1s}(2)$$
$$\psi = \frac{1}{\sqrt{2}}[\alpha(1)\beta(2) - \beta(1)\alpha(2)]\psi_{1s}(1)\psi_{1s}(2)$$

Of these four functions the first three are symmetrical in the coordinates of particles 1 and 2, the fourth being antisymmetrical. To bring the results derived so far from the three postulates of Chap. 5 into agreement with experimental data, we need an additional postulate:

All wave functions must be antisymmetric in the coordinates (spin as well as space coordinates) of all pairs of electrons.

This fourth postulate is called the "exclusion principle"; it incorporates the principle of indistinguishability of electrons, which makes all wave functions either antisymmetrical or symmetrical but, in addition, it excludes the symmetrical functions. Of the four possible wave functions we just listed for the ground state of helium, the first three violate the exclusion principle, so that only the fourth one is possible. It should be noted that the product of a symmetrical and an antisymmetrical function is antisymmetrical; for instance, the exclusion principle permits a function that is symmetrical in space coordinates, as long as it is paired with a function antisymmetrical in spin coordinates.

In general, when two electrons have the same value of n, l, and m_l, then the orbital factor in the wave function is necessarily symmetrical, so that the spin factor must be $(1/\sqrt{2})[\alpha(1)\beta(2) - \beta(1)\alpha(2)]$. On the other hand, when both electrons are in the same spin state, or if the spin factor in the wave function is $(1/\sqrt{2})[\alpha(1)\beta(2) + \beta(1)\alpha(2)]$, then the orbital factor must be antisymmetrical, and consequently the two electrons cannot have identical values of n, l, and m simultaneously. In other words, two electrons in an atomic system cannot have simultaneously an identical set of four quantum numbers n, l, m_l, m_s. This is the conventional statement of the exclusion principle; we have just shown that it follows from the antisymmetry requirement.

When two electrons have different sets of orbital quantum numbers, then the following four wave functions satisfy the exclusion principle:

$$\tfrac{1}{2}[\psi_a(1)\psi_b(2) + \psi_b(1)\psi_a(2)][\alpha(1)\beta(2) - \beta(1)\alpha(2)] \quad (16\text{-}22a)$$

$$\frac{1}{\sqrt{2}}[\psi_a(1)\psi_b(2) - \psi_b(1)\psi_a(2)]\begin{cases} \alpha(1)\alpha(2) & (16\text{-}22b) \\ \beta(1)\beta(2) & (16\text{-}22c) \\ \dfrac{1}{\sqrt{2}}[\alpha(1)\beta(2) + \beta(1)\alpha(2)] & (16\text{-}22d) \end{cases}$$

Of these four functions the first has a symmetrical orbital factor, while the other three have an antisymmetrical orbital factor. The latter three therefore have identical probability densities, and all properties that do not depend on spin are identical for these three states. They are therefore called triplet states, distinguished from each other by their values of $\sigma_z(+\hbar, -\hbar$, and 0, respectively). The first of the four wave functions listed above has a different orbital factor and is called a singlet. When the interelectronic repulsion is neglected, all four states have the same energy value, but we shall see later that the interelectronic repulsion removes the fourfold degeneracy, so that the triplet level is more stable than the corresponding singlet one. In the triplet states the electron spins are always aligned parallel, while in the singlet state they are aligned antiparallel. The net spin angular momentum in the triplet states has a magnitude $\sqrt{2}\,\hbar$, and has three allowed orientations in space; the net spin angular momentum in the singlet state is zero.

---

problem 16-13. Assuming that the outer electron in a silver atom moves in a central field, find the degeneracy of the ground state of this atom. (*Hint:* The outer electron has $n = 5$.)

16-11 The vector diagram for addition of electron spins. Figures 16-2 to 16-4 are exact, but not very convenient for representing the various spin states. These drawings are usually simplified to the diagrams of Fig. 16-6.

Spin Wave Functions

$\alpha(1)\,\alpha(2)$

$\frac{1}{\sqrt{2}}[\alpha(1)\beta(2)+\beta(1)\alpha(2)]$

$\beta(1)\,\beta(2)$

$\frac{1}{\sqrt{2}}[\alpha(1)\beta(2)-\beta(1)\alpha(2)]$

Vector Diagrams

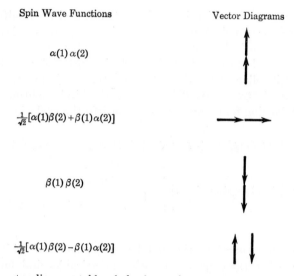

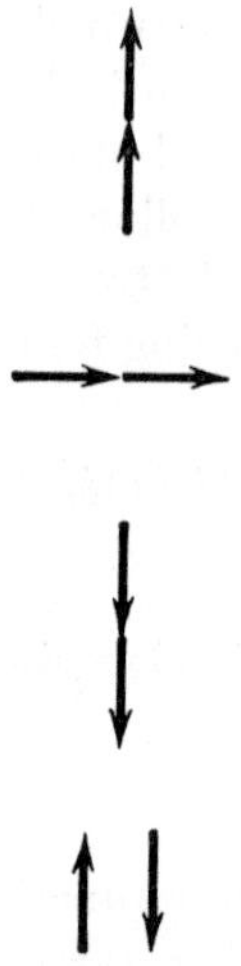

fig. 16-6 vector-diagram table of the four spin states of a two-electron system

16-12 Summary. We have considered the electron spin by analogy with orbital angular momentum. The observation that only two spin states exist per electron has led to the quantization of the Z component of spin angular momentum: $\sigma_z = \pm\frac{1}{2}\hbar$. In accordance with the uncertainty principle the spin-angular-momentum vector makes a finite angle with the Z axis and can be anywhere along the surface of a cone whose axis is the Z axis. Two quantum numbers were introduced: $s = \frac{1}{2}$ and $m_s = \pm\frac{1}{2}$.

For a two-electron system, a correlation was found between the spins of the electrons which was independent of the electrostatic and magnetic forces between the electrons in the classical sense. According to the fourth postulate (the exclusion principle), states having total spin momentum equal to $\sqrt{2}\,\hbar$ have antisymmetric orbital wave functions, while the state having net spin equal to zero has a symmetric orbital wave function.

In order to compare the energies of triplet and singlet states we need to find the expectation value of the electrostatic repulsion between the electrons for both states. Since this repulsion perturbs the spherical symmetry of the potential-energy function, we need first to learn how to deal with such perturbations. This will be done in Chap. 17, after which we shall return to multielectron systems in Chaps. 18 and 19.

perturbation theory

chapter

17

17-1 Introduction. In Chaps. 9, 10, and 11 we discussed a method for solving Schroedinger's stationary wave equation. This method is applicable only to certain systems whose Hamiltonian operator has a form appropriate for factoring. In the present chapter we shall discuss perturbation theory, which allows the approximate solution of the Schroedinger equation. This method is very important because it has more general applicability than any of the methods discussed before, although it is based on the assumption that for at least some systems an exact analytic or numerical solution is available. As an illustration of the use of the theory we shall consider here, in some detail, the case of a particular anharmonic oscillator.

Perturbation theory is based on the expansion in terms of orthogonal sets of functions, which was discussed extensively in Chap 2. We start by expressing the unknown wave function in terms of a known orthogonal set of functions, namely, all stationary wave functions of a system for which Schroedinger's equation has already been solved. The coefficients in the expansion are unknown, and perturbation theory provides the means of approximating their values.

17-2 Perturbations. Whether or not Schroedinger's equation can be solved analytically depends on the form of the potential-energy function. In the case of the helium atom neglect of the repulsion between the electrons permitted an analytical solution, but inclusion of this repulsion prevents the separation of variables that allowed the analytical solution. Similarly, the inclusion in the potential-energy function of terms higher than the second order in the displacement, complicates the solution of the wave equation for an oscillator. As stated in the introduction, we use as a frame of reference a set of known wave functions. These wave functions are called the "unperturbed" wave functions. The success of the perturbation method depends on a suitable choice of such unperturbed wave functions. In Chap 5 we pointed out that stationary wave functions are eigenfunctions of the Hamiltonian operator and that to each form of the potential-energy function there corresponds a characteristic set of (eigen) functions. The set of orthogonal functions chosen as frame of reference is one that corresponds to a potential-energy function (called the unperturbed potential energy), which equals as nearly as possible the potential energy of the system under consideration. The latter is called the perturbed potential energy. The difference between the perturbed and the unperturbed potential energies is called the "perturbation." In the case of the helium atom the perturbation equals the repulsive energy between the electrons; in the case of the oscillator all terms in the potential energy that are of degree 3 or higher in the displacement constitute the perturbation. The orthogonal functions used as a frame of reference are called the unperturbed wave functions; the Hamiltonian that is determined by the unperturbed potential function is called the unperturbed Hamiltonian.

In this chapter two assumptions will be made, and the following notation will be used:

1. The unperturbed stationary wave functions form a normalized nondegenerate set, denoted by Ψ_n^0. The superscript ^{0} indicates any property of the unperturbed system; the subscript n denotes the nth (unperturbed) state.

Since the unperturbed wave functions are nondegenerate, they are orthogonal. It was shown in Chap. 2 that degenerate stationary wave functions are not necessarily orthogonal, but can be linearly combined to form an orthogonal set. Therefore this assumption is not one that principally limits the discussion of this chapter.

2. The relative differences between all properties of the perturbed, or actual, and the unperturbed systems are small. Specifically, we assume that the difference $\mathcal{H}'$ between perturbed and unperturbed Hamiltonian is small compared to the differences between any eigenvalues of the Hamiltonian in the unperturbed system. This means that there is a one-to-one correspondence between the perturbed and unperturbed

eigenstates, for any perturbed energy level must lie closer to one particular unperturbed energy level than to all other unperturbed energy levels. This is illustrated in Fig. 17-1.

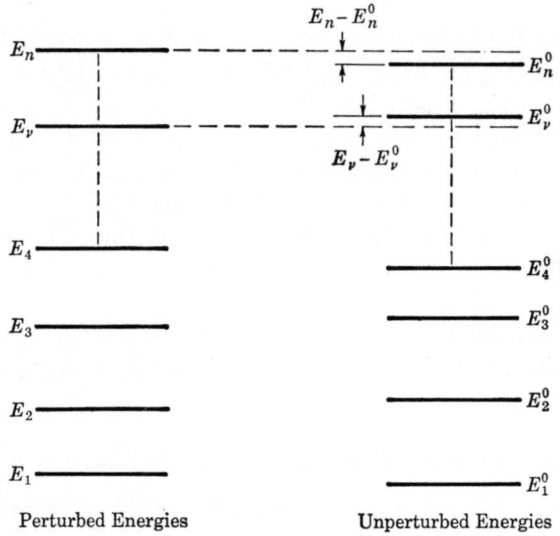

fig. 17-1 schematic representation of the one-to-one correspondence of perturbed and unperturbed levels

We denote the perturbed stationary states by the Greek subscript ν. The unperturbed energy level closest to the νth perturbed level is accordingly denoted by $E_\nu{}^0$, while the perturbed energy level closest to the nth unperturbed level is denoted by E_n.

Since the set $\Psi_n{}^0$ is orthogonal, each perturbed wave function can be expanded in terms of this orthogonal set (see Sec. 2-13),

$$\Psi_\nu = \sum_n C_{\nu n} \Psi_n{}^0 \tag{17-1}$$

Since Ψ_ν and $\Psi_n{}^0$ are stationary wave functions,

$$\Psi_\nu = \psi_\nu \exp -i \frac{E_\nu t}{\hbar} \qquad \text{and} \qquad \Psi_n{}^0 = \psi_n{}^0 \exp - i \frac{E_n{}^0 t}{\hbar}$$

Therefore

$$\psi_\nu = \sum_n C_{\nu n} \exp [i\hbar^{-1}(E_\nu - E_n{}^0)t] \psi_n{}^0 \tag{17-2}$$

Here the coefficient $C_{\nu n}$ expresses the amount of "admixture" of the nth unperturbed state in constructing Ψ_ν. The index n runs through *all* solutions of the unperturbed wave equation. Since Ψ_ν is a function of time, $C_{\nu n}$ is generally also a function of time, but is independent of coordinates.

The set $\Psi_n{}^0$ has been chosen as a system of reference; only when all the coefficients $C_{\nu n}$ are known is Ψ_ν also known. To find the coefficients $C_{\nu n}$, substitute Eq. (17-2) into the wave equation. Since we assumed one-to-one correspondence between the unperturbed and perturbed systems, we can expect one of the coefficients $C_{\nu n}$, namely, $C_{\nu\nu}$, to be close to unity, and the others to be close to zero; this means that Ψ_ν is made up mostly of $\Psi_\nu{}^0$, with some admixture of the other unperturbed wave functions.

17-3 Approximation to the energy levels. When Eq. (17-2) is substituted in the stationary wave equation, $\mathcal{H}\psi_\nu = E_\nu\psi_\nu$, we obtain

$$\sum_n C_{\nu n} \exp\,[i\hbar^{-1}(E_\nu - E_n{}^0)t](\mathcal{H}\psi_n{}^0 - E_\nu\psi_n{}^0) = 0 \tag{17-3}$$

Multiplication of both sides of Eq. (17-3) by $\overset{*}{\psi}{}_m^0$, where $\psi_m{}^0$ is any solution of the stationary unperturbed wave function, and integration over all values of all coordinates, gives

$$\sum_n c_{\nu n}\,[\oint \overset{*}{\psi}{}_m^0 \mathcal{H}\psi_n{}^0\,dq - E_\nu \oint \overset{*}{\psi}{}_m^0 \psi_n{}^0\,dq] = 0 \tag{17-4}$$

where $c_{\nu n} \equiv C_{\nu n} \exp i\hbar^{-1}(E_\nu - E_n{}^0)t$.

Equation (17-4) can be written explicitly for each particular value of m; since $\psi_m{}^0$ and $\psi_n{}^0$ are orthogonal, $\oint \overset{*}{\psi}{}_m^0 \psi_n{}^0\,dq$ differs from zero only for those terms in the series that have $n = m$. The result is as shown on page 251.

The explicit form of Eq. (17-4) is observed to be a set of linear, homogeneous equations, which only has nontrivial solutions if the determinant of the coefficients vanishes. Therefore, if we write

$$H_{mm} = \oint \overset{*}{\psi}{}_m^0 \mathcal{H}\psi_n{}^0\,dq \tag{17-5}$$

$$
\begin{array}{llllll}
 & \overbrace{\qquad\qquad\qquad}^{n=1} & \overbrace{\qquad\qquad\qquad}^{n=2} & & \overbrace{\qquad\qquad\qquad}^{n=\nu} & \\
m = 1: & c_{\nu 1}\left(\oint \overset{*}{\psi}{}_1^0 \mathcal{H} \psi_1{}^0 \, dq - E_\nu\right) & + c_{\nu 2} \oint \overset{*}{\psi}{}_1^0 \mathcal{H} \psi_2{}^0 \, dq & + \cdots & + c_{\nu\nu} \oint \overset{*}{\psi}{}_1^0 \mathcal{H} \psi_\nu{}^0 \, dq & + \cdots = 0 \\
m = 2: & c_{\nu 1} \oint \overset{*}{\psi}{}_2^0 \mathcal{H} \psi_1{}^0 \, dq & + c_{\nu 2}\left(\oint \overset{*}{\psi}{}_2^0 \mathcal{H} \psi_2{}^0 \, dq - E_\nu\right) & + \cdots & + c_{\nu\nu} \oint \overset{*}{\psi}{}_2^0 \mathcal{H} \psi_\nu{}^0 \, dq & + \cdots = 0 \\
\cdots & \cdots & \cdots & & \cdots & \\
\text{Any } m: & c_{\nu 1} \oint \overset{*}{\psi}{}_m^0 \mathcal{H} \psi_1{}^0 \, dq & + c_{\nu 2} \oint \overset{*}{\psi}{}_m^0 \mathcal{H} \psi_2{}^0 \, dq & + \cdots & + c_{\nu\nu} \oint \overset{*}{\psi}{}_m^0 \mathcal{H} \psi_\nu{}^0 \, dq & + \cdots = 0 \\
\cdots & \cdots & \cdots & & \cdots & \\
m = \nu: & c_{\nu 1} \oint \overset{*}{\psi}{}_\nu^0 \mathcal{H} \psi_1{}^0 \, dq & + c_{\nu 2} \oint \overset{*}{\psi}{}_\nu^0 \mathcal{H} \psi_2{}^0 \, dq & + \cdots & + c_{\nu\nu}\left(\oint \overset{*}{\psi}{}_\nu^0 \mathcal{H} \psi_\nu{}^0 \, dq - E_\nu\right) & + \cdots = 0
\end{array}
$$

Explicit Form of Eq. (17-4)

then we find for the determinant the following equation:

$$\begin{vmatrix} H_{11} - E_\nu & H_{12} & \cdots & \cdots & H_{1\nu} & \cdots \\ H_{21} & H_{22} - E_\nu & \cdots & \cdots & H_{2\nu} & \cdots \\ \cdots & \cdots & \cdots & \cdots & \cdots & \cdots \\ H_{\nu 1} & H_{\nu 2} & \cdots & \cdots & H_{\nu\nu} - E_\nu & \cdots \\ \cdots & \cdots & \cdots & \cdots & \cdots & \cdots \end{vmatrix} = 0 \qquad (17\text{-}6)$$

Equation (17-6) represents a restriction on the possible values for E_ν; we shall now proceed to evaluate the allowed values of E_ν. The degree of this equation, in the unknown E_ν, equals the number of rows and columns of the determinant, which in turn equals the number of unperturbed states; this number may be infinite. There are, therefore, as many different values of E_ν as there are unperturbed states.

---

problem 17-1. Show that $H_{mn} = E_n{}^0\delta_{mn} + \oint \overset{*}{\psi}{}_m^0 \mathcal{H}' \psi_n{}^0 \, dq$, where $\delta_{mn} = 0$, when $m \neq n$, $\delta_{mn} = 1$ when $m = n$; $\mathcal{H}' \equiv \mathcal{H} - \mathcal{H}^0$.

---

problem 17-2. (*a*) Show that when $\mathcal{H}' = 0$, the determinant in Eq. (17-6) is diagonal, that is, all terms having $n \neq m$ vanish.

(*b*) Solve Eq. (17-6) for the special case, $\mathcal{H}' = 0$.

(*c*) How many solutions are there?

---

problem 17-3. (*a*) Show that one of the diagonal elements in Eq. (17-6) is much smaller than all other diagonal elements. Which element is the smallest one?

(*b*) Show that, with one exception, all off-diagonal terms are small compared to the diagonal element in the same row and to the diagonal element in the same column. In other words, show that, for example,

$$H_{13} \ll H_{11} - E_\nu \qquad \text{and} \qquad H_{13} \ll H_{23} - E_\nu$$

17-4 First-order perturbation theory. From Prob. 17-3 we conclude that the elements of the determinant in Eq. (17-6) can be divided into two classes:

1. All, except one, of the diagonal elements, which are comparatively large
2. All off-diagonal elements, and the remaining diagonal element, which are comparatively small

When the determinant is expanded, there is not a single term containing *only* large factors. The term containing all diagonal elements contains one small factor, and all other terms contain at least two small factors (off-diagonal elements). As a first approximation we shall retain only the term containing *not more than one small factor* (i.e., the term equaling the product of all the diagonal elements) and we shall neglect all other terms in the expansion of the determinant. Then Eq. (17-6) becomes approximately

$$(H_{11} - E_\nu)(H_{22} - E_\nu) \cdots (H_{mm} - E_\nu) \cdots (H_{\nu\nu} - E_\nu) \cdots = 0 \quad (17\text{-}7)$$

From Prob. (17-1) it follows that

$$H_{mm} = E_m{}^0 + \oint \overset{*}{\psi}{}_m^0 \mathcal{H}' \psi_m{}^0 \, dq \equiv E_m{}^0 + H'_{mm}$$
$$H_{\nu\nu} = E_\nu{}^0 + \oint \overset{*}{\psi}{}_\nu^0 \mathcal{H}' \psi_\nu{}^0 \, dq \equiv E_\nu{}^0 + H'_{\nu\nu}$$

From the definition of our subscripts,

$$|E_\nu{}^0 - E_\nu| \ll |E_m{}^0 - E_\nu|_{m \neq \nu}$$

and thus

$$|H_{\nu\nu} - E_\nu| \ll |H_{mm} - E_\nu|_{m \neq \nu}$$

Therefore if any factor on the left side of Eq. (17-7) be zero, it must be $(H_{\nu\nu} - E_\nu)$, so that

$$E_\nu = H_{\nu\nu} = E_\nu{}^0 + H'_{\nu\nu} \equiv E_\nu{}^0 + \oint \overset{*}{\psi}{}_\nu^0 \mathcal{H}' \psi_\nu{}^0 \, dq \quad (17\text{-}8)$$

Equation (17-8) is the result of *first-order* perturbation theory; it states that the νth perturbed energy value equals the νth unperturbed energy value plus the perturbation averaged over the νth unperturbed state. Thus to a first approximation only the νth unperturbed state contributes to the νth peturbed energy value. The contribution of other unperturbed levels occurs in terms of smaller order than $H'_{\nu\nu}$, as will be seen when the result of second-order perturbation theory is derived.

---

problem 17-4. An anharmonic oscillator has the following potential $V = \frac{1}{2}k_0q^2 + \frac{1}{4}kq^4$, where the second term is much smaller in magnitude than the first. Find the expression for the ground-state energy of this system, using first-order perturbation theory.

17-5 Second-order perturbation theory. As a second approximation to the solution of Eq. (17-6), all terms containing not more than two small factors are included in the expansion of the determinant. The leading term is, of course, the left-hand side of Eq. (17-7); the other terms are obtained by expanding the determinant around the row containing the only small diagonal element, $H_{\nu\nu} - E_\nu$. The terms in the expansion have the general form

$$-\frac{H_{\nu m}H_{m\nu}(H_{11} - E_\nu)(H_{22} - E_\nu) \cdots (H_{mm} - E_\nu) \cdots (H_{\nu\nu} - E_\nu) \cdots}{(H_{mm} - E_\nu)(H_{\nu\nu} - E_\nu)}$$

---

problem 17-5. Expand, explicitly, the following 5×5 determinant, arranging the terms in decreasing order of magnitude. Confirm that the expansion given just above represents the term containing two small factors.

$$\begin{vmatrix} (H_{11} - E_4) & H_{12} & H_{13} & H_{14} & H_{15} \\ H_{21} & (H_{22} - E_4) & H_{23} & H_{24} & H_{25} \\ H_{31} & H_{32} & (H_{33} - E_4) & H_{34} & H_{35} \\ H_{41} & H_{42} & H_{43} & (H_{44} - E_4) & H_{45} \\ H_{51} & H_{52} & H_{53} & H_{54} & (H_{55} - E_4) \end{vmatrix}$$

Accordingly, Eq. (17-6) becomes, to a second approximation,

$$(DP)\left(1 - \frac{1}{(H_{\nu\nu} - E_\nu)} \sum_{n \neq \nu} \frac{H_{\nu n}H_{n\nu}}{H_{nn} - E_\nu}\right) = 0$$

where DP is equal to the product of all diagonal elements in the determinant. Since the first-order perturbation theory led to the result $DP = 0$, we may assume that the solution which we are seeking is not the one where $DP = 0$. If $DP \neq 0$, then

$$1 - \frac{1}{H_{\nu\nu} - E_\nu} \sum_{n \neq \nu} \frac{H_{\nu n} H_{n\nu}}{H_{nn} - E_\nu} = 0$$

Therefore
$$E_\nu = H_{\nu\nu} - \sum_{n \neq \nu} \frac{H_{\nu n} H_{n\nu}}{H_{nn} - E_\nu}$$

The first term on the right equals the result of first-order perturbation theory; the summation represents the second-order terms, involving levels other than the νth one. From Prob. 17-1 it follows that

$$\begin{aligned} H_{\nu\nu} &= E_\nu{}^0 + H'_{\nu\nu} \\ H_{\nu n} &= H'_{\nu n} \\ H_{n\nu} &= H'_{\nu n} \equiv \oint \overset{*}{\psi}{}_n^0 \mathcal{H}' \psi_\nu{}^0 \, dq = \oint \psi_\nu{}^0 \mathcal{H}' \overset{*}{\psi}{}_n^0 \, dq \\ &= [\oint \overset{*}{\psi}{}_\nu^0 \mathcal{H}' \psi_n{}^0 \, dq]^* \equiv (H'_{\nu n})^* \end{aligned}$$

Therefore
$$E_\nu = H_{\nu\nu} - \sum_{n \neq \nu} \frac{|H'_{\nu n}|^2}{H_{nn} - E_\nu} \tag{17-9}$$

Since this summation contains second-order terms only, replacing H_{nn} by $E_n{}^0$ and E_ν by $E_\nu{}^0$ in the summation will only introduce errors of third order of smallness. To second-order accuracy, therefore,

$$E_\nu = H_{\nu\nu} - \sum_{n \neq \nu} \frac{|H'_{\nu n}|^2}{E_n{}^0 - E_\nu{}^0} \tag{17-10}$$

Of all the terms in the summation of Eq. (17-10), the largest are those for which $(E_n{}^0 - E_\nu{}^0)$ is smallest. Thus, while in first-order perturbation theory only the νth unperturbed energy level contributes toward E_ν, in second-order perturbation theory, all unperturbed levels contribute to E_ν; those unperturbed levels contribute most that lie closest to $E_\nu{}^0$. The calculation of the νth perturbed energy level involves the evaluation of all integrals $\oint \overset{*}{\psi}{}_\nu^0 \mathcal{H}' \psi_n{}^0 \, dq$, where all unperturbed wave functions are known a priori and the perturbation Hamiltonian is known by definition.

17-6 The perturbed wave functions. To find Ψ_ν, we recall that

$$\psi_\nu = \sum_n c_{\nu n} \psi_n{}^0$$

from Eq. (17-2) and the definition $c_{\nu n} \equiv C_{\nu n} \exp i\hbar^{-1}(E_\nu - E_n{}^0)t$.

The coefficients $c_{\nu n}$ can be found by solving Eq. (17-4), using the values of E_ν given by Eq. (17-10). Consider the equation written for any value of m:

$$c_{\nu 1}H_{m1} + c_{\nu 2}H_{m2} + \cdots + c_{\nu m}(H_{mm} - E_\nu) + + \cdots + c_{\nu\nu}H_{m\nu} + \cdots = 0$$

In this equation only $c_{\nu\nu}$, E_ν, and H_{mm} can be considered "large." We have shown that H_{mn} is small except when $m = n$, and because of the one-to-one correspondence of perturbed and unperturbed states $c_{\nu\nu} \gg c_{\nu m}$, $m \neq \nu$. Therefore we neglect all terms in the last equation having two small factors, and accordingly only retain

$$c_{\nu\nu}H_{m\nu} + c_{\nu m}H_{mm} = E_\nu c_{\nu m}$$

Therefore $$c_{\nu m} = c_{\nu\nu}\frac{H_{m\nu}}{E_\nu - H_{mm}} \qquad \text{for } m \neq \nu$$

Since $H_{mm} = E_m{}^0 + H'_{mm}$ and $E_\nu = E_\nu{}^0 + H'_{\nu\nu}$,

$$E_\nu - H_{mm} = E_\nu{}^0 - E_m{}^0 + \text{terms of smaller order}$$

Since, furthermore, in the expansion of ψ_ν all terms with $m \neq \nu$ are small compared with the term $c_{\nu\nu}\psi_\nu{}^0$, we can replace the factor $(E_\nu - H_{mm})$ in the expression for $c_{\nu m}$ by $(E_\nu{}^0 - E_m{}^0)$, so that

$$c_{\nu m} = c_{\nu\nu}\frac{H_{m\nu}}{E_\nu{}^0 - E_m{}^0}$$

and $$\psi_\nu = c_{\nu\nu}\left[\psi_\nu{}^0 + \sum_n{}' \frac{H'_{n\nu}}{E_\nu{}^0 - E_n{}^0}\psi_n{}^0\right] \tag{17-11}$$

---

problem 17-6. Prove that ψ_ν, as given by Eq. (17-11), is normalized within the accuracy of the derivation, if $c_{\nu\nu} = 1$.

Equation (17-11) can be interpreted as follows: The wave function ψ_ν consists of a linear combination of all unperturbed wave functions, of which one, $\psi_\nu{}^0$, is most strongly admixed (in accordance with the assumption of one-to-one correspondence), and of which those of the other unperturbed wave functions are most strongly admixed whose unperturbed energy eigenvalues are closest to $E_\nu{}^0$.

17-7 An anharmonic oscillator. As an example of the application of second-order perturbation theory let us find the energy of an anharmonic oscillator in its ground state. In general, the potential energy of an oscillator can be expressed as a Taylor series in the displacement from equilibrium q:

$$V(q) = V(0) + \left(\frac{dV}{dq}\right)_{q=0} q + \frac{1}{2}\left(\frac{d^2V}{dq^2}\right)_{q=0} q^2 + + \frac{1}{6}\left(\frac{d^3V}{dq^3}\right)_{q=0} q^3 + \frac{1}{24}\left(\frac{d^4V}{dq^4}\right)_{q=0} q^4 + \cdots$$

If we choose as the zero of energy the potential energy when the oscillator is in its equilibrium position, then $V(0)$ is zero. Since, furthermore, the restoring force vanishes at the equilibrium position $(dV/dq)_{q=0}$ vanishes as well, so that

$$V(q) = \frac{1}{2}\left(\frac{d^2V}{dq^2}\right)_{q=0} q^2 + \frac{1}{6}\left(\frac{d^3V}{dq^3}\right)_{q=0} q^3 + \frac{1}{24}\left(\frac{d^4V}{dq^4}\right)_{q=0} q^4 + \cdots$$

and the restoring force is

$$F = -\frac{dV}{dq} = -\left(\frac{d^2V}{dq^2}\right)_{q=0} q - \frac{1}{2}\left(\frac{d^3V}{dq^3}\right)_{q=0} q^2 - \frac{1}{6}\left(\frac{d^4V}{dq^4}\right)_{q=0} q^3 - \cdots$$

The second term in this series (and every even term following it) is independent of the direction of the displacement from equilibrium. We shall choose as our example an oscillator in which all contributions to the restoring force are directed toward the equilibrium position, i.o.w. are odd functions of the displacement q. Furthermore, we neglect all terms in the restoring force of order five and higher. Therefore our example deals with an oscillator whose restoring force is given by

$$F = -\left(\frac{d^2V}{dq^2}\right)_{q=0} q - \frac{1}{6}\left(\frac{d^4V}{dq^4}\right)_{q=0} q^3$$

and whose potential is

$$V = \frac{1}{2}\left(\frac{d^2V}{dq^2}\right)_{q=0} q^2 + \frac{1}{24}\left(\frac{d^4V}{dq^4}\right)_{q=0} q^4$$

The first term in this expression corresponds to a harmonic oscillator. If we define $k_0 \equiv (d^2V/dq^2)_{q=0}$, then we can use a linear harmonic oscillator with restoring force $(-k_0q)$ as our unperturbed system, and consider the term $\frac{1}{24}(d^4V/dq^4)_{q=0}q^4$ as the perturbation. If we define $k = \frac{1}{6}\left(\frac{d^4V}{dq^4}\right)_{q=0}$, there results

$$V = \tfrac{1}{2}k_0q^2 + \tfrac{1}{4}kq^4 \tag{17-12}$$

The assumption of a small perturbation imposes the following condition on the amplitude of oscillation:

$$q^2 \ll \frac{2k_0}{k}$$

This condition is most easily satisfied when k_0 is comparatively large and k is comparatively small. The energy values of the anharmonic oscillator are then approximately equal to those of the unperturbed harmonic one, namely, $(n + \frac{1}{2})\hbar\omega_0$, where $\omega_0 = (k_0/\mu)^{1/2}$. To find the perturbed energy levels due to the term $\frac{1}{4}kq^4$ in the potential energy, we must evaluate the integrals $\oint \overset{*}{\psi_\nu^0}\mathcal{H}\psi_n{}^0\,dq$ in Eq. (17-10). Since the perturbation $\mathcal{H}$ equals $\frac{1}{4}kq^4$ and the unperturbed wave functions $\psi_n{}^0$ are given by Eq. (10-6), these integrals become

$$\oint \overset{*}{\psi_\nu^0}\mathcal{H}'\psi_n{}^0\,dq = \tfrac{1}{4}k\oint (q^2\overset{*}{\psi_\nu^0})(q^2\psi_n{}^0)\,dq \tag{17-13}$$

The energy for the ground state of this anharmonic oscillator is

$$E_0 = \tfrac{1}{2}\hbar\omega_0 + \tfrac{1}{4}k\oint|q^2\psi_0{}^0|^2\,dq - \tfrac{1}{16}k^2\sum_{n=1}^{\infty}\frac{|\oint q^2\overset{*}{\psi_0^0}q^2\psi_n{}^0\,dq|^2}{n\hbar\omega_0}$$

First evaluate the second term on the right of the equality. From Eq. (10-10) it follows that

$$q^2\psi_0{}^0 = q(q\psi_0{}^0) = \frac{-i\hbar^{1/2}}{(4k_0\mu)^{1/4}}\,q\psi_1{}^0 = \frac{-\hbar}{(4k_0\mu)^{1/2}}\,[\sqrt{2}\,\psi_2{}^0 - \psi_0{}^0]$$

Therefore

$$\oint|q^2\psi_0{}^0|^2\,dq = \frac{\hbar^2}{4k_0\mu}\oint\left[2|\psi_2{}^0|^2 - \sqrt{2}\,(\overset{*}{\psi_0^0}\psi_2{}^0 + \overset{*}{\psi_2^0}\psi_0{}^0) + |\psi_0{}^0|^2\right]dq$$

Since $\psi_0{}^0$ and $\psi_2{}^0$ are part of an orthonormal set,

$$\oint|q^2\psi_0{}^0|^2\,dq = \frac{3\hbar^2}{4k_0\mu}$$

and hence

$$\tfrac{1}{4}k\oint|q^2\psi_0{}^0|^2\,dq = \frac{3k\hbar^2}{16k_0\mu} = \frac{3k\hbar^2}{16\mu^2\omega_0{}^2}$$

Next evaluate the summation in the expression for E: apply Eq. (10-10) once more:

$$q^2\psi_n{}^0 = q(q\psi_n{}^0) = \frac{-i\hbar^{1/2}}{(4k_0\mu)^{1/4}}\,[(n+1)^{1/2}q\psi_{n+1}^0 - n^{1/2}q\psi_{n-1}^0] =$$

$$= \frac{-\hbar}{(4k_0\mu)^{1/2}}\,[(n+1)^{1/2}(n+2)^{1/2}\psi_{n+2}^0 + \\ - (2n+1)\psi_n{}^0 + n^{1/2}(n-1)^{1/2}\psi_{n-2}^0]$$

Therefore $\quad (q^2\psi_0{}^0)^*(q^2\psi_n{}^0) = \dfrac{\hbar^2}{4k_0\mu}\,[\sqrt{2}\,(n+1)^{1/2}(n+2)^{1/2}\overset{*}{\psi}{}_2^0\psi_{n+2}^0 +$

$$- \overset{*}{\psi}{}_0^0\,(n+1)^{1/2}(n+2)^{1/2}\psi_{n+2}^0 - \sqrt{2}\,(2n+1)\overset{*}{\psi}{}_2^0\psi_n{}^0 + \\ + (2n+1)\overset{*}{\psi}{}_0^0\psi_n{}^0 + \sqrt{2}\,n^{1/2}(n-1)^{1/2}\psi_2{}^0\psi_{n-2}^0 - n^{1/2}(n-1)^{1/2}\overset{*}{\psi}{}_0^0\psi_{n-2}^0]$$

Therefore, since the functions $\psi_n{}^0$ form an orthonormal set,

when $n = 0$,

$$\oint(q^2\psi_0{}^0)^*(q^2\psi_n{}^0)\,dq = \frac{3\hbar^2}{4k_0\mu} \qquad \text{(first and fourth terms of bracket)}$$

when $n = 2$,

$$\oint(q^2\psi_0{}^0)^*(q^2\psi_n{}^0)\,dq = \frac{-6\sqrt{2}\,\hbar^2}{4k_0\mu} \qquad \text{(third and last terms)}$$

when $n = 4$,

$$\oint(q^2\psi_0{}^0)^*(q^2\psi_n{}^0)\,dq = \frac{2\sqrt{6}\,\hbar^2}{4k_0\mu} \qquad \text{(next to last term)}$$

The integral vanishes for all other values of n. Therefore

$$E_0 = \tfrac{1}{2}\hbar\omega_0 + \frac{3k\hbar^2}{16\mu^2\omega_0{}^2} - \frac{21}{128}\frac{k^2\hbar^3}{\mu^4\omega_0{}^5} =$$

$$= \tfrac{1}{2}\hbar\omega_0\left(1 + \frac{3k\hbar}{8\mu^2\omega_0{}^3} - \frac{21}{64}\frac{k^2\hbar^2}{\mu^4\omega_0{}^6}\right) \qquad (17\text{-}14)$$

Note that the sign of k affects the first-order, but not the second-order contribution.

Equation (17-14) could be considered the beginning of a series expansion in $(k\hbar/\mu_0^2\omega_0^3)$; the leading term represents the LHO, the second term the first-order perturbation, and the third term the second-order perturbation. Higher-order perturbation theories would presumably contribute terms in $k^3\hbar^3/\mu_0^6\omega_0^9$, etc.

---

problem 17-7. Prove that odd terms in the expansion of V in terms of q do not contribute to the first-order perturbation. (*Hint:* Remember the parities of the stationary wave functions of the LHO.)

---

problem 17-8. Find the first excited vibrational energy of the oscillator whose potential is given by Eq. (17-12).

It should be observed that in applying perturbation theory to an anharmonic oscillator that it is not necessary to know the eigenfunctions of the LHO explicitly; all that is required is the very important recursion relation, Eq. (10-10), between adjacent functions of the "ladder." This recursion relation followed directly from the operator method of generating eigenfunctions. Thus we have shown by this example that it is sometimes at least as useful to know the rule for generating eigenfunctions as it is to know these eigenfunctions explicitly.

17-8 Summary. A general approximation method has been considered for solving the wave equation for a system whose potential function resembles but is not quite the same as the potential function for which solutions have already been obtained. As an example, an anharmonic oscillator has been considered.

Certain limiting assumptions have been made here, notably the one-to-one correspondence of unperturbed and perturbed levels, which implies nondegeneracy of the unperturbed levels. In Chap. 18 it will be shown how a system with degenerate levels may be treated.

the helium atom

chapter

18

18-1 Introduction. In this chapter the results of Chaps. 16 and 17 will be applied to find expressions for the energy of the ground state and of several low-lying states of the helium atom. From these expressions we shall interpret details of the spectrum of the helium atom, and in Chap. 19 we shall extrapolate the results to the structure of more complex atoms. Furthermore, we shall in Chap. 18 establish the basis of magnetic interactions.

As outlined in Chap. 17, the Hamiltonian of the helium atom is split into two terms, an unperturbed one and a perturbation. Here the unperturbed system consists of two electrons in the spherically symmetrical field of an α particle, the interaction between the electrons being neglected. The perturbation consists of the electrostatic repulsion between the electrons. The unperturbed wave functions are combinations of the central-field wave functions found in Chaps. 11 and 13.

18-2 The ground state of the helium atom. The unperturbed wave function for the ground state of the helium atom is found from Eq. (16-22*a*) by setting $a = b = 1s$. After normalization,

$$\psi = \frac{1}{\sqrt{2}} \psi_{1s}(1)\psi_{1s}(2)[\alpha(1)\beta(2) - \beta(1)\alpha(2)] \tag{18-1}$$

where

$$\psi_{1s}(1) = \sqrt{\frac{Z^3}{\pi a_0{}^3}} \exp \frac{-Z\mathbf{r}_1}{a_0}$$

$$\psi_{1s}(2) = \sqrt{\frac{Z^3}{\pi a_0{}^3}} \exp \frac{-Z\mathbf{r}_2}{a_0}$$

Z, the atomic number of the element, is 2 here
a_0 is the Bohr radius of the hydrogen atom ($= \hbar^2/e^2\mu$)

The perturbation equals e^2/r_{12}, being entirely electrostatic; it has been shown that magnetic-dipole interactions between the electrons are much smaller than the electrostatic repulsion; the magnetic-dipole interactions will therefore be neglected here.

According to first-order perturbation theory the principal contribution to the perturbed ground-state energy comes from the unperturbed ground state. The perturbation energy is

$$H'_{00} = \oint \psi_0{}^0 \mathcal{H}' \psi_0{}^0 \, dq \, d\omega$$

Since α and β are normalized,

$$\oint \frac{1}{\sqrt{2}} [\alpha(1)\beta(2) - \beta(1)\alpha(2)]^* \frac{1}{\sqrt{2}} [\alpha(1)\beta(2) - (\beta(1)\alpha(2)] \, d\omega = 1$$

(see Sec. 16-3). Therefore

$$H'_{00} = \frac{Z^3}{\pi a_0{}^3} \oint \frac{e^2}{r_{12}} \exp\left(\frac{-Z(\mathbf{r}_1 + \mathbf{r}_2)}{a_0}\right) dq_1 \, dq_2 = \frac{5}{4} \frac{Ze^2}{2a_0}\dagger$$

This result can be compared with experimental observations on the first ionization potential of a helium atom. When the atom is ionized,

$$\text{He } (1s^2) \rightarrow \text{He}^+ \ (1s) + e$$

Since the singly charged helium ion is hydrogen like, its energy is $-Z^2e^2/2a_0$. Therefore the energy involved in the ionization of a helium atom is

$$\Delta E = E[\text{He}^+ \ (1s) + e] - E[\text{He } (1s^2)]$$

Since the electron removed from the helium atom has been moved to infinity, it does not contribute to the energy of the ionized system. The energy of the atom equals twice the energy of an electron in the

† L. Pauling and E. B. Wilson, Jr., "Introduction to Quantum Mechanics," p. 446, McGraw Hill Book Company, Inc., New York, 1935.

field of an α particle, plus the perturbation energy. Therefore

$$\Delta E = \frac{-4e^2}{2a_0} - \left(\frac{-8e^2}{2a_0} + \frac{5}{2}\frac{e^2}{2a_0}\right) = \frac{3}{2}\left(\frac{e^2}{2a_0}\right) = 20.5 \text{ ev}$$

The experimental value obtained for the first ionization potential of the helium atom is 24.58 volts. Considering that the value 20.5 ev was obtained using only first-order perturbation theory, the agreement between calculated and measured values is reasonable.

---

problem 18-1. Using the first and second ionization potentials of He, calculate the interaction energy of two electrons in the ground state of He. (*Hint:* Use results of Prob. 16-8.)

18-3 The sixteen first excited states. Having found the energy required to remove an electron from a helium atom, let us next consider the energy involved in raising one of the two electrons in a helium atom from $n = 1$ to $n = 2$. To be sure, this will require less than the 24.58 ev required above. For this excitation there are 16 states corresponding to appropriate combinations of the 4 different spin functions of 2 electrons (see Chap. 16) with the 4 orbital functions having $l = 0$ or 1. In Sec. 11-11 we discussed the wave functions having $l = 1$, of which there are three independent wave functions. Two sets were discussed: ψ_{2p_1}, ψ_{2p_0}, and $\psi_{2p_{-1}}$, which are eigenfunctions of $\mathcal{L}_z$, and the hybrid set ψ_{2p_x}, ψ_{2p_y}, and ψ_{2p_z}. There is no a priori reason to choose one set over the other when we select the unperturbed set of wave functions; certainly there is no reason to require these to be eigenfunctions of $\mathcal{L}_z$. Some physical foresight can simplify the computations considerably, however. The charge distributions corresponding to the wave functions ψ_{2p_1} and $\psi_{2p_{-1}}$ are doughnut-shaped, and cylindrically symmetrical about the Z axis. The distributions for ψ_{2p_x}, ψ_{2p_y}, and ψ_{2p_z} (which is identical with that for ψ_{2p_0}) each have the identical "dumbbell" shape, although they differ in orientation. The solution of the determinantal equation [Eq. (17-6)] requires the evaluation of integrals of the form H'_{mn}; since the integration is to be carried out over all of space, the absolute orientation in space of the integrand is immaterial. Therefore, all integrals H'_{mn} in which the integrands only differ in their absolute orientation in space, are equal to each other. The trio ψ_{2p_x}, ψ_{2p_y}, and ψ_{2p_z} thus is preferable to the trio ψ_{2p_1}, ψ_{2p_0}, and $\psi_{2p_{-1}}$. The sixteen unperturbed functions selected are therefore

$$\left.\begin{aligned}
&P: \frac{1}{\sqrt{2}}[\psi_{1s}(1)\psi_{2s}(2) + \psi_{2s}(1)\psi_{1s}(2)]\\
&Q: \frac{1}{\sqrt{2}}[\psi_{1s}(1)\psi_{2p_x}(2) + \psi_{2p_x}(1)\psi_{1s}(2)]\\
&R: \frac{1}{\sqrt{2}}[\psi_{1s}(1)\psi_{2p_y}(2) + \psi_{2p_y}(1)\psi_{1s}(2)]\\
&S: \frac{1}{\sqrt{2}}[\psi_{1s}(1)\psi_{2p_z}(2) + \psi_{2p_z}(1)\psi_{1s}(2)]
\end{aligned}\right\} \cdot \frac{1}{\sqrt{2}}[\alpha(1)\beta(2) - \beta(1)\alpha(2)]$$

$$\left.\begin{aligned}
&T: \frac{1}{\sqrt{2}}[\psi_{1s}(1)\psi_{2s}(2) - \psi_{2s}(1)\psi_{1s}(2)]\\
&U: \frac{1}{\sqrt{2}}[\psi_{1s}(1)\psi_{2p_x}(2) - \psi_{2p_x}(1)\psi_{1s}(2)]\\
&V: \frac{1}{\sqrt{2}}[\psi_{1s}(1)\psi_{2p_y}(2) - \psi_{2p_y}(1)\psi_{1s}(2)]\\
&W: \frac{1}{\sqrt{2}}[\psi_{1s}(1)\psi_{2p_z}(2) - \psi_{2p_z}(1)\psi_{1s}(2)]
\end{aligned}\right\} \cdot \left\{\begin{aligned}
&\alpha(1)\alpha(2)\\
&\frac{1}{\sqrt{2}}[\alpha(1)\beta(2) + \beta(1)\alpha(2)]\\
&\beta(1)\beta(2)
\end{aligned}\right.$$

18-4 Degenerate perturbation theory. In Chap. 17 we developed, from Schroedinger's equation, the determinantal equation (17-6), whose solution was approximated by assuming that the perturbation Hamiltonian is small compared to the differences in the unperturbed energy levels (see Fig. 17-1). In the case of the helium atom the energy of the unperturbed states depends only on the principal quantum numbers, n_1 and n_2, of the two electrons; the 16 first excited unperturbed states are therefore degenerate. Thus the perturbation energy cannot be small compared to the difference between the unperturbed energies since the latter difference is zero for degenerate levels. We can, however, apply the results of Chap. 17 to the extent that we may neglect, to a first approximation, the effect of all except the first 16 excited unperturbed states in finding the energy levels of the first 16 excited states of the helium atom.

The general degenerate perturbation theory will not be considered here: the present example will serve to illustrate some of its features.

Equation (17-6) now reduces to a 16×16 determinantal equation which must be solved exactly. The orthogonality of the four spin functions, as well as the foresight used in selecting the hybrid functions ψ_{2p_x}, ψ_{2p_y}, and ψ_{2p_z}, will reduce the determinant to a more manageable 4×4 determinant.

The evaluation of each element in Eq. (17-6) requires integration of the form

$$H'_{mn} = \oint \psi_m^{0*} \left(\frac{e^2}{r_{12}}\right) \psi_n{}^0 \, dq \, d\omega$$

where $\psi_m{}^0$ and $\psi_n{}^0$ are now any two of the 16 unperturbed wave functions listed above. The integral can be factored into a spin-independent and a space-independent part, with the perturbation e^2/r_{12} entering in the spin-independent part. A typical integral is

$$\oint \frac{1}{\sqrt{2}} [\psi_{1s}(1)\psi_{2s}(2) + \psi_{2s}\psi_{1s}(2)]^* \frac{e^2}{r_{12}} \frac{1}{\sqrt{2}} [\psi_{1s}(1)\psi_{2s}(2) - \psi_{2s}(1)\psi_{1s}(2)] \, dq \times$$
$$\times \oint \frac{1}{\sqrt{2}} [\alpha(1)\beta(2) - \beta(1)\alpha(2)]\alpha(1)\alpha(2) \, d\omega$$

We observe that the spin functions $\frac{1}{\sqrt{2}} [\alpha(1)\beta(2) - \beta(1)\alpha(2)]$ and $\alpha(1)\alpha(2)$ are mutually orthogonal, for

$$\oint \frac{1}{\sqrt{2}} [\alpha(1)\beta(2) - \beta(1)\alpha(2)]^*\alpha(1)\alpha(2) \, d\omega =$$
$$= \frac{1}{\sqrt{2}} \oint \alpha^*(1)\alpha(1) \, d\omega_1 \cdot \oint \beta^*(2)\alpha(2) \, d\omega_2 +$$
$$- \frac{1}{\sqrt{2}} \oint \beta^*(1)\alpha(1) \, d\omega_1 \cdot \oint \alpha^*(2)\alpha(2) \, d\omega_2 =$$
$$= \frac{1}{\sqrt{2}} \cdot 1 \cdot 0 - \frac{1}{\sqrt{2}} 0 \cdot 1 = 0$$

For the same reason all elements vanish that involve integration of two *different* spin wave functions. Accordingly, the 16×16 determinant can be represented schematically as follows, where use is made of the fact that all orbital and spin wave functions are normalized:

$$\frac{1}{2}\begin{vmatrix} A & 0 & 0 & 0 \\ 0 & B & 0 & 0 \\ 0 & 0 & B & 0 \\ 0 & 0 & 0 & B \end{vmatrix}$$

where A and B are each 4×4 arrays and 0 indicates a 4×4 array with all elements equal to zero. The A array is shown in Table 18-1. P, Q, R, and S refer to the wave functions listed in Sec. 18-3.

---

problem 18-2. By analogy with the A array in Table 18.1, draw the B array.

It is now necessary to evaluate the elements of the determinants A and B. Since the functions ψ_{1s} and ψ_{2s} are independent of the angles θ and ϕ, the many integrals in arrays A and B reduce to only a few. Consider the first diagonal term in the determinant

$$\oint[\psi_{1s}(1)\psi_{2s}(2) + \psi_{2s}(1)\psi_{1s}(2)]^* \frac{e^2}{r_{12}} [\psi_{1s}(1)\psi_{2s}(2) + \psi_{2s}(1)\psi_{1s}(2)]\, dq =$$
$$= \oint|\psi_{1s}(1)\psi_{2s}(2)|^2 \frac{e^2}{r_{12}}\, dq + \oint|\psi_{2s}(1)\psi_{1s}(2)|^2 \frac{e^2}{r_{12}}\, dq +$$
$$+ \oint[\psi_{1s}(1)\psi_{2s}(2)]^* \frac{e^2}{r_{12}} [\psi_{2s}(1)\psi_{1s}(2)]\, dq +$$
$$+ \oint[\psi_{2s}(1)\psi_{1s}(2)]^* \frac{e^2}{r_{12}} [\psi_{1s}(1)\psi_{2s}(2)]\, dq$$

If we write

$$J_S \equiv \oint|\psi_{1s}(1)\psi_{2s}(2)|^2 \frac{e^2}{r_{12}}\, dq = \oint|\psi_{2s}(1)\psi_{1s}(2)|^2 \frac{e^2}{r_{12}}\, dq \qquad (18\text{-}2)$$

and $$K_S \equiv \oint[\psi_{1s}(1)\psi_{2s}(2)]^* \frac{e^2}{r_{12}} [\psi_{2s}(1)\psi_{1s}(2)]\, dq =$$
$$= \oint[\psi_{2s}(1)\psi_{1s}(2)]^* \frac{e^2}{r_{12}} [\psi_{1s}(1)\psi_{2s}(2)]\, dq \qquad (18\text{-}3)$$

table 18-1

---

the *A* array

$E_\nu^0 - E + \oint P^* \frac{e^2}{r_{12}} P\, dq$	$\oint P^* \frac{e^2}{r_{12}} Q\, dq$	$\oint P^* \frac{e^2}{r_{12}} R\, dq$	$\oint P^* \frac{e^2}{r_{12}} S\, dq$
$\oint Q^* \frac{e^2}{r_{12}} P\, dq$	$E_\nu^0 - E_\nu + \oint Q^* \frac{e^2}{r_{12}} Q\, dq$	$\oint Q^* \frac{e^2}{r_{12}} R\, dq$	$\oint Q^* \frac{e^2}{r_{12}} S\, dq$
$\oint R^* \frac{e^2}{r_{12}} P\, dq$	$\oint R^* \frac{e^2}{r_{12}} Q\, dq$	$E_\nu^0 - E_\nu + \oint R^* \frac{e^2}{r_{12}} R\, dq$	$\oint R^* \frac{e^2}{r_{12}} S\, dq$
$\oint S^* \frac{e^2}{r_{12}} P\, dq$	$\oint S^* \frac{e^2}{r_{12}} Q\, dq$	$\oint S^* \frac{e^2}{r_{12}} R\, dq$	$E_\nu^0 - E_\nu + \oint S^* \frac{e^2}{r_{12}} S\, dq$

then

$$\oint[\psi_{1s}(1)\psi_{2s}(2) + \psi_{2s}(1)\psi_{1s}(2)]^* \frac{e^2}{r_{12}} [\psi_{1s}(1)\psi_{2s}(2) + \psi_{2s}(1)\psi_{1s}(2)]\, dq = $$
$$= 2(J_s + K_s)$$

The other diagonal terms of A have similar integrals; because of symmetry,

$$\oint[\psi_{1s}(1)\psi_{2p_x}(2) + \psi_{2p_x}(1)\psi_{1s}(2)]^* \frac{e^2}{r_{12}} [\psi_{1s}(1)\psi_{2p_x}(2) + \psi_{2p_x}(1)\psi_{1s}(2)]\, dq =$$
$$= \oint[\psi_{1s}(1)\psi_{2p_y}(2) + \psi_{2p_y}(1)\psi_{1s}(2)]^* \frac{e^2}{r_{12}} [\psi_{1s}(1)\psi_{2p_y}(2) + \psi_{2p_y}\psi_{1s}(2)]\, dq =$$
$$= \oint[\psi_{1s}(1)\psi_{2p_z}(2) + \psi_{2p_z}(1)\psi_{1s}(2)]^* \frac{e^2}{r_{12}} [\psi_{1s}(1)\psi_{2p_z}(2)+\psi_{2p_z}(1)\psi_{1s}(2)]\, dq=$$
$$= 2(J_p + K_p)$$

where the definitions of J_p and K_p are analogous to those of J_s and K_s

In the off-diagonal terms the integrands are always odd in one of the coordinates, since $\psi_{2p_x} \sim x$, $\psi_{2p_y} \sim y$, and $\psi_{2p_z} \sim z$. Therefore all off-diagonal terms vanish. We have thus reduced the 16×16 determinant to a diagonal one: array B can be found in a manner completely analogous to that of finding A. Thus only four integrals, namely, J_s, K_s, J_p, and K_p, need be evaluated. The resulting equation for the perturbed energy levels is shown on page 268.

Thus we find 16 solutions, 15 of which are multiple ones. The solutions are shown schematically in Fig. 18-1. It should be noted that while the 16 unperturbed states were completely degenerate, the degeneracy is partially removed by the perturbation. It might be well to examine here the nature of the removal of the degeneracy. In the first place, there is the subdivision into the 4 levels centered around $E_\nu{}^0 + J_s$ and the 12 levels centered around $E_\nu{}^0 + J_p$. While we have not explicitly evaluated the J_s and J_p integrals, it is not difficult to understand why $J_p > J_s$. It was shown in Chap. 11 that the s orbitals are spherically symmetrical, while the p orbitals are concentrated along the cartesian axes. The $2p$ orbitals penetrate, as it were, the $1s$ orbitals, while the $2s$ orbitals are concentric with the $1s$ orbitals, but have a larger mean radius. Therefore electrons in a $2s$ orbital avoid those in $1s$ orbitals, while the $2p$ electrons often come close to $1s$ electrons. It is not surprising, therefore, that the states with one electron in one of the $2p$ orbitals and the other in a $1s$ orbital are less stable than the ones having one electron in a $2s$ and the other in a $1s$ orbital. The fact that the states

$$
\begin{vmatrix}
E_\nu^0+J_s+K_s-E_\nu & 0 & 0 & 0 & 0 & 0 & 0 & 0 & 0 & 0 & 0 & 0 & 0 & 0 & 0 & 0 \\
0 & E_\nu^0+J_p+K_p-E_\nu & 0 & 0 & 0 & 0 & 0 & 0 & 0 & 0 & 0 & 0 & 0 & 0 & 0 & 0 \\
0 & 0 & E_\nu^0+J_p+K_p-E_\nu & 0 & 0 & 0 & 0 & 0 & 0 & 0 & 0 & 0 & 0 & 0 & 0 & 0 \\
0 & 0 & 0 & E_\nu^0+J_p+K_p-E_\nu & 0 & 0 & 0 & 0 & 0 & 0 & 0 & 0 & 0 & 0 & 0 & 0 \\
0 & 0 & 0 & 0 & E_\nu^0+J_s-K_s-E_\nu & 0 & 0 & 0 & 0 & 0 & 0 & 0 & 0 & 0 & 0 & 0 \\
0 & 0 & 0 & 0 & 0 & E_\nu^0+J_p-K_p-E_\nu & 0 & 0 & 0 & 0 & 0 & 0 & 0 & 0 & 0 & 0 \\
0 & 0 & 0 & 0 & 0 & 0 & E_\nu^0+J_p-K_p-E_\nu & 0 & 0 & 0 & 0 & 0 & 0 & 0 & 0 & 0 \\
0 & 0 & 0 & 0 & 0 & 0 & 0 & E_\nu^0+J_p-K_p-E_\nu & 0 & 0 & 0 & 0 & 0 & 0 & 0 & 0 \\
0 & 0 & 0 & 0 & 0 & 0 & 0 & 0 & E_\nu^0+J_s-K_s-E_\nu & 0 & 0 & 0 & 0 & 0 & 0 & 0 \\
0 & 0 & 0 & 0 & 0 & 0 & 0 & 0 & 0 & E_\nu^0+J_p-K_p-E_\nu & 0 & 0 & 0 & 0 & 0 & 0 \\
0 & 0 & 0 & 0 & 0 & 0 & 0 & 0 & 0 & 0 & E_\nu^0+J_p-K_p-E_\nu & 0 & 0 & 0 & 0 & 0 \\
0 & 0 & 0 & 0 & 0 & 0 & 0 & 0 & 0 & 0 & 0 & E_\nu^0+J_p-K_p-E_\nu & 0 & 0 & 0 & 0 \\
0 & 0 & 0 & 0 & 0 & 0 & 0 & 0 & 0 & 0 & 0 & 0 & E_\nu^0+J_s-K_s-E_\nu & 0 & 0 & 0 \\
0 & 0 & 0 & 0 & 0 & 0 & 0 & 0 & 0 & 0 & 0 & 0 & 0 & E_\nu^0+J_p-K_p-E_\nu & 0 & 0 \\
0 & 0 & 0 & 0 & 0 & 0 & 0 & 0 & 0 & 0 & 0 & 0 & 0 & 0 & E_\nu^0+J_p-K_p-E_\nu & 0 \\
0 & 0 & 0 & 0 & 0 & 0 & 0 & 0 & 0 & 0 & 0 & 0 & 0 & 0 & 0 & E_\nu^0+J_p-K_p-E_\nu
\end{vmatrix} = 0
$$

Here the A and B determinants are enclosed by dotted rectangles.

centered around $E_\nu^0 + J_p$ are thrice as numerous as those around $E_\nu^0 + J_s$ is owing to the fact that there is only one $2s$ orbital, but that there are three $2p$ orbitals. The degeneracy would be further resolved if the helium atom were placed in strong electric field.

The splitting of levels into $(J + K)$ and $(J - K)$ sublevels is due to the electron spin. The $(J - K)$ levels are triplets; in these levels, the orbital factor in each wave function is antisymmetrical in the coordinates of the two electrons, and for each orbital wave function there are the three symmetrical spin functions, corresponding to parallel alignment of the two electron spins. The $(J + K)$ levels are singlets: the wave function for each level is the product of a symmetrical orbital function and the antisymmetrical spin function

$$\frac{1}{\sqrt{2}}[\alpha(1)\beta(2) - \beta(1)\alpha(2)]$$

Since the perturbation (e^2/r_{12}) is positive, both the J and K integrals are positive, so that $(J + K) > (J - K)$. For any given combination of orbital quantum numbers, the triplet levels are therefore more stable than the singlet level. The following argument confirms this conclusion on the basis of physical insight.

18-5 Physical interpretation of J and K. Since $|\psi_{1s}(1)|^2$ is the probability density for electron 1 and $|\psi_{2s}(2)|^2$ is the probability density for electron 2, the J_s and J_p integrals each represent the repulsion between two charge clouds. The K_s and K_p integrals cannot be given such a classical interpretation. These result from the requirement that a system of electrons must be invariant to the exchange of the electrons; K_s and K_p are called exchange integrals.

The triplet levels have symmetric spin functions and antisymmetric orbital functions, the latter being of the form

$$\frac{1}{\sqrt{2}}[\psi_a(1)\psi_b(2) - \psi_b(1)\psi_a(2)]$$

where the a and b designate different combinations of the orbital quantum numbers. The probability of finding electron 1 at position $\mathbf{r}_1$ and simultaneously electron 2 at position $\mathbf{r}_2$ is given by

$$P_t = \tfrac{1}{2}|\psi_a(\mathbf{r}_1)\psi_b(\mathbf{r}_2) - \psi_b(\mathbf{r}_1)\psi_a(\mathbf{r}_2)|^2$$

Similarly, the probability of finding the two electrons at the same location, for singlet states is given by

$$P_s = \tfrac{1}{2}|\psi_a(\mathbf{r}_1)\psi_b(\mathbf{r}_2) + \psi_b(\mathbf{r}_1)\psi_a(\mathbf{r}_2)|^2$$

Classically, the probability of finding one electron at $\mathbf{r}_1$ and the other at $\mathbf{r}_2$ would be the product of the two independent probabilities

$$P_c = |\psi_a(\mathbf{r}_1)|^2|\psi_b(\mathbf{r}_2)|^2 \qquad \text{or} \qquad P_c = |\psi_a(\mathbf{r}_2)|^2|\psi_b(\mathbf{r}_1)|^2$$

We see, therefore, that even in the unperturbed system, where there is no force acting between the two electrons, their motions cannot be considered to be independent of each other, but are correlated by their spins. To compare P_t, P_s, and P_c, let us allow $\mathbf{r}_1$ to become approximately equal to $\mathbf{r}_2$ in P_t and P_s, i.o.w., let us compare the probabilities of finding two electrons close together, for each case. When $\mathbf{r}_1$ approaches $\mathbf{r}_2$, P_t approaches zero, whereas P_s becomes proportional to the two expressions for P_c, which become identical to each other. Thus the spin correlation causes nonclassical behavior for the triplet levels, in that the two electrons are less likely to approach each other than would be expected classically if their motions were truly independent. The expectation value of $|r_{12}|$ is therefore greater and that of $|1/r_{12}|$ smaller for triplets than for singlets. Therefore, the repulsion between the electrons has a smaller expectation value for triplets than it does for singlets, so that the triplets are more stable than the singlets.

The stabilization due to parallel alignment of spins has important consequences in determining the relative stability of different states of complex atoms and in explaining some of the magnetic properties of materials. The first of these topics will be discussed in Chap. 19 (Hund's rule); detailed discussion of magnetism is beyond the scope of this volume. It must suffice to say here that magnetic interactions are interpreted in terms of the exchange energy, since it stabilizes parallel orientations of electron spins whenever environmental conditions are favorable.

It is well to compare the exchange energy discussed in this chapter with the resonance energy discussed in Chap. 14. Both energies cause stabilization; neither can be linked to classical phenomena. They differ from one another in that the resonance-energy integral involves the space coordinates of only one electron, whereas the exchange energy involves integration over the space coordinates of a pair of electrons and also involves the spin coordinates of the electrons. The resonance-energy stabilization results from the fact that an electron can find itself in two (or more) distinct configurations having the same energy. The exchange energy results from the fact that electrons are indistinguishable so that exchange of any two electrons in a system does not change any properties of the system.

18-6 The term value diagram for helium. The numbers in parentheses in Fig. 18-1 are the term values (term value ≡ − energy)

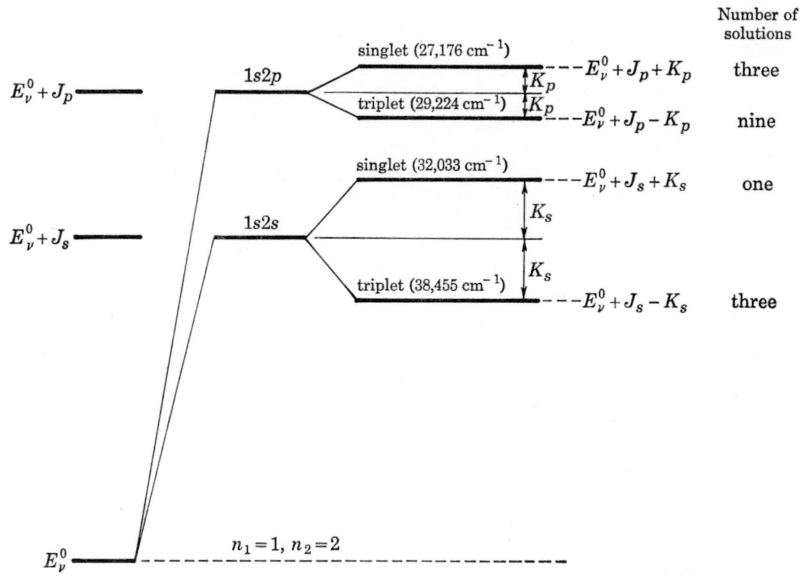

fig. 18-1 sixteen energy levels of helium in the 1*s* 2*s* and 1*s* 2*p* configurations

for the states resulting from the 1*s* 2*s* and 1*s* 2*p* configurations of the helium atom, as derived from measurements on the helium spectrum. The zero term value would correspond to term value for He^+ (1*s*); the term value for the ground state of helium ($1s^2$) is not shown in Fig. 18-1; it lies at 198,298 cm^{-1} (24.58 ev), much below the lowest entry in the figure. It is observed that the magnitudes of J and of K constitute a significant correction to the unperturbed energies of the helium atom.

18-7 Summary. We have applied perturbation theory to the helium atom, which had been treated in Chap. 16 without consideration of the electronic repulsion. By considering this repulsion as a perturbation of the system treated in Chap. 16, we have resolved some degeneracies found in that chapter, and have supplemented Chap. 17 by treating a system having highly degenerate unperturbed wave functions. It should perhaps be noted that the electronic repulsion in the helium atom is not small enough to be treated as a mere perturbation; more refined calculations would give better agreement with experiment than for the simple model assumed here. Nevertheless, the results derived here give a striking qualitative agreement with the spectroscopic results.

electronic configurations of atoms

chapter

19

19-1 Introduction. Many of the principles used in the treatment of the helium atom in Chap. 18 may be extended to a discussion of atoms having a higher atomic number. With the aid of perturbation theory, a systematic classification of the seventeen lowest energy levels of the helium atoms was achieved in Chap. 18. Whereas the magnitude of the energies of the various levels can be computed only by the numerical evaluation of various complex integrals, these magnitudes can be determined experimentally by spectroscopic methods. An important aspect of the theoretical treatment is the recognition of the nature of the forces that resolve the high degeneracy of the unperturbed central-field system.

When elements containing more than two electrons are considered, a numerical evaluation of the energy levels becomes a formidable problem. However, a systematic evaluation of spectroscopic and other experimental data is greatly aided by the use of certain semiempirical rules that are based on the principles of wave mechanics discussed in previous chapters.

19-2 The exclusion principle. It is recalled that the state of an electron in a central field is described by four quantum numbers, n, l, m_l, and m_s, and that as a consequence of the exclusion principle no more than one electron in an atom may have the same set of values for these four quantum numbers. As was done in the case of the helium atom, we shall first neglect the electrostatic interaction between electrons and find the number of orbitals available to electrons in the field of an atomic nucleus.

When the quantum number n equals unity, l can have only one possible value, namely, zero. A single electron may have m_s equal to $+\frac{1}{2}$ or to $-\frac{1}{2}$. When two electrons move in the field of an atomic nucleus, both may have $n = 1$, $l = 0$, but in this case the exclusion principle requires one electron to have $m_s = +\frac{1}{2}$ and the other electron to have $m_s = -\frac{1}{2}$. This is the case for the ground state of the helium atom, whose wave function was found in Chap. 16 to be

$$\frac{1}{\sqrt{2}} \Psi_{1s}(1)\Psi_{1s}(2)[\alpha(1)\beta(2) - \beta(1)\alpha(2)]$$

In the case of the element lithium there are three electrons moving in the field of a triply charged nucleus; these three electrons all must have different sets of the quantum numbers n, l, m_l, m_s. Since there are only two states available that have $n = 1$, at least one of the electrons must have a larger value of n. Since the level $n = 1$ has the lowest energy, lithium in its ground state has two electrons in the $n = 1$ level, the third in the $n = 2$ level. The two electrons having $n = 1$ together have no net orbital angular momentum. They have a spherical charge distribution, and have no net spin moment (the two spins are oriented in opposite directions). These two electrons form an inert shell, so that the electron having $n = 2$ moves in a central field caused by the triply charged lithium nucleus and the electron cloud in the level $n = 1$. There are four possible orbital states available to the electron having $n = 2$, and for each of these the electron has two possible spin states. Consequently, the degeneracy of the $n = 2$ level is eight.

This argument can be extended to any value of n. For any value of n, the quantum number l may have any value from zero to $(n - 1)$, each value of l corresponding to $(2l + 1)$ possible values of m_l. Since, furthermore, each orbital state corresponds to two spin states, the degeneracy of a level having principal quantum number n is given by

$$D(n) = 2 \sum_{l=0}^{n-1} (2l + 1) = 2[1 + 3 + 5 + \cdots (2n - 1)]$$

In the sum inside the square bracket, the first and last term add up to $2n$, as do the second and one-but-last term, etc. Since there are n

terms in the summation,

$$D(n) = 2 \cdot \frac{n}{2}(2n) = 2n^2 \qquad \text{when } n \text{ is even,}$$

$$= 2 \cdot \frac{n-1}{2}(2n) + 2n = 2n^2 \qquad \text{when } n \text{ is odd}$$

Therefore

$$D(n) = 2n^2 \tag{19-1}$$

---

problem 19-1. Consider an excited state of a lithium atom where two electrons are in $n = 1$ states, while a third electron is excited to an $n = 3$ level.

(*a*) Find the degeneracy of this excited state.

(*b*) List all possible wave functions of the third electron.

The next element beyond lithium, namely, beryllium, contains two electrons in the $n = 1$ level and two electrons in the $n = 2$ level when it is in its ground state. The spin interactions are similar to those between the electrons in the helium atom in its ground state, but the ground state of beryllium (considering only central-field forces) is more highly degenerate than the ground state of helium.

---

problem 19-2. List all possible wave functions (orbital and spin dependence) for the ground state of the beryllium atom. (Do not explicitly consider the two electrons having $n = 1$. Assume only central-field forces. Take as unperturbed single-electron wave functions ψ_{2s}, ψ_{2p_x}, ψ_{2p_y}, ψ_{2p_z}.)

19-3 Resolution of the orbital degeneracies. We shall now consider the resolution of the degeneracies when electron interaction is taken into account. According to the result of Prob. 19-2 the ground state of beryllium is 28-fold generate for a spherically symmetrical potential field. Just as was the case for the helium atom in its excited states, perturbations of the spherical symmetry partially resolve this degeneracy. In evaluating the effect of various perturbations, we use the result of Chap. 17, that, to a first approximation the wave functions may be assumed unaffected by the perturbation, so that the energy values can be evaluated by averaging the perturbation over the unperturbed wave functions.

The first perturbation we consider is the one imposed by external constraints. The geometry of the various eigenfunctions of the $\mathfrak{L}^2$ operator, as derived in Chap. 11, is such that in a crystalline environment certain hybrid orbitals are more stable than others. For instance, the p_x, p_y, and p_z orbitals are particularly stable in a cation that is surrounded tetrahedrally by anions, for the orbitals have their

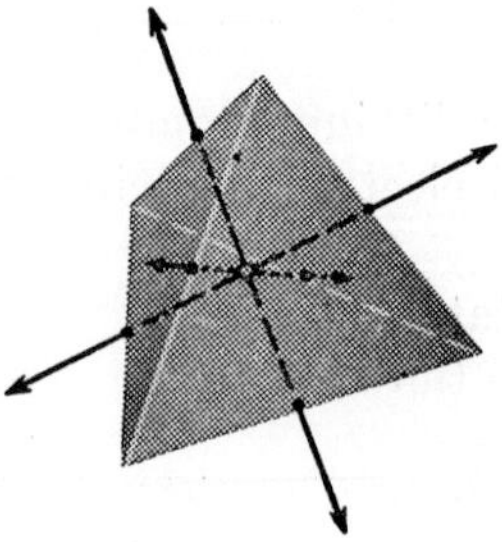

fig. 19-1 octahedrally directed orbitals

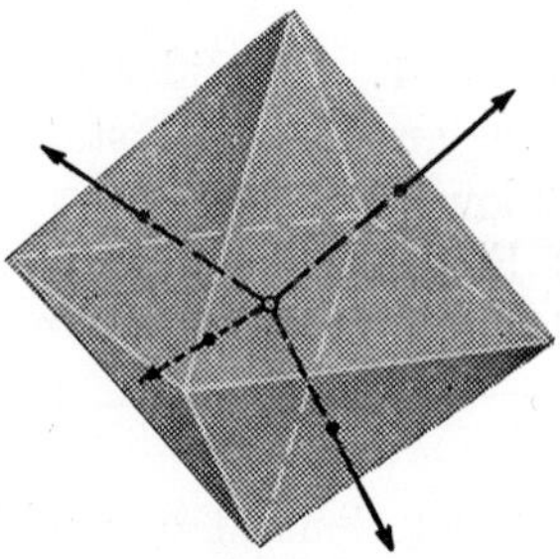

fig. 19-2 tetrahedrally directed orbitals

charge densities concentrated in directions perpendicular to the edges of the tetrahedra, that is, away from the corners where the anions are located (see Fig. 19-1). In this environment the repulsion between the electrons on the cation and the anions is therefore much smaller than this repulsion would be in an octahedral environment, where the orbitals have their maximum densities in the directions of the anions. This phenomenon of "crystalline field splitting," that is, the resolution of the degeneracy of orbitals in an atom or ion by the field due to surrounding atoms or ions has found numerous applications in solid-state physics.

Similar splitting occurs between hybrid orbitals of the so-called transition elements (see Sec. 19-7). In this case both tetrahedrally and octahedrally directed orbitals are formed by *spd* hybridization;† Figs. 19-2 and 19-1 show the stabilization of both of these in, respectively, octahedral and tetrahedral environments.

More subtle are the perturbations inside isolated (e.g., gaseous) atoms and ions. In Sec. 19-2 we stated that the two electrons having

† L. Pauling "The Nature of the Chemical Bond," 3d ed., chap. V, Cornell University Press, Ithaca, N.Y., 1960.

$n = 1$ form an inert shell because their charge distribution is spherically symmetrical, and there is no net orbital and no net spin angular momentum. The same can be said about any level denoted by the quantum number n whose n^2 orbitals are *all* occupied by electrons.

---

problem 19-3 Show that the charge density due to four electrons that occupy, respectively, $2s$, $2p_x$, $2p_y$, and $2p_z$ orbitals is spherically symmetrical. Extend the argument to a complete $n = 2$ shell.

The electrons in a partially filled "outer" shell of an atom or ion are called "valence electrons." As long as the valence electrons do not penetrate the inner, inert shells, they all move in the same spherically symmetrical field because of the combined effects of the nucleus and the filled inert shells. In Chap. 11 we found, however, that orbitals having higher values of l are more strongly directional than the ones having low values of l. Therefore orbitals with $l > 0$ penetrate the inner shells more than do the s valence orbitals, which are concentric with the inner shells but have a larger radius (see Chaps. 13 and 18). When we take into account the repulsion between electrons, therefore, we expect the repulsion between the inner shells and the s-valence electron to be less than the repulsion between the inner shells and the p-valence electrons, etc. Therefore for any value of n the electrons having smaller values of l are more stable than those having larger values of l. While we found in Chap. 13 that the energy in a coulombic field depends only on the quantum number n, we have now shown that the perturbations in an atom or ion make the energy somewhat dependent on l as well.

19-4 Resolution of spin degeneracies. Having considered the interaction of valence electrons with their crystalline environment and with the inner, inert shells, we now consider the interactions between the valence electrons themselves. In Chap. 18 we discussed the exchange energy, which stabilizes electrons that have their spins aligned parallel. We found that in its ground state a helium atom has its two electron spins oriented antiparallel, but that in excited states a parallel spin alignment is more stable than its antiparallel counterpart. The spins are oriented antiparallel in the ground state because the exclusion principle does not permit two $1s$ electrons to have parallel spins and because the energy necessary to raise an electron from the $n = 1$ level to the $n = 2$ level far exceeds the exchange energy gained by parallel alignment. Beryllium has in its ground state two valence electrons in the $n = 2$ level; since $2s$ states are more stable than $2p$ states, parallel alignment of the spins in the ground state would be possible only if the energy difference between $2s$ and $2p$ states is less than the exchange energy. The results of experiment show that there is no net spin on a beryllium atom in its ground state; we conclude therefore that the exchange energy is less than the energy gap between $2s$ and $2p$ states. Consequently, in the $n = 2$ level, the most stable configuration is one in which the two electrons have $l = 0$, with spins antiparallel.

The elements boron, carbon, nitrogen, oxygen, and fluorine have, respectively, 3, 4, 5, 6, and 7 electrons in the $n = 2$ shell. Of these, two electrons have the quantum numbers $l = 0$, $m_l = 0$, $m_s = \pm\frac{1}{2}$; the others are all in p states ($l = 1$). Since there are three degenerate states ($m_l = +1, 0, -1$), up to six electrons can be accommodated in the ($n = 2$, $l = 1$) level. Of these, three electrons can align their spins parallel; in a nitrogen atom, in its ground state, for instance, the seven electrons have the quantum numbers given in Table 19-1. This atom therefore has a net spin momentum in its ground state.

19-5 Multiplet structure; symmetric spin function of three electrons. In Chap. 16 the addition of the spins of two electrons was discussed; this discussion can be extended to include three or more electrons. Here we shall find the spin momentum for the three $2p$ electrons in the nitrogen atom.

table 19-1

electron configuration of nitrogen in its ground state

n	l	m_l	m_s
1	0	0	$+\frac{1}{2}$
1	0	0	$-\frac{1}{2}$
2	0	0	$+\frac{1}{2}$
2	0	0	$-\frac{1}{2}$
2	1	1	$+\frac{1}{2}$
2	1	0	$+\frac{1}{2}$
2	1	-1	$+\frac{1}{2}$

$$\sigma^2 = (\boldsymbol{\sigma}_1 + \boldsymbol{\sigma}_2 + \boldsymbol{\sigma}_3)^2 = \sigma_1{}^2 + \sigma_2{}^2 + \sigma_3{}^2 + 2(\boldsymbol{\sigma}_1 \cdot \boldsymbol{\sigma}_2 + \boldsymbol{\sigma}_1 \cdot \boldsymbol{\sigma}_3 + \boldsymbol{\sigma}_2 \cdot \boldsymbol{\sigma}_3) =$$
$$= \sigma_1{}^2 + \sigma_2{}^2 + \sigma_3{}^2 + (\sigma_x + i\sigma_y)_1(\sigma_x - i\sigma_y)_2 + (\sigma_x - i\sigma_y)_1(\sigma_x + i\sigma_y)_2 +$$
$$+ (\sigma_x + i\sigma_y)_1(\sigma_x - i\sigma_y)_3 + (\sigma_x - i\sigma_y)_1(\sigma_x + i\sigma_y)_3 +$$
$$+ (\sigma_x + i\sigma_y)_2(\sigma_x - i\sigma_y)_3 + (\sigma_x - i\sigma_y)_2(\sigma_x + i\sigma_y)_3 + 2\sigma_{z_1}\sigma_{z_2} + 2\sigma_{z_1}\sigma_{z_3} +$$
$$+ 2\sigma_{z_2}\sigma_{z_3} \qquad (19\text{-}2)$$

$$\sigma_z = \sigma_{z_1} + \sigma_{z_2} + \sigma_{z_3} \qquad (19\text{-}3)$$

Possible spin wave functions are

$$\alpha(1)\alpha(2)\alpha(3)$$
$$\alpha(1)\alpha(2)\beta(3) + \alpha(1)\beta(2)\alpha(3) + \beta(1)\alpha(2)\alpha(3)$$
$$\alpha(1)\beta(2)\beta(3) + \beta(1)\alpha(2)\beta(3) + \beta(1)\beta(2)\alpha(3)$$
$$\beta(1)\beta(2)\beta(3)$$

all of which are symmetrical in the spin coordinates, and hence must be paired with functions antisymmetrical in the space coordinates.

Such an antisymmetrical function of space coordinates may be expressed in the form of a determinant:

$$\psi(\mathbf{r}_1,\mathbf{r}_2,\mathbf{r}_3) = \begin{bmatrix} \psi_{2p_x}(1) & \psi_{2p_y}(1) & \psi_{2p_z}(1) \\ \psi_{2p_x}(2) & \psi_{2p_y}(2(& \psi_{2p_z}(2) \\ \psi_{2p_x}(3) & \psi_{2p_y}(3) & \psi_{2p_z}(3) \end{bmatrix} \qquad (19\text{-}4)$$

---

problem 19-4. Prove that Eq. (19-4) represents a function antisymmetric in the coordinates of all three electrons.

The four states whose orbital wave function is given by Eq. (19-4) and whose four symmetrical spin functions are listed above are called "quartets." The names "singlet," "triplet," and "quartet" refer to the multiplicity; they correspond to the magnitude of $(2S + 1)$ where S is the quantum number representing the resultant spin in an atomic species. The value of $(2S + 1)$ gives the number of component levels (degeneracy) due to spin. The multiplicity may be related to the number of "unpaired" electrons in an atom; it is equal to $(2N \times \frac{1}{2} + 1)$, where N is the number of unpaired electrons, each with a spin quantum number $s = \frac{1}{2}$. In describing the state of an atom, one lists only the outer electron configuration if all the inner shells have their full complement of electrons.

---

problem 19-5. Determine the multiplicity and the number of unpaired electrons for the following ground-state configurations:

(*a*) $3s^2$
(*b*) $2p$
(*c*) $3s^23p^3$
(*d*) $3d^34s^2$
(*e*) $3s^23p^4$
(*f*) $3d^54s^2$

We shall evaluate the total spin and its Z component for the symmetrical three-electron spin function $\alpha(1)\alpha(2)\alpha(3)$, given above. According to Eq. (19-2),

$$\begin{aligned}
\sigma^2\alpha(1)\alpha(2)\alpha(3) &= \\
&= [\sigma_1{}^2\alpha(1)]\alpha(2)\alpha(3) + \alpha(1)[\sigma_2{}^2\alpha(2)]\alpha(3) + \alpha(1)\alpha(2)[\sigma_3{}^2\alpha(3)] + \\
&+ (\sigma_x + i\sigma_y)_1\alpha(1)(\sigma_x - i\sigma_y)_2\alpha(2)\alpha(3) + \\
&+ (\sigma_x - i\sigma_y)_1\alpha(1)(\sigma_x + i\sigma_y)_2\alpha(2)\alpha(3) + \\
&+ (\sigma_x + i\sigma_y)_1\alpha(1)\alpha(2)(\sigma_x - i\sigma_y)_3\alpha(3) + \\
&+ (\sigma_x - i\sigma_y)_1\alpha(1)\alpha(2)(\sigma_x + i\sigma_y)_3\alpha(3) + \\
&+ \alpha(1)(\sigma_x + i\sigma_y)_2\alpha(2)(\sigma_x - i\sigma_y)_3\alpha(3) + \\
&+ \alpha(1)(\sigma_x - i\sigma_y)_2\alpha(2)(\sigma_x + i\sigma_y)_3\alpha(3) + \\
&+ 2\sigma_{z_1}\alpha(1)\sigma_{z_2}\alpha(2)\alpha(3) + 2\sigma_{z_1}\alpha(1)\alpha(2)\sigma_{z_3}\alpha(3) + 2\alpha(1)\sigma_{z_2}\alpha(2)\sigma_{z_3}\alpha(3)
\end{aligned}$$

Since $\sigma^2\alpha = \frac{3}{4}\hbar^2\alpha$, $(\sigma_x + i\sigma_y)\alpha = 0$ and $\sigma_z\alpha = \frac{1}{2}\hbar\alpha$:

$$\begin{aligned}
\sigma^2\alpha(1)\alpha(2)\alpha(3) &= 3\cdot\tfrac{3}{4}\hbar^2\alpha(1)\alpha(2)\alpha(3) + 3\cdot\tfrac{1}{2}\hbar^2\alpha(1)\alpha(2)\alpha(3) = \\
&= \tfrac{3}{2}(\tfrac{3}{2}+1)\hbar^2\alpha(1)\alpha(2)\alpha(3) \qquad (19\text{-}5)
\end{aligned}$$

Also, from Eq. (19-3),

$$\begin{aligned}
\sigma_z\alpha(1)\alpha(2)\alpha(3) &= [\sigma_{z_1}\alpha(1)]\alpha(2)\alpha(3) + \alpha(1)[\sigma_{z_2}\alpha(2)]\alpha(3) + \\
&+ \alpha(1)\alpha(2)[\sigma_{z_3}\alpha(3)] = \tfrac{3}{2}\hbar\alpha(1)\alpha(2)\alpha(3) \qquad (19\text{-}6)
\end{aligned}$$

The results obtained for one-, two-, and three-electron systems can now be generalized. The total spin is quantized according to the expression $\sqrt{S(S+1)}\hbar$, where $S = \frac{1}{2}$ for a single electron, $S = 1$ for two unpaired electrons, $S = \frac{3}{2}$ for three unpaired electrons, and, in general, $S = \frac{1}{2}N$ for N unpaired electrons. The Z component was found for a single electron to have the possible values $+\frac{1}{2}\hbar$ and $-\frac{1}{2}\hbar$; for two electrons it was found to be $\hbar$, 0, or $-\hbar$. For one of the symmetric three-electron spin functions we have found a Z component of spin angular moment equal to $\frac{3}{2}\hbar$; it is similarly proved that the other possible values of this Z component are $\frac{1}{2}\hbar$, $-\frac{1}{2}\hbar$, and $-\frac{3}{2}\hbar$.

problem 19-6. Find the magnitude and Z component of spin angular momentum for the three remaining symmetrical three-electron spin functions.

When these last results are generalized, we see that there are $(2S + 1)$ different spin states, having respective Z components of spin angular momentum equal to $S\hbar$, $(S - 1)\hbar$, $(S - 2)\hbar$ . . . , $-(S - 2)\hbar$, $-(S - 1)\hbar$, $-S\hbar$.

19-6 Other spin functions for three electron systems. In the discussion of the helium atom it was shown that the triplet states

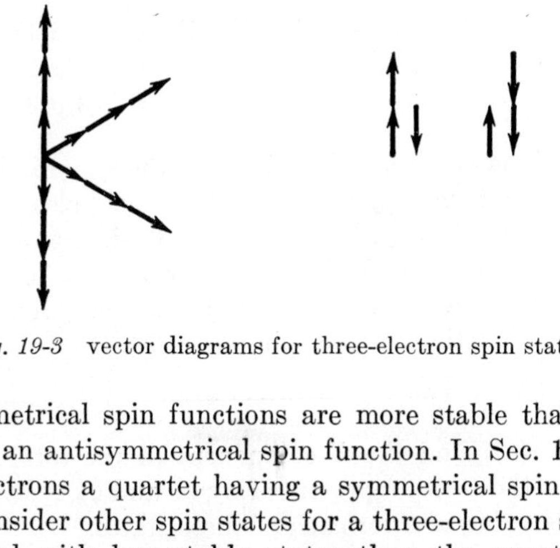

fig. 19-3 vector diagrams for three-electron spin states

having symmetrical spin functions are more stable than the singlet state having an antisymmetrical spin function. In Sec. 19-5 we found for three electrons a quartet having a symmetrical spin function; we shall now consider other spin states for a three-electron system; these are associated with less stable states than the quartets found in Sec. 19-5.

A vector diagram is helpful in constructing the spin functions for these less stable states; one of the states corresponds to two electrons in the α state and the third in the β state, while the other one corresponds to two electrons in the β state, and the third electron in the α state (see Fig. 19-3). One would be tempted to write, in analogy with the symmetric quartets,

$$\alpha(1)\alpha(2)\beta(3) - \alpha(1)\beta(2)\alpha(3) + \beta(1)\alpha(2)\alpha(3) \qquad (A)$$

and

$$\alpha(1)\beta(2)\beta(3) - \beta(1)\alpha(2)\beta(3) + \beta(1)\beta(2)\alpha(3) \qquad (B)$$

It is observed that by interchanging the symbols (1) and (2) in functions (A) and (B) that these functions are not antisymmetrical, for

$$\alpha(1)\alpha(2)\beta(3) - \alpha(1)\beta(2)\alpha(3) + \beta(1)\alpha(2)\alpha(3) \neq -[\alpha(1)\alpha(2)\beta(3) - \beta(1)\alpha(2)\alpha(3) + \alpha(1)\beta(2)\alpha(3)]$$

A necessary condition for the function to be antisymmetrical is, therefore, that the term $\alpha(1)\alpha(2)\beta(3)$ be preceded by a coefficient whose sign changes as electrons 1 and 2 are interchanged. Two satisfactory wave functions for the three $2p$ electrons in nitrogen are, written in determinantal form,

$$\psi_\alpha \equiv \begin{vmatrix} \psi_{2p_x}(1)\alpha(1) & \psi_{2p_y}(1)\alpha(1) & \psi_{2p_z}(1)\beta(1) \\ \psi_{2p_x}(2)\alpha(2) & \psi_{2p_y}(2)\alpha(2) & \psi_{2p_z}(2)\beta(2) \\ \psi_{2p_x}(3)\alpha(3) & \psi_{2p_y}(3)\alpha(3) & \psi_{2p_z}(3)\beta(3) \end{vmatrix} \tag{19-7}$$

and

$$\psi_\beta \equiv \begin{vmatrix} \psi_{2p_x}(1)\alpha(1) & \psi_{2p_y}(1)\beta(1) & \psi_{2p_z}(1)\beta(1) \\ \psi_{2p_x}(2)\alpha(2) & \psi_{2p_y}(2)\beta(2) & \psi_{2p_z}(2)\beta(2) \\ \psi_{2p_x}(3)\alpha(3) & \psi_{2p_y}(3)\beta(3) & \psi_{2p_z}(3)\beta(3) \end{vmatrix} \tag{19-8}$$

In neither of these two wave functions are the space and spin coordinates separated. Satisfactory wave functions could also be obtained by replacing ψ_{2p_x} by ψ_{2p_z} in Eqs. (19-7) and (19-8), since two electrons having different spin states may be in the same orbital state. Since the spin and orbital coordinates are not separated here, these functions are not necessarily eigenfunctions of the spin operators.

---

problem 19-7. (*a*) Find the Z component of the total spin angular momentum for the states represented by ψ_α and ψ_β.

(*b*) Find the value of S for each of these states.

By a procedure analogous to, but more involved than that used in Chap. 18, it is shown that the doublet states, in which one spin is antiparallel to the other two, are less stable than the quartet states, whose wave functions were found in Sec. 19-5.

In general, $S = \Sigma m_s$, the sum over all electrons of their quantum numbers m_s (see Sec. 16-2).

19-7 Hund's rule. The most stable spin configuration of a group of electrons in an atom that have the same values of the quantum numbers n and l corresponds to a state of *maximum* multiplicity consistent with the exclusion principle. This rule was deduced by Hund from spectroscopic results; the explanation of the rule is that a state of high multiplicity is a state of high total spin quantum number and that a high total spin quantum number implies parallel alignment of the electron spins, and hence a favorable condition for exchange stabilization. As an example, let us consider the outer-electron configuration of the elements Na (at. no. 11) through Ar (at. no. 18) in their ground states. Their outer electrons all have $n = 3$ (see Table 19-2). Since the $n = 1$ and $n = 2$ shells together may not contain more than 10 electrons, the $n = 3$ shell of Na contains only one electron, so that $\Sigma m_s = \frac{1}{2}$, and the multiplicity equals 2. Magnesium (at. no. 12) contains two $3s$ electrons; therefore $\Sigma m_s = 0$, and the multiplicity equals 1. The multiplicity of the ground state of the sulphur atom (at. no. 16) is found to be 3. Since a maximum of three p electrons can have their spins parallel, the fourth $3p$ electron has its spin antiparallel to that of the other three electrons, hence $\Sigma m_s = 1$.

19-8 Hybridization and Hund's rule. An interesting configuration is that of copper. This element has the atomic number 29: since the shells having $n \leq 3$ jointly accommodate only twenty-eight electrons, the copper atom contains a single valence electron in a $4s$ state. Loss of the $4s$ electron gives the Cu^+ ion, with ten $3d$-electrons. The Cu^{++} ion, which is more common than the Cu^+ ion, contains nine $3d$ electrons; its existence indicates that it is relatively easy to remove one electron from the $3d$ shell, so that the $3d$ shell is not much more stable than the $4s$ shell, here. In Chap. 13 we found that the energy of an electron in a coulomb field is inversely proportional to the square of the principal quantum number n; the difference between the energies of successive levels therefore decreases with increasing n, i.o.w. the energy values crowd together as n increases.

---

problem 19-8. Compute and compare the energy gap between $n = 1$ and $n = 2$ states and the gap between $n = 3$ and $n = 4$ states for an electron in a spherically symmetrical coulomb field.

Since the energy of a d state is increased because of the penetration of the inner shells, we can understand that $3d$ and $4s$ states are nearly degenerate. In view of this near degeneracy we should reexamine

Hund's rule. The original interpretation of this rule was that in a shell half-filled, or less than half-filled, all electron spins are aligned parallel and that in a shell more than half-filled, electrons pairwise compensate each other's spins in such a way that a maximum net spin is preserved. We must now broaden this interpretation, and specifically the interpretation of the word "shell." Originally a shell was thought of as an assembly of electrons having common values of the quantum numbers n and l. When the $3d$ and $4s$ levels are sufficiently close together to allow a $4s$ electron to align its spin parallel to that of $3d$ electrons, the resulting gain in exchange energy more than compensates for the energy needed to excite the electron from the $3d$ to the $4s$ level. The $3d$ and $4s$ electrons would then belong to one combined shell in the sense of Hund's rule.

Under suitable conditions hybridization of three of the $3d$ orbitals with the $4s$ orbital further bridges the gap between $3d$ and $4s$ states. It is believed that conduction electrons in transition metals exist in the hybrid $(3d)^3\ 4s$ state, because d^3s orbitals have maximum density along four directions 109° apart in space, and these directions are favorable for the metallic bonds between closely packed metal atoms.

A similar hybridization of orbitals occurs in many organic compounds. It is recalled that carbon, with atomic number 6, has two electrons in the $n = 1$ shell, two electrons in the shell having $n = 2$, $l = 1$. For this configuration, $\Sigma m_s = 1$. However, if one electron is excited from its $2s$ to a $2p$ state, and the $2s$ and $2p$ orbitals are combined into a $2sp^3$ orbital, then the four valence electrons of carbon can occupy the four sp^3 hybrid orbitals, and align their spins parallel; this configuration is then stabilized by the exchange energy due to the four parallel electron spins. When the carbon atom is surrounded by four other atoms, for instance, by four hydrogens in the case of CH_4, then each of these four electrons may further stabilize the system by "resonating" between the C and an H (see Chap. 14).

---

problem 19-9. In your opinion, which of the systems given below are stabilized by resonance and which by exchange (some may be stabilized by both, others by neither)? Explain.

(*a*) H_2^+
(*b*) NH_4^+
(*c*) C_6H_6
(*d*) C(diamond)
(*e*) C(graphite)

The maximum density of sp^3 orbitals, like that of d^3s orbitals, is found in directions that point toward the corners of a tetrahedron with the carbon nucleus at the center. This geometrical arrangement is particularly favorable both for exchange energy (hybridization) and for resonance bond formation, because it maximizes the distance between the hydrogen nuclei for a given C-H distance, and hence minimizes the repulsion between the protons, and because it maximizes the distance between parallel electron spins, as required by the exclusion principle. The very common carbon bonds with their characteristic 109° angle are thus seen to be due to orbital hybridization.

19-9. The aufbau principle. The electron configuration of the elements is summarized by the aufbau principle according to which electrons are successively added to a nucleus, each electron occupying a state characterized by a given unique set of values of four quantum numbers. As each electron is added to the system it will occupy an orbital, available according to the exclusion principle. For the ground state of the system, the electrons will select the orbitals with the lowest possible energy. In some cases the relative stability of the different orbitals is determined by a delicate balance between the various interactions discussed above.

---

problem 19-10. Draw a spin diagram, and determine the multiplicity of the ground state of the following:

(*a*) Fe^{+3}
(*b*) Fe^{++}
(*c*) Mn^{+4}
(*d*) Co^{+3}
(*e*) Cu^{+}
(*f*) Cu^{++}
(*g*) V
(*h*) V^{+4}

As a first approximation we can state that the $2n^2$ states having a given value of n must all be occupied before a state having a higher value of n can be occupied. We have seen above that there are exceptions to this first approximation. The occupancy of the $2n^2$ states constituting a level having a given value of n is determined primarily by Hund's rule. Just which values of m_l and which hybrid orbitals give the most stable configuration is determined by external constraints.

Table 19-2 lists the ground-state electron configurations of the elements to atomic number 96, as well as their multiplicities, as deter-

table 19-2

the electron configuration of the elements in the ground state

	orbital	1*s*	2*s*	2*p*	3*s*	3*p*	3*d*	4*s*	4*p*	4*d*	4*f*	5*s*	5*p*	5*d*	
	n	1	2		3			4				5			
	l	0	0	1	0	1	2	0	1	2	3	0	1	2	
atomic number	element														$2S+1$
1	H	1													2
2	He	2													1
3	Li	2	1												2
4	Be	2	2												1
5	B	2	2	1											2
6	C	2	2	2											3
7	N	2	2	3											4
8	O	2	2	4											3
9	F	2	2	5											2
10	Ne	2	2	6											1
11	Na	2	2	6	1										2
12	Mg				2										1
13	Al				2	1									2
14	Si				2	2									3
15	P				2	3									4
16	S				2	4									3
17	Cl				2	5									2
18	Ar				2	6									1
19	K	2	2	6	2	6		1							2
20	Ca							2							1
21	Sc						1	2							2
22	Ti						2	2							3
23	V						3	2							4
24	Cr						5	1							7
25	Mn						5	2							6
26	Fe						6	2							5
27	Co						7	2							4
28	Ni						8	2							3
29	Cu	2	2	6	2	6	10	1							2
30	Zn							2							1
31	Ga							2	1						2
32	Ge							2	2						3
33	As							2	3						4
34	Se							2	4						3
35	Br							2	5						2
36	Kr							2	6						1
37	Rb	2	2	6	2	6	10	2	6			1			2
38	Sr											2			1
39	Y									1		2			2
40	Zr									2		2			3
41	Cb									4		1			6
42	Mo									5		1			7
43	Tc									6		1			6
44	Ru									7		1			5
45	Rh									8		1			4
46	Pd									10					1

	orbital	1s	2s	2p	3s	3p	3d	4s	4p	4d	4f	5s	5p	5d	5f	6s	6p	6d	7s	
	n	1	2		3			4				5				6			7	
	l	0	0	1	0	1	2	0	1	2	3	0	1	2	3	0	1	2	0	
atomic number	element																			$2S+1$
47	Ag	2	2	6	2	6	10	2	6	10		1								2
48	Cd											2								1
49	In											2	1							2
50	Sn											2	2							3
51	Sb											2	3							4
52	Te											2	4							3
53	I											2	5							2
54	Xe											2	6							1
55	Cs	2	2	6	2	6	10	2	6	10		2	6			1				2
56	Ba															2				1
57	La													1		2				2
58	Ce										2	2	6			2				3
59	Pr										3	2	6			2				4
60	Nd										4	2	6			2				5
61	Pm										5	2	6			2				6
62	Sm										6	2	6			2				7
63	Eu										7	2	6			2				8
64	Gd										7	2	6	1		2				9
65	Tb										8	2	6	1		2				8
66	Dy										10	2	6			2				5
67	Ho										11	2	6			2				4
68	Er										12	2	6			2				3
69	Tm										13	2	6			2				2
70	Yb										14	2	6			2				1
71	Lu										14	2	6	1		2				2
72	Hf	2	2	6	2	6	10	2	6	10	14	2	6	2		2				3
73	Ta													3		2				4
74	W													4		2				5
75	Re													5		2				6
76	Os													6		2				5
77	Ir													7		2				4
78	Pt													9		1				3
79	Au	2	2	6	2	6	10	2	6	10	14	2	6	10		1				2
80	Hg															2				1
81	Tl															2	1			2
82	Pb															2	2			3
83	Bi															2	3			4
84	Po															2	4			3
85	At															2	5			2
86	Rn															2	6			1
87	Fr	2	2	6	2	6	10	2	6	10	14	2	6	10		2	6		1	2
88	Ra															2	6		2	1
89	Ac															2	6	1	2	2
90	Th														2	2	6		2	
91	Pa														3	2	6		2	
92	U														3	2	6	1	2	
93	Np													?	5	2	6		2	
94	Pu														6	2	6		2	
95	Am														7	2	6		2	
96	Cm														7	2	6	1	2	
97	Bk																			
98	Cf																			
99	Es																			
100	Fm																			

mined by experiment. To resolve the $(2l + 1)$-fold degeneracy of states with a common value of l, we have assumed the presence of a magnetic field in the z direction. The table illustrates that although to a first approximation the energy increases with increasing n, there are exceptions to this behavior. For example, in K ($Z = 19$) the valence electron occupies a 4*s* rather than 3*d* orbital; similarly in Rb ($Z = 37$) the valence electron is in a 5*s* rather than a 4*d* orbital; on the other hand in $Y(Z = 39)$ the 4*d* orbital is more stable than the 5*p* orbital. Other exceptions are evident in the heavier elements where, for example, in La (57), the 5*p*, 5*d*, and 6*s* orbitals are more stable than the 4*f* orbitals; the *g* orbitals do not begin to be populated until the 6*p*, 6*d*, and 7*s* orbitals are filled [Th(90) or V(92)].

appendix 1

reference books

O. Oldenberg "Introduction to Atomic and Nuclear Physics," 3d ed., McGraw-Hill Book Company, Inc., New York, 1961.

M. Born "Atomic Physics," 7th ed., Hafner Publishing Company, Inc., New York, 1962.

R. M. Eisberg "Fundamentals of Modern Physics," John Wiley & Sons, Inc., New York, 1961.

C. W. Sherwin "Introduction to Quantum Mechanics," Holt, Rinehart and Winston, New York, 1959.

L. Pauling and E. B. Wilson, Jr. "Introduction to Quantum Mechanics," McGraw-Hill Book Company, Inc., New York, 1935.

V. B. Rojanski "Introductory Quantum Mechanics," Prentice-Hall, Inc., Englewood Cliffs, N.J., 1938.

D. Bohm "Quantum Theory," Prentice-Hall, Inc., Englewood Cliffs, N.J., 1951.

L. I. Schiff "Quantum Mechanics," 2d ed., McGraw-Hill Book Company, Inc., New York, 1955.

R. H. Dicke and J. P. Wittke "Introduction to Quantum Mechanics," Addison Wesley Publishing Company, Inc., Reading, Mass., 1960.

L. D. Landau and E. M. Lifshitz "Quantum Mechanics," translated by J. B. Sykes and J. S. Bell, Addison Wesley Publishing Company, Inc., Reading, Mass., 1958.

L. Pauling "The Nature of the Chemical Bond," 3d ed., Cornell University Press, Ithaca, N.Y., 1960.

H. Eyring, J. Walter, and G. E. Kimble "Quantum Chemistry," John Wiley & Sons, Inc., New York, 1944.

W. Kauzmann "Quantum Chemistry," Academic Press Inc., New York, 1957.

J. C. Slater "Quantum Theory of Matter," McGraw-Hill Book Company, Inc., New York, 1951.

R. B. Leighton "Principles of Modern Physics," McGraw-Hill Book Company, Inc., New York, 1959.

G. Herzberg "Atomic Spectra and Atomic Structure," 2d ed., Dover Publications, Inc., New York, 1944.

G. Herzberg "Spectra of Diatomic Molecules," 2d ed., D. Van Nostrand Company, Inc., Princeton, N.J., 1950.

index